The Ultimate
PUB QUIZ
Book

Editor
Martin H. Manser

Compilers
Andrew Bianchi
Alexandra Clayton
Saira Dunnakey
Alison Farrell
Alice Grandison

Editorial Assistants
Lynda Drury
Linda Eley
Wendy Kempster

The Ultimate
PUB QUIZ
Book

Martin H. Manser

Cartoons by
Martin Angel

CHANCELLOR
PRESS

Designer
Angela Ashton

Project Management
Sarah Eason

Editorial Assistance
Liz Dalby and Helen Parker

Artwork Commissioning
Susanne Grant

Production
Jenni Cozens and Ian Paulyn

Editorial Director
Paula Borton

Art Director
Clare Sleven

Director
Jim Miles

This edition published by Chancellor Press
an imprint of Bounty Books, a Division of the Octopus Publishing Group Ltd,
2-4 Heron Quays, London, E14 4JP

© Octopus Publishing Group Ltd

Printed in 1999

Produced by Miles Kelly Publishing Ltd
Bardfield Centre, Great Bardfield, Essex, England CM7 4SL

ISBN 0-75370143-X

Printed in the United Kingdom

The Ultimate Pub Quiz Book is divided into quiz sessions.
Each session is divided into eight categories, shown
below with their icons:

 TV, Music & Entertainment

 History

 Sports

 General Knowledge

 Science & Technology

 Geography

 The Arts

 Pot Luck

Session 1	8
Session 2	16
Session 3	24
Session 4	32
Session 5	40
Session 6	48
Session 7	56
Session 8	64
Session 9	72
Session 10	80
Session 11	88
Session 12	96
Session 13	104
Session 14	112
Session 15	120
Session 16	128
Session 17	136
Session 18	144
Session 19	152
Session 20	160
Session 21	168
Session 22	176
Session 23	184
Session 24	192

Session 25   200

Session 26   208

Session 27   216

Session 28   224

Session 29   232

Session 30   240

Session 31   248

Session 32   256

Session 33   264

Session 34   272

Session 35   280

Session 36   288

Session 37   296

Session 38   304

Session 39   312

Session 40   320

Session 41   328

Session 42   336

Session 43   344

Session 44   352

Session 45   360

Session 46   368

Session 47   376

Session 48   384

SESSION 1

QUIZ 1

TV, music & entertainment

1　Who was Grant Mitchell's first wife in *EastEnders*?

2　Who played the inept hit man Vincent Vega in the film *Pulp Fiction*?

3　Which band is fronted by Jarvis Cocker?

4　Who was the choreographer and star of the show *Lord of the Dance*?

5　Which operatic tenor is nicknamed 'Big Lucy'?

6　Which Teletubby is dressed in red?

7　Which US chat-show host had an acting role in the film *The Color Purple*?

8　What is the real name of Bono from U2?

9　Which singer starred with Kevin Costner in the film *The Bodyguard*?

10　Name the characters in *Friends* who are brother and sister.

11　For whom did Paul McCartney write 'Hey Jude'?

12　In the film *It's a Wonderful Life*, what happens every time an angel gets his wings?

13　What is the name of the housekeeper in *Father Ted*?

14　What is the heroine's name in Walt Disney's *Beauty and the Beast*?

15　Who was George Michael's partner in Wham!?

ANSWERS

1. Sharon Watts. 2. John Travolta. 3. Pulp. 4. Michael Flatley. 5. Luciano Pavarotti. 6. Po. 7. Oprah Winfrey. 8. Paul Hewson. 9. Whitney Houston. 10. Ross and Monica. 11. Julian Lennon. 12. A bell rings. 13. Mrs Doyle. 14. Belle. 15. Andrew Ridgeley.

SESSION 1 — QUIZ 2

History

1 Who was British prime minister at the outbreak of war with Germany in 1939?

2 Who founded Virginia?

3 Who died in 323 BC?

4 When did Captain Cook first claim part of Australia for Britain? Was it (a) 1770, (b) 1790 or (c) 1800?

5 Who took the throne after Queen Victoria?

6 In what year did Napoleon retreat from Moscow?

7 Where was the Magna Carta signed?

8 Who was the first Tudor king, crowned in 1485?

9 Which school, Eton or Harrow, was founded in 1440?

10 Who was known as the 'Tyrant of Geneva'?

11 In 79 AD Pliny the Younger witnessed the destruction of what?

12 Palmerston was a member of which political party?

13 Who lost the battle of Naseby in 1645?

14 When did women over 21 get the vote?

15 What was the predominant drink at a party held in North America in 1773?

ANSWERS

1. Neville Chamberlain. 2. Walter Raleigh. 3. Alexander the Great. 4. (a) 1770. 5. Edward VII. 6. 1812. 7. Runnymede. 8. Henry VII. 9. Eton. 10. John Calvin. 11. Pompeii. 12. Liberal. 13. The Royalists. 14. 1929. 15. Tea.

SESSION 1　QUIZ 3

Sports

1　Who were the two goal scorers for England in the 1966 World Cup Final?

2　What do the initials W. G. in W. G. Grace stand for?

3　What number does the scrum half in Rugby Union usually wear?

4　What is two strokes under par in golf called?

5　What nationality is Rod Laver?

6　What distance is a marathon run over?

7　Which American won seven gold medals at the 1972 Munich Olympics?

8　What is the first leg of a medley swimming race?

9　Which Italian club did Diego Maradona play for?

10　Which station lies between Income Tax and The Angel Islington in Monopoly?

11　How many players are there in a basketball team?

12　In which county is Goodwood racecourse?

13　Who was the first black player to score a goal for England?

14　Alan and Chris Old played for England at which two sports?

15　Where were the 1940 Olympics held?

ANSWERS

1. Geoff Hurst and Martin Peters. 2. William Gilbert. 3. Nine. 4. Eagle. 5. Australian. 6. 26 miles 385 yards. 7. Mark Spitz. 8. Backstroke. 9. Napoli. 10. Kings Cross. 11. Five. 12. Sussex. 13. Luther Blissett. 14. Rugby and cricket. 15. They didn't take place because of World War II.

SESSION 1   QUIZ 4

General knowledge

1   What gas mark is equivalent to 350 degrees Fahrenheit?

2   In the American sitcom *Frasier* what is Frasier Crane's brother called?

3   In US military slang what does 'Charley' mean?

4   What does a lexicographer do?

5   Who played opposite Dustin Hoffman in *The Graduate*?

6   Beta-blockers stop secretion of what chemical?

7   What colour is Chinese Red?

8   Gourami is a large fish. True or false?

9   Name the 19th full-length Disney cartoon which featured three Liverpudlian vultures and a hypnotic snake amongst its cast?

10   How many graces were there in Greek mythology?

11   If you had a pissaladière, would you (a) eat it, (b) play it or (c) wear it?

12   Who is the patron saint of doctors?

13   What is the name of the first bridge captured on D-Day?

14   Name the yellow Tellytubby.

15   Who wrote the poem *Penmaenpool*?

ANSWERS

1. Mark 4. 2. Niles. 3. Vietcong. 4. Write or compile dictionaries. 5. Anne Bancroft. 6. Adrenaline. 7. Red. 8. True. 9. *Jungle Book*. 10. Three. 11. (a) eat it. 12. Luke. 13. Pegasus. 14. Laa Laa. 15. Gerard Manley Hopkins.

SESSION 1 QUIZ 5

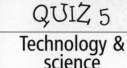

Technology & science

1 Which woman scientist was awarded two Nobel Prizes in the early part of the 20th century?

2 What did Flamsteed, Halley, Bradley and Bliss all have in common?

3 What is the name of the branch of mathematics that deals with the sides and angles of triangles?

4 What is the name of the worldwide organization initiated by Jean Henri Dunant in 1862?

5 What do the letters ISDN stand for?

6 How many points are there to a compass?

7 Name the national bird of New Zealand.

8 Which law states that at a constant temperature, the pressure of a gas is inversely proportionate to its volume?

9 Which group of mammals are the only ones to lay eggs?

10 Name the plant that translates from the Latin as 'fair lady'.

11 What is controlled by a rheostat?

12 Agar-agar is often used in cooking. What is it?

13 What is the exposive that consists of nitroglycerine, nitrocellulose, wood pulp and potassium nitrate?

14 Who was the US Space Shuttle Captain of *Challenger*?

15 What is the common name for diamorphine?

ANSWERS

1. Marie Curie. 2. They were all Astronomers Royal. 3. Trigonometry. 4. The Red Cross. 5. Integrated Services Digital Network. 6. 32. 7. Kiwi. 8. Boyle's law. 9. Monotremes (platypus and spiny anteater). 10. *Bella Donna*, deadly nightshade. 11. Electric current. 12. A type of gelatine made from seaweed. 13. Gelignite. 14. Bruce McCandless. 15. Heroin.

SESSION 1   QUIZ 6

Geography

1   In which British city would you find Arthur's Seat?

2   Where would you find Queen Maud Land, Marie Byrd Land and Wilkes Land?

3   What is the capital of Barbados?

4   In which city would you see the Brandenburg Gate?

5   The River Danube flows into the Black Sea. True or false?

6   Which desert lies in Mongolia and North East China?

7   Where is Mount McKinley?

8   Which one of these countries lies on the Equator: (a) Ethiopia, (b) Angola or (c) Kenya?

9   What is the name for the device used to record the vibrations caused by earthquakes?

10   What is the capital of the American state of Massachusetts?

11   What is the name of the longest river in Ireland, which flows through Limerick?

12   The island of Mauritius is in which ocean?

13   The depth of the deepest part of the ocean is greater than the height of Mount Everest. True or false?

14   Which of these ports is furthest west: (a) Ostend, (b) Calais or (c) Dunkerque?

15   Which country's fishing industry is the largest: (a) Japan, (b) Iceland or (c) Russia?

ANSWERS

1. Edinburgh. 2. Antarctica. 3. Bridgetown. 4. Berlin. 5. True. 6. Gobi desert. 7. Alaska. 8. (c) Kenya. 9. Seismometer. 10. Boston. 11. River Shannon. 12. Indian Ocean. 13. True. 14. (b) Calais. 15. (a) Japan.

SESSION 1 | QUIZ 7

The Arts

1 'Their's not to reason why, Their's but to do and die'; who rode into the Valley of Death?

2 Whose operas are performed by the D'Oyly Carte company?

3 In *Oliver Twist*, how is the thief Jack Dawkins better known?

4 Who was the author of *Rob Roy* and *Ivanhoe*?

5 Rossetti, Millais and Holman Hunt were all members of which artistic brotherhood?

6 Which writers disguised themselves as Currer, Ellis and Acton Bell?

7 In which Spanish city is the Guggenheim Museum?

8 What was Moby Dick?

9 With which famous beauty did the Trojan prince Paris elope?

10 Who wrote *The Moor's Last Sigh* and *Midnight's Children*?

11 Which composer wrote the music of *Rule Britannia*?

12 'Four legs good; two legs bad', according to whom?

13 Who painted *Primavera* and *The Birth of Venus*?

14 In *Alice in Wonderland* who sleeps in a teapot?

15 Who travelled to Brobdingnag, the land of the giants?

ANSWERS

1. The Light Brigade, called the Five Hundred (in the poem by Tennyson). 2. Gilbert and Sullivan. 3. The Artful Dodger. 4. Sir Walter Scott. 5. The Pre-Raphaelites. 6. The Brontë sisters: Charlotte, Emily and Anne. 7. Bilbao. 8. A whale. 9. Helen of Troy. 10. Salman Rushdie. 11. Thomas Arne. 12. The animals in *Animal Farm*, by George Orwell. 13. Sandro Botticelli. 14. The Dormouse. 15. Gulliver.

SESSION 1 — QUIZ 8

Pot Luck

1 Sextiles, Oostmaand, Weodmonath and Thermidor are old names for which summer month?

2 Why did the Spanish Inquisition burn their victims instead of beheading them?

3 A group of larks is: (a) an exaltation, (b) an exhibition or (c) an exhalation?

4 Which British prime minister was the only one to marry a divorcee?

5 What is the origin of the term 'scouse' applied to natives of Liverpool?

6 Which purple gemstone did the Romans believe prevented drunkenness?

7 What flower is called the 'Fair Maid of February'?

8 A griffin has the body of a lion and the head of what?

9 What are graylings, dabs and groupers?

10 Kannada, Telegu, Tamil and Marathi are among the official languages of which country?

11 Which two words, sounding alike, mean the same as these two phrases: a branch of a tree/bending of the head or body?

12 What type of animal brays?

13 What is the main ingredient of fondue?

14 Why is Saint Sebastian the patron saint of pinmakers?

15 What material was the first motorbike made from?

ANSWERS

1. August. 2. They were forbidden to shed blood. 3. (a) an exaltation. 4. Margaret Thatcher. 5. Lobscouse, meaning 'sailors' stew'. 6. Amethyst. 7. Snowdrop. 8. Eagle. 9. Fish. 10. India. 11. Bough/bow. 12. Donkey or ass. 13. Cheese. 14. He was shot full of arrows. 15. Wood.

SESSION 2   QUIZ 1

TV, music & entertainment

1 Which film actor played the part of David Addison in the TV show *Moonlighting*?

2 Of which boy band was Robbie Williams a member?

3 Who owns the chip shop in *Brookside*?

4 What was the name of the piano player in the film *Casablanca*?

5 What are the first names of Mulder and Scully in *The X Files*?

6 Which musical instrument did Stéphane Grappelli play?

7 From which feature film was Celine Dion's hit 'My Heart Will Go On' the theme song?

8 What is the name of the fictional town where 'The Simpsons' live?

9 Who played Malcolm X in the film of the same name?

10 Which country does Dame Kiri Te Kanawa come from?

11 Which character in *Neighbours* is played by Ian Smith?

12 What was the first name of Doctor Zhivago?

13 Which famous singer and actor was born in Hoboken, New Jersey?

14 Which *Blue Peter* presenter was fired in 1998 for using cocaine?

15 Which Scottish historical character was played by Mel Gibson in the film *Braveheart*?

ANSWERS

1. Bruce Willis. 2. Take That. 3. Mick Johnson. 4. Sam. 5. Fox and Dana. 6. Violin. 7. *Titanic*. 8. Springfield. 9. Denzel Washington. 10. New Zealand. 11. Harold Bishop. 12. Yuri. 13. Frank Sinatra. 14. Richard Bacon. 15. William Wallace.

SESSION 2   QUIZ 2

History

1. Who was the first prime minister during the reign of Queen Victoria?

2. Which king said, 'Let not poor Nelly starve!'

3. What religious group did Ignatius of Loyola found?

4. How many Opium wars were there?

5. Where did the Etruscans live?

6. Which Spaniard razed the Aztec city Tenochtitlan in 1521?

7. Who were the victims of the Anschluss?

8. In which year did the Korean War begin?

9. Which philosopher was condemned for corrupting the youth of Athens?

10. What book did theologian Thomas à Kempis write?

11. What was the name of Yuri Gagarin's spacecraft?

12. The emperor Caligula made which animal a senator?

13. What was the name of the queen who sponsored Christopher Columbus on his voyage of discovery?

14. Which famous trading and shipping company was based in Bombay?

15. Who outfoxed General Montcalm at Quebec?

ANSWERS

1. Viscount Melbourne. 2. Charles II. 3. The Jesuits. 4. Two. 5. Central Italy. They lived prior to the Romans. 6. Cortes. 7. The Austrians in 1938. It was the annexation of their country by Germany. 8. 1950. 9. Socrates. 10. *The Imitation of Christ*. 11. Vostok 1. 12. A horse. 13. Isabella. 14. The East India Company. 15. General Wolfe.

SESSION 2 — QUIZ 3

Sports

1. Why did Björn Borg never shave during Wimbledon?

2. Canadian Wayne Gretzky is renowned for which sport?

3. At which event was Ed Moses the king?

4. Which county did Viv Richards play for?

5. Which Italian scored a hat-trick against Brazil in 1982?

6. How many countries were represented at the 1896 Olympics?

7. Cassius Clay won which boxing division at the 1964 Olympics?

8. Which mountains lie to the south of Gleneagles?

9. In which Australian state was Greg Norman born?

10. What was Eddy Merckx's sport?

11. What do marathon runners often hit?

12. What lies immediately before the take-off board in the long jump?

13. Who scored for England in the infamous 'Hand of God' game?

14. Who won the men's singles title at Wimbledon in 1992?

15. Who did Italy beat in the semi finals of the 1994 World Cup?

ANSWERS

1. It was a superstition. 2. Ice hockey. 3. 400-metre hurdles. 4. Somerset. 5. Paolo Rossi. 6. 14. 7. Light heavyweight. 8. Ochill mountains. 9. Queensland. 10. Cycling. 11. The wall - a phase when all energy seems to disappear. 12. Plasticine which helps to see if a jumper has taken off before the board. 13. Gary Lineker. 14. Andre Agassi. 15. Bulgaria.

SESSION 2 · QUIZ 4

General knowledge

1   What do panphobics suffer from?

2   What is the 'cakewalk'?

3   How many teeth does an adult human have?

4   What is the longest Psalm in the Bible?

5   Who is the God of war in Norse mythology?

6   What opened on 6 May 1994?

7   What is cipolin?

8   What is the currency of Finland called?

9   Does the Titanic lie at a depth of (a) 10,000, (b) 13,000 or (c) 20,000 feet?

10   What is the chemical symbol for copper?

11   What was seen in 1835, 1910 and 1985?

12   What sign of the zodiac runs from 19 February – 20 March?

13   By what name is the order of animals, chiroptera, better known?

14   How many yards are there in a chain?

15   How many stripes does a sergeant have on his or her arm?

ANSWERS

1. A fear of everything. 2. An American Negro dance. 3. 32. 4. Psalm 119 with 176 verses. 5. Thor. 6. The Channel Tunnel. 7. Italian marble. 8. Markka. 9. (b) 13,000 feet. 10. Cu. 11. Halley's Comet. 12. Pisces. 13. Bats. 14. 22. 15. Three.

SESSION 2   QUIZ 5

Technology & science

1 What did Christopher Cockerell invent in 1955?

2 To which profession do members of the BDA belong?

3 From where does the term 'electricity' derive?

4 What is the name of the smallest bird in the world?

5 The binary system of numbers uses only two numbers. What are they?

6 What was the name of the mathematician who devised a mechanical calculating machine in 1834?

7 What is the common name for hydrated magnesium sulphate?

8 What do Wyandotte, Buff Orpington and Rhode Island Red have in common?

9 Who discovered the metal titanium in 1791?

10 What was the name of the US project for manned exploration to the Moon?

11 Bell metal is an alloy of which two metals?

12 What is the name of the only monkey native to Europe?

13 Which gas is sometimes referred to as 'marsh gas'?

14 Name two of the three main constituents of glass.

15 What is the name given to the hard reddish brick-like earthenware used for making pots and vessels?

ANSWERS

1. The hovercraft. 2. Dentists (British Dental Association). 3. From the Greek *electrum*, meaning amber (an electrical charge can be created by rubbing amber). 4. The bee hummingbird. 5. 0 and 1. 6. Charles Babbage. 7. Epsom salts. 8. All are breeds of chicken. 9. William Gregor. 10. The Apollo programme. 11. Copper and tin. 12. Barbary ape. 13. Methane. 14. Sand, soda, limestone. 15. Terracotta.

SESSION 2   QUIZ 6

Geography

1. In which country is the Great Slave Lake?

2. Which country shares an island with the Dominican Republic?

3. Which river flows through the German city of Bonn?

4. What is the capital of Liechtenstein?

5. Which island group includes Lewis, Benbecula and Barra?

6. Which city is Strathclyde University in?

7. What is the name for the high wave caused by an earthquake or a volcano?

8. Lake Volta is in which African country?

9. Riga is the capital of: (a) Lithuania, (b) Moldavia or (c) Latvia?

10. Which country does the River Ebro flow through?

11. In which English county is Crewe?

12. In which American state would you find Norfolk, Lincoln and Cambridge: (a) Nebraska, (b) Pennsylvania or (c) Alabama?

13. The Maldives are south of the Equator. True or false?

14. What is the name of the strait that separates Australia from Tasmania?

15. Baja California is part of which country?

ANSWERS

1. Canada. 2. Haiti. 3. Rhine. 4. Vaduz. 5. Outer Hebrides. 6. Glasgow. 7. Tsunami. 8. Ghana. 9. (c) Latvia. 10. Spain. 11. Cheshire. 12. (a) Nebraska. 13. False. 14. Bass Strait. 15. Mexico.

SESSION 2 QUIZ 7

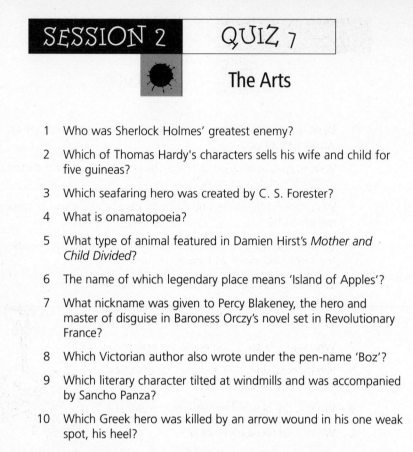

The Arts

1 Who was Sherlock Holmes' greatest enemy?

2 Which of Thomas Hardy's characters sells his wife and child for five guineas?

3 Which seafaring hero was created by C. S. Forester?

4 What is onamatopoeia?

5 What type of animal featured in Damien Hirst's *Mother and Child Divided*?

6 The name of which legendary place means 'Island of Apples'?

7 What nickname was given to Percy Blakeney, the hero and master of disguise in Baroness Orczy's novel set in Revolutionary France?

8 Which Victorian author also wrote under the pen-name 'Boz'?

9 Which literary character tilted at windmills and was accompanied by Sancho Panza?

10 Which Greek hero was killed by an arrow wound in his one weak spot, his heel?

11 Who was the narrator of the stories of *The One Thousand and One Nights*?

12 In Aesop's fables, what did the fox eventually decide about the grapes that he was unable to reach?

13 Who wrote a play set in the forest of Arden?

14 What decorative style is associated with the 1920s and 1930s?

15 William Wordsworth, Lord Tennyson and Ted Hughes all held which official literary post?

ANSWERS

1. Professor Moriarty. 2. Mayor of Casterbridge (Michael Henchard). 3. Horatio Hornblower. 4. A word that imitates a sound, such as 'hiss'. 5. A cow and a calf. 6. Avalon. 7. 'The Scarlet Pimpernel'. 8. Charles Dickens. 9. Don Quixote. 10. Achilles. 11. Scheherazade. 12. That they were sour. 13. Shakespeare - *As You Like It*. 14. Art Deco. 15. Poet Laureate.

SESSION 2   QUIZ 8

Pot Luck

1   Dandie Dinmont, Border, Cairn and Kerry Blue are all breeds of which type of dog?

2   What travels at a speed of 5.9 million million miles, or 9.4 million million kilometres per year?

3   What type of business is traditionally denoted by a sign of three golden balls?

4   What word, used to address a woman in a formal letter, reads the same backwards as forwards?

5   In the phonetic alphabet the letter J is represented by which girl's name?

6   Why is the White Sea so called?

7   Who said, 'To err is human, to forgive, divine'?

8   What unusual feature is shared by ostriches, emus and kiwi birds?

9   What is the nineteenth letter of the alphabet?

10   What is salinity a measure of?

11   The eggs of the sturgeon fish are an expensive delicacy. What are they called?

12   What happened to people who failed to pay the 'nose tax' imposed by the Danes in the 9th century?

13   From what is silk produced?

14   Bamboo is: (a) a grass, (b) a tree or (c) a fern?

15   At least a quarter of cars in Brazil run on fermented sugar cane. True or false?

ANSWERS

1. Terrier. 2. Light. 3. Pawnbroker. 4. Madam. 5. Juliet. 6. It is covered in ice for most of the year. 7. Alexander Pope. 8. They are birds that cannot fly. 9. N. 10. Salt. 11. Caviar. 12. Their noses were slit. 13. Cocoon of the silk worm. 14. (a) a grass. 15. True.

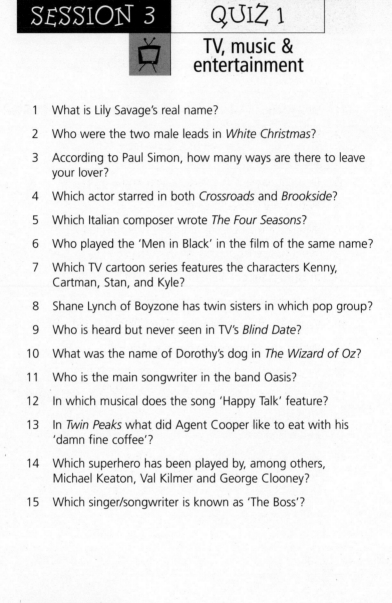

SESSION 3 — QUIZ 1

TV, music & entertainment

1 What is Lily Savage's real name?

2 Who were the two male leads in *White Christmas*?

3 According to Paul Simon, how many ways are there to leave your lover?

4 Which actor starred in both *Crossroads* and *Brookside*?

5 Which Italian composer wrote *The Four Seasons*?

6 Who played the 'Men in Black' in the film of the same name?

7 Which TV cartoon series features the characters Kenny, Cartman, Stan, and Kyle?

8 Shane Lynch of Boyzone has twin sisters in which pop group?

9 Who is heard but never seen in TV's *Blind Date*?

10 What was the name of Dorothy's dog in *The Wizard of Oz*?

11 Who is the main songwriter in the band Oasis?

12 In which musical does the song 'Happy Talk' feature?

13 In *Twin Peaks* what did Agent Cooper like to eat with his 'damn fine coffee'?

14 Which superhero has been played by, among others, Michael Keaton, Val Kilmer and George Clooney?

15 Which singer/songwriter is known as 'The Boss'?

ANSWERS

1. Paul O'Grady. 2. Bing Crosby and Danny Kaye. 3. 50. 4. Steven Pinder. 5. Antonio Vivaldi.
6. Tommy Lee Jones and Will Smith. 7. *South Park*. 8. B*Witched. 9. Our Graham.
10. Toto. 11. Noel Gallagher. 12. *South Pacific*. 13. Cherry pie. 14. Batman.
15. Bruce Springsteen.

SESSION 3   QUIZ 2

History

1   Which king of England styled himself as 'Defender of the Faith'

2   What did the Canada Act of 1791 do?

3   Who was the longest serving American president?

4   By what name is Eva Peron better known?

5   How many Crusades were there?

6   Who kept the Persians at bay at Thermopylae?

7   What happened to George III in 1811?

8   In which year did Emperor Hirohito of Japan die?

9   What did Henry Wood begin in 1895?

10   What was the comfortable period before World War I known as?

11   Which age came before the Iron Age?

12   Who won the US presidential election in 1968?

13   Who invented a device for measuring radioactivity in 1913?

14   Which Eastern philosopher's teaching was distilled in the *Analects*?

15   What was Hannibal's secret weapon?

ANSWERS

1. Henry VIII. 2. It divided the country into English and French parts. 3. F. D. Roosevelt. 4. Evita. 5. Four. 6. A small band of Spartans. 7. He was declared insane. 8. 1989. 9. The Promenade Concerts. 10. La belle poque. 11. The Bronze Age. 12. Richard Nixon. 13. Geiger. 14. Confucius. 15. Elephants with which he famously crossed the Alps.

SESSION 3   QUIZ 3

Sports

1 Who was BBC sports personality of the year in 1998?

2 Where were the 1994 Winter Olympics held?

3 Who is Matthew Simmons?

4 What nationality is athlete Rosa Mota?

5 What is Barcelona's stadium called?

6 What did William Webb Ellis do?

7 If you were at Garmisch-Partenkirchen, which sport would you be taking part in?

8 What were used in football for the first time in 1890?

9 Gaston Roelants is a national of which country?

10 How many sports have been present at all the summer Olympics?

11 Where are the 2002 Winter Olympics due to be held?

12 Which is the oldest football league club? Is it (a) Notts County, (b) Nottingham Forest or (c) Stoke City?

13 What sport did Alberto Tomba compete in?

14 Which athlete won the most Olympic gold medals ever?

15 At which sport can you see nose walking?

ANSWERS

1. Michael Owen. 2. Lillehammer, Norway. 3. He was the spectator kicked by Eric Cantona. 4. Portuguese. 5. Nova Campa. 6. He picked up a ball and thus invented rugby. 7. Skiing. 8. Goal nets. 9. Belgium. 10. 5 - Cycling, fencing, gymnastics, swimming and athletics. 11. Salt Lake City. 12. (a) Notts County founded in 1862. 13. Skiing. 14. Ray Ewry, who won 10 from 1900-08. 15. Surfing.

SESSION 3   QUIZ 4

General knowledge

1 What are the colours of the Italian flag?

2 What is ovicide?

3 Which suburb of southwest London hosts the annual All England Lawn Tennis championships?

4 What are Centenary, Black Star of Africa and Jubilee?

5 What was invented in roughly 3,500 BC in Mesopotamia?

6 Where can you find the oldest Underground system in the world?

7 What does RAM stand for?

8 What is a penny farthing?

9 What is the first wedding anniversary called?

10 When is the second dog watch at sea?

11 If you see a car with the letters AND on it where has it come from?

12 Who regard Haile Selassie as god?

13 What is the commonest metal used in light-bulbs?

14 Jim Morrison sang for which pop group?

15 Urdu is the national language of Pakistan. True or false?

ANSWERS

1. Red, white and green. 2. Sheep killing. 3. Wimbledon. 4. Diamonds. 5. The wheel. 6. London. 7. Random Access Memory. 8. A type of bicycle. 9. Cotton. 10. 6 pm - 8 pm. 11. Andorra. 12. Rastafarians. 13. Tungsten. 14. The Doors. 15. True.

SESSION 3 QUIZ 5

Technology & science

1 Which mineral substance found near Whitby, Yorkshire, is popularly used in jewellery?

2 How many sides has a dodecagon?

3 What do nitrous oxide, sodium pentothal and cyclopropane have in common?

4 If you studied hippology, what would you be studying?

5 With which invention of 1783 do you associate the brothers Jacques and Joseph Montgolfier?

6 What do the initials BST stand for?

7 What is the name of the process by which water moves to balance the concentration of fluids?

8 What is the collective name for beavers, porcupines, hares, squirrels, guinea pigs, water voles and lemmings?

9 What chemical element is the common constituent of coal?

10 Where does the plant fuchsia get its name?

11 What is a young hare called?

12 What element has atomic number 1?

13 Who was one of the first women to enter the medical profession, in 1875?

14 By what name is solid carbon dioxide known?

15 What is a shipworm?

ANSWERS

1. Jet. 2. 12. 3. They are all general anaesthetics. 4. Horses. 5. Hot-air balloon. 6. British Summer Time. 7. Osmosis. 8. Rodents. 9. Carbon. 10. From the 16th century botanist Leonhard Fuchs, who brought it to Europe. 11. A leveret. 12. Hydrogen. 13. Elizabeth Garrett Anderson. 14. Dry ice. 15. A mollusc.

SESSION 3   QUIZ 6

Geography

1 In which country are the Harz mountains?

2 The River Darling is in which country?

3 Molten rock at the surface is called lava; what is it called when it is deep in the Earth?

4 What is the capital of the Bahamas?

5 Which is the largest lake in Switzerland?

6 Which lies further south, Algiers or Cadiz?

7 Baffin Bay is between Canada and which other country?

8 Which country lies between Nicaragua and Panama?

9 Which mountain in Scotland dominates the town of Fort William?

10 Which strait separates Asia from North America?

11 Which former Olympic city is the capital of South Korea?

12 What is the name for the French-speaking population of southern Belgium?

13 In which ocean are the Galapagos Islands?

14 The Columbia River forms the boundary of Oregon and what other state?

15 Which of these Balearic Islands is furthest south: (a) Ibiza, (b) Minorca or (c) Majorca?

ANSWERS

1. Germany. 2. Australia. 3. Magma. 4. Nassau. 5. Lake Geneva. 6. Cadiz. 7. Greenland. 8. Costa Rica. 9. Ben Nevis. 10. Bering Strait. 11. Seoul. 12. Walloon. 13. Pacific Ocean. 14. Washington. 15. (a) Ibiza.

SESSION 3 QUIZ 7

The Arts

1 Which prize is awarded every October to the book judged to be the best published that year by a British or Commonwealth author?

2 In which Parisian gallery are the *Mona Lisa* and the *Venus de Milo*?

3 Who wrote *The Faerie Queene*?

4 In Hamlet, what is the name of the prince's sister who goes mad and drowns?

5 Who was the moody master of *Wuthering Heights*?

6 Who painted the *Haywain*?

7 Which century of the Italian Renaissance is called the 'Quintocento'?

8 From what is silk produced?

9 Which Spanish artist turned up to the London Surrealist exhibition in 1936 wearing a diving suit?

10 Who wrote nonsense poems about the 'Owl and the Pussycat' and the 'Quangle Wangle's Hat'?

11 In architecture, what is a cupola?

12 Which composer's last words are believed to have been, 'I shall hear in heaven'?

13 What was the sequel to *The Hitchhiker's Guide to the Galaxy* by Douglas Adams?

14 Who was the bear of very little brain, created by A. A. Milne?

15 Which poet was the sister of the painter Dante Gabriel Rossetti?

ANSWERS

1. The Booker Prize. 2. The Louvre. 3. Edmund Spenser. 4. Ophelia. 5. Heathcliff. 6. John Constable. 7. Sixteenth ('Fifteen Hundreds'). 8. Silkworms. 9. Salvador Dali. 10. Edward Lear. 11. A dome. 12. Ludwig van Beethoven. 13. *The Restaurant at the End of the Universe*. 14. Winnie the Pooh. 15. Christina Rossetti.

SESSION 3   QUIZ 8

Pot Luck

1   At twelve noon GMT in London what time is it in Auckland, New Zealand?

2   Which expensive red spice is extracted from a crocus flower?

3   What is 'plagiarism'?

4   What substance found in the human body is also used in the manufacture of matches?

5   Which of the following does not live under water: (a) sea cucumber, (b) sea urchin or (c) sea pink?

6   If all the water in the air fell at the same time, what depth of rain would cover the Earth?

7   What type of animals are 'porcine'?

8   What is geographically significant about the rocks of Muckle Flugga?

9   What is special about the phrase, 'The quick brown fox jumps over the lazy dog'?

10   From what tropical disease did Oliver Cromwell die?

11   Which English girl's name is derived from a Hebrew word meaning 'a female sheep'?

12   Which item of clothing when first worn in 1797, caused dogs to bark, women to faint and a boy's arm to be broken?

13   How many deadly sins are there?

14   On what date is All Fools' Day?

15   Which Australian outlaw said, just before he was hanged, 'Such is life'?

ANSWERS

1. Twelve midnight. 2. Saffron. 3. Copying somebody else's work. 4. Phosphorous. 5. (c) sea pink; it is a flower. 6. 1 inch or 25 mm. 7. Pigs. 8. Most northerly point of the British Isles. 9. It contains all of the letters of the alphabet. 10. Malaria. 11. Rachel. 12. Top hat. 13. Seven. 14. 1 April. 15. Ned Kelly.

SESSION 4

QUIZ 1

TV, music & entertainment

1 Who are the team leaders in *Have I Got News for You*?

2 Who was Michael Jackson's first wife?

3 Who played Randle P. McMurphy in the film *One Flew over the Cuckoo's Nest*?

4 What does 'Nessun Dorma' mean?

5 What was the first feature-length cartoon?

6 What nationality is singer k. d. lang?

7 What is the name of the dog in *Frasier*?

8 Who wrote the score of the musical *West Side Story*?

9 What is the name of the school in *Home and Away*?

10 What is Scary Spice's real name?

11 Which 1996 film had 'Choose life' as its advertising slogan?

12 Which film actor played Mork in the sitcom *Mork and Mindy*?

13 Who is Radiohead's lead singer?

14 In *Coronation Street*, who was the first landlady of the Rovers Return?

15 What is Boy George's surname?

ANSWERS

1. Paul Merton and Ian Hislop. 2. Lisa Marie Presley. 3. Jack Nicholson. 4. None shall sleep. 5. *Snow White and the Seven Dwarfs*. 6. Canadian. 7. Eddie. 8. Leonard Bernstein. 9. Summer Bay High. 10. Melanie Brown. 11. *Trainspotting*. 12. Robin Williams. 13. Thom Yorke. 14. Annie Walker. 15. O'Dowd.

SESSION 4   QUIZ 2

History

1   For how long did Pope John Paul I hold office?

2   What nationality was statesman Ho Chi Minh?

3   Jan Huss was a Hungarian reformer of the church. True or False?

4   Where is Trafalgar?

5   Which queen was succeeded by her second cousin, Mary?

6   What name is given to a British Royal Dynasty?

7   By what name is the Roman city Deva currently known?

8   Who said, 'Kinquering Congs their title take'?

9   What name was given to the remnant of the Long Parliament dismissed by Cromwell?

10   Which religious group was founded by William Booth?

11   How many of Henry VIII's wives were beheaded?

12   In what year did prisoners first arrive in Australia? Was it (a) 1788, (b) 1808 (c) or 1856?

13   Which European countries were united by the Kalmar Union in 1397?

14   Who was the leader of the Khmer Rouge from 1962–85?

15   The battle of Crécy took place during which war?

ANSWERS

1. 33 days, in 1978.   2. Vietnamese.   3. False. He was Czech.   4. Off the south coast of Spain. 5. Jane.   6. A House.   7. Chester.   8. William Spooner, who was renowned for mixing up the first letters of words.   9. Rump.   10. The Salvation Army.   11. Two.   12. (a) 1788. 13. Denmark, Norway and Sweden.   14. Pol Pot.   15. The Hundred Years War.

SESSION 4 — QUIZ 3

Sports

1 Who is football's Mr Chin?

2 In what year was Peter Swan found guilty of bribery in football?

3 Sir Stanley Rous once refereed an FA Cup Final. True or false?

4 Tamara Press won an Olympic title on two occasions at what sport?

5 How many players take the field at any one time in American football?

6 What sport was one started with a bully-off, but now begins with a pass back?

7 Which football team are known as the Seagulls?

8 Who resigned as Chief Executive of the FA in 1998?

9 In what county is Royal Birkdale?

10 What was unusual about the baseball player Pete Gray?

11 How many medals did Great Britain win at the 1998 winter Olympics?

12 What position did rugby player Bill Beaumont play?

13 Who got 1,000 runs and 100 wickets in 21 Tests?

14 Who won the Superbowl in 1983?

15 Where is the first race of the Flat season held?

ANSWERS

1. Jimmy Hill. 2. 1965. 3. True in 1934. 4. Shot put. 5. 11. 6. Hockey. 7. Brighton and Hove Albion. 8. Graham Kelly. 9. Lancashire. 10. He had only one arm. 11. 1 bronze. 12. Lock forward. 13. Ian Botham. 14. The Washington Redskins. 15. Doncaster.

SESSION 4 — QUIZ 4

General knowledge

1 Which American state is known as the 'Land of Opportunity'?

2 Kofi Annan is the head of which organization?

3 In which city would you find the 'Notre Dame'?

4 Who wrote the banned book *Spycatcher*?

5 Did the world's first heart transplant patient live (a) 10 days, (b) 13 days or (c) 18 days after the operation?

6 Where would you find an inner and outer bailey?

7 How many people were there in Noah's Ark?

8 What is the most primitive of all animal groups?

9 What are the official reports of Parliamentary proceedings called?

10 In the name W. B. Yeats, what do the initials W. B. stand for?

11 Which is the coldest planet in our solar system?

12 What went into space for the first time on 3 November 1957?

13 What was seen in 1681 for the last time?

14 What is a B-52?

15 What is another name for $CHCl_3$?

ANSWERS

1. Arkansas. 2. The United Nations. 3. Paris. 4. Peter Wright. 5. (c) 18 days. 6. In a castle. 7. Eight. 8. The protozoans. 9. Hansard. 10. William Butler. 11. Pluto. 12. A dog. 13. The dodo. 14. An American bomber plane. 15. Chloroform.

SESSION 4 QUIZ 5

Technology & science

1 What do puncheon, butt, hogshead and kilderkin have in common?

2 With what is the science of ergonomics concerned?

3 To which group of animals does the slow-worm belong?

4 From where does the term 'ozone' come?

5 What is craniology?

6 What is the name of the gas used in balloons and airships?

7 In computer technology, what do the initials COBOL mean?

8 In Roman numerals what does LXX stand for?

9 What are the four dimensions?

10 Who developed the theory of relativity?

11 Name the largest living invertebrate.

12 What would be measured with an anemometer?

13 Which nationality was Galileo?

14 What is the chemical symbol for sodium?

15 What is the British equivalent of US Plexiglas?

ANSWERS

1. They are all measures. 2. The study of the efficiency of workers in their working environment. 3. Lizards (a legless lizard). 4. From the Greek *ozein*, to smell. 5. The study of skulls. 6. Helium. 7. Common Business Oriented Language. 8. 70. 9. Length, width, depth and time. 10. Albert Einstein. 11. Giant squid. 12. Wind velocity. 13. Italian. 14. Na. 15. Perspex.

SESSION 4 — QUIZ 6

Geography

1 Which country is enclosed by Colombia and Peru?

2 In which country is the Kiel Canal?

3 The Nullarbor Plain is in which country?

4 Which is the largest state of the United States of America?

5 What is the capital of Canada?

6 Which mountain range is between Aviemore and Braemar in Scotland?

7 What is the name for rock formed by solidification from a molten state: (a) sedimentary, (b) metamorphic or (c) igneous?

8 In which ocean is Ascension Island?

9 Funchal is the capital of which island?

10 Which is further north, Halifax in England or Halifax in Canada?

11 In which English county is the open air Minack Theatre?

12 Which river joins the Rhine at Koblenz?

13 In which Spanish city would you find the Prado museum?

14 Which of these African countries has the shortest coastline: (a) Angola, (b) Namibia or (c) Kenya?

15 In which Australian state would you find the Ninety Mile beach?

ANSWERS

1. Ecuador. 2. Germany. 3. Australia. 4. Alaska. 5. Ottawa. 6. Cairngorms. 7. (c) igneous. 8. Atlantic Ocean. 9. Madeira. 10. Halifax in England. 11. Cornwall. 12. Moselle. 13. Madrid. 14. (c) Kenya. 15. Victoria.

SESSION 4 QUIZ 7

The Arts

1 Which of Shakespeare's kings decided to divide his kingdom between his three daughters?

2 What nationality was Salvador Dali?

3 What is the literal meaning of the word 'Renaissance'?

4 In which European city is the Musée d'Orsay?

5 Which English artist painted a series of pictures of swimming pools in California?

6 What distilled liquid derived from pine trees is used as a thinner for oil paint?

7 What was Robert Burns's 'wee sleekit, cow'rin' tim'rous beastie'?

8 Who first called a spy a 'mole' in his novel *Tinker, Tailor, Soldier, Spy*?

9 In *The Importance of Being Ernest* in what object was Jack Worthing left in as a baby?

10 Which gentleman thief was the creation of Ernest Hornung?

11 Who wrote the plays *The Cherry Orchard* and *The Seagull*?

12 To whom did Richard Lovelace write a poem from prison?

13 Who wrote the *Just So* stories?

14 Whose skull does Hamlet reminisce over?

15 Who wrote *Sense and Sensibility*?

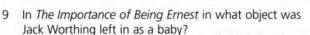

ANSWERS

1. King Lear. 2. Spanish. 3. Rebirth. 4. Paris. 5. David Hockney. 6. Turpentine. 7. A mouse. 8. John Le Carré. 9. A handbag. 10. Raffles. 11. Anton Chekhov. 12. Althea ('To Althea from Prison'). 13. Rudyard Kipling. 14. Yorick. 15. Jane Austen.

SESSION 4 — QUIZ 8

Pot Luck

1 What number is signified by the prefix 'mega-'?

2 What are 'Penny Buns', 'Puffballs' and 'Stinkhorns'?

3 With which organ does a snake hear?

4 What exactly is 'Big Ben'?

5 Who are the 'paparazzi'?

6 Casanova was a librarian. True or false?

7 What colour dye is obtained from woad?

8 In rhyming slang, what would you do with a 'jam-jar'?

9 Whose last written words were 'We shall stick it out to the end but we are getting weaker.... For God's sake look after our people'?

10 Which of the following English words did not come from the Chinese language: (a) ketchup, (b) kowtow or (c) decoy?

11 Until the 1960s which monks spent their lives in perpetual silence?

12 The root of which garden weed is sometimes used as a coffee substitute?

13 What do you do if you 'keep something under your hat'?

14 What fraction of the world's surface is covered with water?

15 Calamity Jane was an actual person. True or false?

ANSWERS

1. One million. 2. Mushrooms. 3. Its tongue. 4. The bell inside the clock tower. 5. Photographers of celebrities. 6. True. 7. Blue. 8. Drive it. It's slang for a car. 9. Captain Robert Scott. 10. (c) decoy, it is from Dutch. 11. Trappist. 12. Dandelion. 13. Keep it a secret. 14. Two-thirds. 15. True.

SESSION 5

QUIZ 1

TV, music & entertainment

1 What is Dorothy's job in the sitcom *Men Behaving Badly*?

2 What is the name of Elvis Presley's Memphis mansion?

3 According to *Forrest Gump*, what is life like?

4 What is the name of the local pub in *Emmerdale*?

5 What is singer Billie's surname?

6 Name the Seven Dwarfs.

7 Name the two Ross brothers who are both TV and radio presenters.

8 Which musical instrument did Jacqueline du Pré play?

9 In which romantic film did the two main characters meet when he removed a piece of grit from her eye?

10 What was John Lennon's middle name?

11 Who was the father of Michelle Fowler's daughter 'Vicky' in *EastEnders*?

12 Which jazz singer was known as 'Lady Day'?

13 Who duetted with Aretha Franklin on 'Sisters Are Doing it for Themselves'?

14 What was the final line in the film *Gone With the Wind*?

15 In *Only Fools and Horses*, what does Trigger call Rodney?

ANSWERS

1. Nurse. 2. Graceland. 3. A box of chocolates. 4. The Woolpack. 5. Piper. 6. Doc, Happy, Grumpy, Sneezy, Sleepy, Bashful and Dopey. 7. Jonathan and Paul. 8. Cello. 9. *Brief Encounter*. 10. Winston. 11. Dirty Den Watts. 12. Billie Holiday. 13. Annie Lennox. 14. Tomorrow is another day. 15. Dave.

SESSION 5 | QUIZ 2

History

1 Which Roman governor died in 36 AD?

2 Which battle took place in 1415?

3 What nearly happened in London in 1605?

4 What nationality was Josef Tito?

5 Akbar the Great was Mogul emperor of which country?

6 Who, according to Clement Atlee, was 'Fifty per cent genius and fifty per cent bloody fool'?

7 What did Admiral Tirpitz create?

8 What was found in California in 1848?

9 Whose *Book of Household Management* was published in parts from 1859–60?

10 How many times was Disraeli prime minister?

11 Who had a Grand Armée?

12 Who was the grandson of Genghis Khan?

13 What did Nelson turn at Copenhagen?

14 What crippling disease struck F. D. Roosevelt?

15 Which king executed Sir Thomas More?

ANSWERS

1. Pontius Pilate. 2. Agincourt. 3. An explosion at the Houses of Parliament. 4. Croatian. 5. India. 6. Churchill. 7. Germany's World War I fleet. 8. Gold. 9. Mrs Beeton. 10. Twice. 11. Napoleon. 12. Kublai Khan. 13. A blind eye. He looked through his telescope with the wrong eye thus ignoring a signal from his commander. 14. Polio. 15. Henry VIII.

SESSION 5 — QUIZ 3

Sports

1 What did Sebastian Coe retain in Los Angeles?

2 Des Drummond played which sport?

3 What do Lucinda Prior-Palmer and Lucinda Green have in common?

4 Which commentator said, 'The crowd holds its joint breath'?

5 Jackie Stewart never won an American Grand Prix. True or false?

6 Apart from Brazil which was the only country to beat Italy in the 1994 World Cup?

7 Who won gold when Ben Johnson was disqualified in the 1988 Olympics?

8 Which cricketer was refused entry into South Africa in 1968?

9 Which country invented 'Total Football'?

10 Where is the Whitbread Gold Cup run?

11 Juventus play in which Italian city?

12 For what sport is the Isle of Man famous?

13 *Bring on the Clown* was a book about which goalkeeper?

14 Before Allan Wells and Linford Christie who was the only other Briton to win an Olympic 100-metre race?

15 In what year was the women's 3,000-metre run in the Olympics for the first time?

ANSWERS

1. 1,500-metre Olympic Title. 2. Rugby League. 3. They are the same person.
4. Murray Walker. 5. False. 6. Ireland. 7. Carl Lewis. 8. Basil d'Oliveira. 9. Holland.
10. Sandown. 11. Turin. 12. Motor cycling. 13. Bruce Grobelaar. 14. Harold Abrahams.
15. 1984.

SESSION 5 | QUIZ 4

General knowledge

1 What is kept in an ossuary?

2 What is a Pyrrhic victory?

3 Who made an 'error of judgment' on Clapham Common?

4 What was the name of the horse injured in the Hyde Park bombing of 1982?

5 What is a manse?

6 What was celebrated on 8 May 1995?

7 Who is the wife of the former Pakistan cricketer, Imran Kahn?

8 What is the name of the last book in the Bible?

9 In Greek mythology are there (a) 6, (b) 9 or (c) 12 muses?

10 What is a doppelgänger?

11 'Othello' was one of the first of Shakespeare's plays to be published. True or false?

12 With what unit is the stature of a horse measured?

13 How many pounds are there in a hundredweight?

14 What is the most densely populated city in the world?

15 Who wrote 'Jonathan Livingstone Seagull'?

ANSWERS

1. Bones. 2. A victory in which the losses of the victor are as great as those of the defeated. 3. Ron Davies the then Welsh Secretary. 4. Sefton. 5. It is the home of a minister of religion. 6. The fiftieth anniversary of Victory in Europe Day. 7. Jemima Goldsmith. 8. Revelation. 9. (b) 9 muses. 10. The ghostly replica of a living person. 11. False. It was published posthumously. 12. The hand, which is equivalent to four inches. 13. 112. 14. Hong Kong. 15. Richard Bach.

SESSION 5   QUIZ 5

Technology & science

1 How many chains are there in a mile?

2 If you were in the ENT Department of a hospital, what would the full name of the Department be?

3 What is the name given to the study of earthquakes?

4 Who, when handed the Order of Merit on her deathbed, said 'Too kind, too kind'?

5 Which is the only common metal which is liquid at room temperature?

6 What is the only venomous snake in Britain?

7 The invention of Auguste and Louis Lumière was first seen in public in 1895. What was it?

8 What is the chief metal alloyed with iron to make stainless steel?

9 When do 'crepuscular' birds hunt for food?

10 How was the name of the flower 'primrose' derived?

11 What is the cube root of 8?

12 What is the chemical symbol for tin?

13 Which animal is known as 'the ship of the desert'?

14 If a clock in a mirror says ten to three, what time is it?

15 Which branch of physics deals with sound?

ANSWERS

1. 80. 2. Ear, Nose and Throat Department. 3. Seismology. 4. Florence Nightingale. 5. Mercury. 6. Adder. 7. The cinema. 8. Chromium. 9. Dawn and dusk. 10. 'Primrose' is a Middle English word, probably derived from Latin *prima rosa*, first rose. 11. Two. 12. Sn. 13. The camel. 14. Ten past nine. 15. Acoustics.

SESSION 5 · QUIZ 6

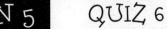

Geography

1 What is the name of the firth between John O'Groats and the Orkney Islands?

2 What is the capital of Austria?

3 Winnipeg is the capital of which Canadian province?

4 What is the point on the Earth's surface directly above an earthquake's focus?

5 In which city would you find the Parthenon?

6 Is Anticosti Island in: (a) Spain, (b) Italy or (c) Canada?

7 Which Dorset seaside town suffered a major landslip on Christmas Day 1839?

8 Captain Cook called them the Friendly Islands, but what are they now known as: (a) Tonga, (b) Fiji or (c) the Cook Islands?

9 Which river flows through New Orleans?

10 Where is the Gulf of Taranto: (a) Brazil, (b) Italy or (c) Spain?

11 Which American state is surrounded by Nebraska, Missouri, Oklahoma and Colorado?

12 Which country has the largest population in South America?

13 In which country is the Aswan Dam?

14 In which ocean is the island of St Helena?

15 Which city is dominated by the Sugar Loaf Mountain?

ANSWERS

1. Pentland Firth. 2. Vienna. 3. Manitoba. 4. Epicentre. 5. Athens. 6. (c) Canada, in the Gulf of St Lawrence. 7. Lyme Regis. 8. (a) Tonga. 9. Mississippi. 10. (b) Italy. 11. Kansas. 12. Brazil. 13. Egypt. 14. Atlantic Ocean. 15. Rio de Janeiro.

46

The Arts

1 Which smiling man was painted by Franz Hals?

2 Who wrote *Watership Down*?

3 Who were John, Susan, Titty, Roger, Peggy and Nancy?

4 Which London art gallery has branches in Liverpool and St Ives?

5 Hans Holbein was official portrait painter to which English king?

6 Which war is the subject of Picasso's painting *Guernica*?

7 Which musical instrument was first built by Bartolomeo Cristofori in Florence in the 17th century?

8 Oscar Wilde described foxhunting as the 'unspeakable in full pursuit' of what?

9 Which satirical magazine, first published in 1841, was also known as *The London Charivari*?

10 In which novel by Agatha Christie does Hercule Poirot first appear?

11 Who wrote *The French Lieutenant's Woman*?

12 What was stolen in Pope's poem *The Rape of the Lock*?

13 In which Lakeland town is William Wordsworth's Dove Cottage?

14 Who wrote *The Sea, The Sea*?

15 Who was the husband of the Indian squaw Minnehaha?

ANSWERS

1. *The Laughing Cavalier*. 2. Richard Adams. 3. *Swallows and Amazons*. 4. The Tate. 5. Henry VIII. 6. Spanish Civil War. 7. Piano. 8. 'The Uneatable'. 9. *Punch*. 10. *The Mysterious Affair at Styles*. 11. John Fowles. 12. A lock of hair. 13. Grasmere. 14. Iris Murdoch. 15. Hiawatha.

SESSION 5 — QUIZ 8

Pot Luck

1 What are cumulus, cirrus and stratus?

2 What was the nickname of the World War I German flying ace Baron von Richthofen?

3 Who originally said, 'Please do not shoot the pianist. He is doing his best'?

4 What makes the cliffs of Dover white?

5 What is the favourite food of the aardvark?

6 How many letters make up the Cambodian alphabet: (a) 14, (b) 74 or (c) 132?

7 In the sign language of British bookmakers at racecourses what odds are indicated by placing your right hand on your nose?

8 What country does 'tequila' come from?

9 From which country did the USA purchase Alaska in 1867?

10 Which British sea captain was mistaken for Lono, the god of fertility, when he landed on Hawaii?

11 How many British monarchs have been deposed since the Norman conquest?

12 Which law relating to the riding of bicycles was abolished in 1930?

13 Which country's car registration mark is PL?

14 What is the word 'perambulator' usually shortened to?

15 What does the abbreviation RSVP mean?

ANSWERS

1. Types of cloud. 2. 'The Red Baron'. 3. Oscar Wilde. 4. Chalk. 5. Ants and termites. 6. (b) 74. 7. 2–1. 8. Mexico. 9. Russia. 10. James Cook. 11. Five. 12. Bell must be rung constantly when in motion. 13. Poland. 14. Pram. 15. Please reply (Répondez s'il vous plaît).

SESSION 6 QUIZ 1

TV, music & entertainment

1. Jim Kerr is lead singer with which band?

2. What is the surname of US comedy actress Ellen?

3. What was the name of the boy who befriended 'E.T.' in the film of the same name?

4. What was the name of Fred and Wilma's daughter in *The Flintstones*?

5. Which US singer opened a theme park called Dollywood?

6. In *Brookside*, there is a character nicknamed Sinbad. What is the character's real name?

7. Who are film actress Jamie Lee Curtis's famous parents?

8. Who provided the voice of Esmeralda in Walt Disney's *The Hunchback of Notre Dame*?

9. In the comedy show *Harry Enfield and Chums*, what is the name of Kevin the Teenager's best friend?

10. Which band had a hit with 'Bittersweet Symphony'?

11. In the film *Muriel's Wedding*, which pop group was Muriel obsessed with?

12. What is The Artist Formerly Known As Prince's original full name?

13. Who played the chauffeur in the film *Driving Miss Daisy*?

14. How did Kurt Cobain of the rock band Nirvana die?

15. Who plays Charlie Fairhead in the BBC drama series *Casualty*?

ANSWERS

1. Simple Minds. 2. DeGeneres. 3. Elliot. 4. Pebbles. 5. Dolly Parton. 6. Thomas Sweeney. 7. Tony Curtis and Janet Leigh. 8. Demi Moore. 9. Perry. 10. The Verve. 11. Abba. 12. Prince Rogers Nelson. 13. Morgan Freeman. 14. He shot himself. 15. Derek Thompson.

SESSION 6   QUIZ 2

History

1   Who was William IV's niece?

2   During which war did the Battle of Naseby occur?

3   Which people lived in modern-day Yucatán, Belize and N. Guatemala?

4   What was printed for the first time in 1611?

5   What nationality was Marco Polo?

6   Who revolted in 1381?

7   In 1817, Sir Robert Peel stood for MP at Oxford University. True or false?

8   Who was Stalin's foreign minister throughout World War II?

9   Who led the Oxford Movement in the 19th century?

10   Which American president couldn't tell a lie?

11   What did William the Conqueror do when he landed on English soil?

12   What did the English take from the Dutch in 1664?

13   Which judge presided at the 'Bloody Assizes'?

14   What is Sunday, 30 January 1972 also known as?

15   Who were the Cathars?

ANSWERS

SESSION 6 | QUIZ 3

Sports

1 Ray Reardon of snooker fame was nicknamed 'Dracula'.
   True or false?

2 In which city were the first World Athletics Championships held?

3 In which European country was John McEnroe born?

4 What was Dick Fosbury's contribution to sport?

5 How many points do you score for a goal in Australian
   rules football?

6 Who play at Carrow Road?

7 The Curtis Cup is competed for by which sportsmen?

8 Who was the Australian Cricket Captain from 1975-82?

9 What number did Gareth Edwards wear on the back of his shirt?

10 What sport did the notorious O. J. Simpson play?

11 Which Australian squash player was born on 11 March 1947?

12 Rod Laver was left-handed. True or false?

13 What did Dick Beardsley win on its first running in 1981?

14 Botham and Kapil Dev have both taken 200 Test wickets and
   scored 3,000 runs. Who was the first person to achieve this feat?

15 For which club did Bobby Windsor play?

ANSWERS

1. True. 2. Helsinki. 3. Germany. 4. He invented a new high jump technique called the
Fosbury Flop. 5. 6 points. 6. Norwich City. 7. Golfers. 8. Greg Chappell. 9. Nine.
10. American football. 11. Geoff Hunt. 12. True. 13. The London Marathon.
14. Gary Sobers. 15. Pontypool.

SESSION 6 | QUIZ 4

General knowledge

1. In computing, what are 'FAQs'?

2. What have the 'Torrey Canyon' and the 'Exxon Valdez' have in common?

3. What is a fosse?

4. What did the prickly Lucien B. Smith invent?

5. How old was Adrian Mole when he first appeared?

6. Cirrus, rhombus, nimbus and stratus; which is the odd one out?

7. How many 'James Bond' novels did Fleming write?

8. Who painted the *Irises*?

9. Italy has produced the most popes. True or false?

10. Which country has the largest Jewish population?

11. On average does the koala sleep: (a) 13, (b) 19 or (c) 22 hours a day?

12. Which country has the highest cattle population in the world?

13. What are Merchant Taylors, Haberdashers and Salters?

14. What is a lycanthrope?

15. The Taj Mahal was built for what purpose?

ANSWERS

1. Frequently asked questions. 2. They are both oil tankers that spilled their cargo. 3. A ditch or moat. 4. Barbed wire. 5. Thirteen and three-quarters. He is the star of the books by Sue Townsend. 6. Rhombus. It is a shape, the others are cloud types. 7. twelve. Amazingly there have been 18 films based on these. 8. Vincent Van Gogh. 9. True. Over 200 popes have been Italian. 10. USA. 11. (c) 22. 12. India, where the cow is sacred. 13. Livery companies. 14. A werewolf: half-man and half-wolf. 15. As a mausoleum built by Shah Jahan in memory of his wife.

SESSION 6   QUIZ 5

Technology & science

1   What is the period of one thousand years called?

2   Which letter of the alphabet is used to denote an unknown quantity?

3   'Love apple' is an old name for which fruit?

4   What did Walter Hunt invent?

5   What is the meaning of the abbreviation EPNS?

6   What is the name given to the study of drugs and their effects?

7   Spider, hermit and masked are varieties of which creature?

8   Which theory is based on the formula $E = mc^2$?

9   From what raw material is aluminium obtained?

10 What animal is known to Australians as the 'jumbuck'?

11 With what is the science of cryogenics concerned?

12 What food flavouring is obtained from the crocus plant?

13 Which town in Essex obtains its name from the crocus plant?

14 What mathematical term means 'without end or limits'?

15 What are pinto, runner and kidney?

ANSWERS

1. A millennium. 2. x. 3. Tomato. 4. The safety pin. 5. Electroplated nickel silver. 6. Pharmacology. 7. Crab. 8. Relativity. 9. Bauxite. 10. Sheep. 11. Production of very low temperatures and resulting physical consequences. 12. Saffron. 13. Saffron Walden; crocuses grew in the surrounding fields in the Middle Ages. 14. Infinity. 15. All are types of bean.

SESSION 6   QUIZ 6

Geography

1   Where would you find the Great Sandy Desert?

2   In which American state is the Great Salt Lake?

3   Which Scottish town at the head of the Firth of Tay shares its name with an Australian city?

4   What is the name for the part of the Earth overlying the mantle?

5   Which river flows through Dublin?

6   Which country lies to the north of Bolivia?

7   On which river would you find the Lorelei Rock?

8   Which is the nearest lake to Verona in Italy?

9   In which country would you be if you were on a pilgrimage to Santiago de Compostela?

10   In June 1997 nineteen people were killed in volcanic eruptions on which island?

11   On what sea is the Crimean town of Yalta?

12   Which of these islands is furthest north: (a) Cyprus, (b) Sicily or (c) Crete?

13   Pico de Aneto is the highest point in which mountain range?

14   Innsbruck is in which country?

15   Lake Victoria is owned by three countries. Two are Kenya and Tanzania, which is the other?

ANSWERS

1. Australia. 2. Utah. 3. Perth. 4. Crust. 5. River Liffey. 6. Brazil. 7. Rhine. 8. Lake Garda. 9. Spain. 10. Montserrat. 11. Black Sea. 12. (b) Sicily. 13. Pyrenees. 14. Austria. 15. Uganda.

54

The Arts

1. Where did Kubla Khan decree that his pleasure dome should be built?

2. What was the name of the hunchback of Notre Dame?

3. Who wrote *Kidnapped* and *Treasure Island*?

4. Doric, Ionic, Corinthian and Tuscan are types of what?

5. Under what name did the French actress Rosine Bernard achieve international success?

6. In *The Hunting of the Snark*, what did the Snark turn out to be?

7. Kipling's 'great grey-green, greasy Limpopo River' is an example of what?

8. What was the name of the miser created by George Eliot?

9. Which artist painted a series of paintings of water lilies?

10. What was Picasso's first name?

11. In a theatre what is the area between the curtain and the orchestra pit called?

12. In which novel does Holden Caulfield declare everyone a 'Phoney'?

13. What are the two cities in Dickens' *A Tale of Two Cities*?

14. Which Polynesian island was the final home of the painter Gauguin?

15. By what name is the Greek painter Domenikos Theotocopoulos better known?

ANSWERS

1. Xanadu. 2. Quasimodo. 3. Robert Louis Stevenson. 4. Columns, also called Orders. 5. Sarah Bernhardt. 6. A Boojum. 7. Alliteration. 8. *Silas Marner*. 9. Claude Monet. 10. Pablo. 11. Proscenium. 12. *Catcher in the Rye*. 13. Paris and London. 14. Tahiti. 15. El Greco.

SESSION 6 QUIZ 8

Pot Luck

1   In 1825, above what speed was it claimed that train passengers would suffer mental disorders and risk suffocation: (a) 12 mph, (b) 32 mph or (c) 62 mph?

2   In the 18th century what was the daily ration of rum for each sailor in the Royal Navy?

3   Which ship first sent the Morse code signal 'SOS'?

4   What colour is azure?

5   St Fiacre is the patron saint of: (a) taxi drivers, (b) nurses or (c) bricklayers?

6   Whose epitaph in St Paul's Cathedral says 'If his monument you seek, look around'?

7   Which day follows All Saints' Day on 1 November?

8   On 22 April 1884 in which English town did the country's most destructive earthquake occur?

9   Which dog's best friend is a bird called Woodstock?

10   What are traditionally eaten on Shrove Tuesday?

11   What is a bestiary?

12   A minaret is: (a) a slow dance, (b) a tall tower or (c) a minor French dignitary?

13   Which brewing company's red triangle was the first registered trademark?

14   In the middle ages which people were branded with the letter B?

15   Where would you find the Wheat State, Bananaland, the Cabbage Patch, Land of the White Ant and Groperland?

ANSWERS

1. (a) 12 mph. 2. One pint. 3. The Titanic. 4. Blue. 5. (a) taxi drivers. 6. Sir Christopher Wren. 7. All Souls' Day. 8. Colchester. 9. 'Snoopy'. 10. Pancakes. 11. An illustrated book of animals. 12. (b) a tall tower. 13. Bass. 14. Blasphemers. 15. Australia.

SESSION 7 QUIZ 1

TV, music & entertainment

1   John Wayne's real name is Marion Michael Morrison. True or false?

2   Name the three children in the sitcom *Roseanne*.

3   Who had a hit in 1998 with 'Brimful of Asha'?

4   Which character in *Coronation Street* is played by Amanda Barrie?

5   Who played Willy Wonka in the film *Willy Wonka and the Chocolate Factory*?

6   Which French composer wrote *Boléro*?

7   Who or what was 'Rosebud' in the film *Citizen Kane*?

8   Singer Louise used to be a member of which group?

9   Which international footballer is co-host of a TV chat show and a team captain in *A Question of Sport*?

10   What kind of animal is Babe in the film of the same name?

11   In *Happy Days*, what was the Fonz's full name?

12   Which musical instrument did Louis Armstrong play?

13   Natasha Richardson and Miranda Richardson are sisters. True or false?

14   What was the name of the police officer in the cartoon series *Top Cat*?

15   Who was the creator of *Fireball XL5*, *Thunderbirds* and *Captain Scarlet*?

ANSWERS

1. True. 2. Becky, Darlene, and D. J. 3. Cornershop. 4. Alma Baldwin.
5. Gene Wilder. 6. Maurice Ravel. 7. 'Kane's childhood sled. 8. Eternal. 9. Ally McCoist.
10. A pig. 11. Arthur Fonzarelli. 12. Trumpet. 13. False. 14. Officer Dibble.
15. Gerry Anderson.

SESSION 7 QUIZ 2

History

1 By what name is the failure of a joint stock company trading with South America, better known?

2 Who was the wife of Louis XVI?

3 Who did Idi Amin oust from office?

4 What was the name of the first Duke of Marlborough?

5 Which king was known as Rufus?

6 Who was Montezuma II?

7 What nationality was statesman Jan Smuts?

8 What were Emmeline and her daughter Christabel?

9 Which Crusade did Richard III lead?

10 To which island was Napoleon banished in 1814?

11 Which dictator was famous for making the trains run on time?

12 What was Henry Shrapnel's invention?

13 Who was also known as Carolus Magnus?

14 Who was the liberator of South America?

15 What happened in South Africa on 21 March 1960?

ANSWERS

1. The South Sea Bubble. 2. Marie-Antoinette. 3. Milton Obote. 4. John Churchill. 5. William II. 6. The last emperor of the Aztecs. 7. South African. 8. They were suffragettes and their surname was Pankhurst. 9. The third, from 1189-92. 10. Elba. 11. Mussolini. 12. The artillery shell. 13. Charlemagne. 14. Simón Bolívar. 15. The Sharpeville massacre.

SESSION 7 QUIZ 3

Sports

1   Which number did Martin Peters wear during the 1966 World Cup Finals?

2   Who was rugby's famous streaker?

3   Where was Peter Allis born?

4   What is the name of the 14th hole at Sandwich?

5   Where were the 1980 Olympics held?

6   Who won the women's Super G at the 1998 Winter Olympics?

7   With what part of his anatomy did Trevor Brooking score in the 1980 FA Cup Final?

8   Which team did Tom Finney play for?

9   Which woman won the first London marathon?

10   Who were the cricket county champions in 1998?

11   Which teams participated in the 1998 Coca Cola Final?

12   At what sport does Steve Backley compete?

13   Who are the Pumas?

14   What is the name of the Irishman who runs the Jordan Formula 1 team?

15   Who did Inter Milan beat in the 1998 EUFA Cup Final?

ANSWERS

1. 16. 2. Erika Roe. 3. Berlin. 4. The Suez. 5. Moscow. 6. Picabo Street. 7. His head.
8. Preston North End. 9. Inge Simonsen. 10. Leicester. 11. Chelsea and Middlesbrough.
12. The Javelin. 13. Argentina Rugby Union team. 14. Eddie Jordan. 15. Lazio, they won 3-1.

SESSION 7   QUIZ 4

General knowledge

1 What four letters did the Romans use to signify the Senate and People of Rome?

2 Who is the 'Enlightened One'?

3 Which family of actors have the Christian names, Henry, Peter and Jane?

4 The horse mackerel is a fish. True or false?

5 What do Americans call aubergines?

6 In C. S. Lewis' *Narnia Chronicles*, what is 'Aslan'?

7 What electronic arcade game is a derivative of bagatelle?

8 What does DNA stand for?

9 Did the potato originate in (a) Sudan, (b) Turkey or (c) Southern Chile?

10 If you have otitis, what part of the body is affected?

11 What nationality was Edgar Allan Poe?

12 What was a heliogram?

13 What has the postcode SW1A 2AA?

14 What do the initials IHS stand for?

15 Where would you find a fuselage?

ANSWERS

1. SPQR. 2. Buddha. 3. Fonda. 4. True. 5. Egg-plant. 6. A lion. 7. Pinball. 8. Deoxyribonucleic acid. 9. (c) Southern Chile. 10. The ear. 11. American. 12. An early type of photograph. 13. 10 Downing Street. 14. Jesus Hominum Salvator – Jesus Saviour of Mankind. 15. In an aircraft. It is the aircraft's body.

SESSION 7 | QUIZ 5

Technology & science

1   What is the chemical symbol for gold?

2   What is the name of the main protein in milk?

3   What are swallowtail, Scottish Angus and Camberwell?

4   ERNIE is the name of the computer which selects Premium Bond winners. What do the letters stand for?

5   What is the name of the process by which plants make food?

6   Who invented dynamite?

7   A female fox is a vixen. What is a male fox called?

8   'Smog' is a contraction of which two words?

9   Which cereal is obtained from the roots of the cassava plant?

10   Name the instrument used for detecting radioactivity.

11   A morello is what kind of fruit?

12   Which mathematician invented logarithms?

13   What is the Roman numeral for 1,000?

14   What name is given to the biological science concerning heredity?

15   A horse is measured in hands. How many centimetres is a hand?

ANSWERS

1. Au. 2. Casein. 3. All are types of butterfly. 4. Electronic Random Number Indicator Equipment. 5. Photosynthesis. 6. Alfred Nobel. 7. A dog. 8. 'Smoke' and 'fog'. 9. Tapioca. 10. Geiger counter. 11. Cherry. 12. John Napier. 13. M. 14. Genetics. 15. Ten centimetres.

SESSION 7 — QUIZ 6

Geography

1   The Thar desert lies in Pakistan and which other country:
(a) India, (b) Iran or (c) Afghanistan?

2   What significant event happened in 1980 at Mount St Helens
in America?

3   The Colorado River flows through Texas. True or false?

4   Which of these Greek islands is not in the Aegean Sea:
(a) Limnos, (b) Kos or (c) Corfu?

5   Which can move the largest sized rock particles, water or ice?

6   The 'Little Mermaid' is a statue in the harbour of which
European city?

7   In which country are the Angel Falls?

8   The Ettrick and Teviot rivers join with which major river in the
Scottish Borders?

9   Which of these Spanish coasts is furthest south: (a) Costa Blanca,
(b) Costa Dorada or (c) Costa Brava?

10   Mount Etna is over twice as high as Mount Vesuvius.
True or false?

11   Which is further, London to Lisbon or London to Rome?

12   The Okavango River in Africa never reaches the sea, but ends in
a landlocked basin in which country?

13   Which city is served by Schiphol airport?

14   What is mined at Bingham Canyon in Utah to make it the largest
man-made hole in the world?

15   Which is larger, Loch Lomond or Lake Windermere?

ANSWERS

1. (a) India. 2. A volcanic eruption. 3. True. There is also another Colorado River in Colorado.
4. (c) Corfu. 5. Ice. 6. Copenhagen. 7. Venezuela. 8. River Tweed. 9. (a) Costa Blanca.
10. True. 11. London to Lisbon. 12. Botswana. 13. Amsterdam. 14. Copper.
15. Loch Lomond.

62

 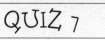
QUIZ 7

The Arts

1 The adventures of which horse were chronicled by Anna Sewell?

2 Who wrote *Lolita*?

3 Which inventor of the sugar cube also founded a London art gallery?

4 Who created the picture *The Scream*?

5 Which artistic movement was begun by Picasso and Braque?

6 Which titled detective appeared in the crime novels of Dorothy L. Sayers?

7 In *A Midsummer Night's Dream* who is the King of the Fairies?

8 Who wrote *Brideshead Revisited*?

9 'Only connect' is the often repeated theme of which novel by E. M. Forster?

10 Which poet was married to Ted Hughes?

11 What happens to Tom and Maggie Tulliver at the end of *The Mill on the Floss*?

12 According to Peter Pan what was created when the first baby laughed for the first time?

13 Which 18th-century Royal portrait painter also painted a famous picture of the actress Mrs Sarah Siddons?

14 Which novel by Daphne du Maurier is set in a remote Cornish inn?

15 Which Italian city featured most often in the paintings of Canaletto?

ANSWERS

1. Black Beauty. 2. Vladimir Nabokov. 3. Tate. 4. Edward Munch. 5. Cubism. 6. Lord Peter Wimsey. 7. Oberon. 8. Evelyn Waugh. 9. Howards End. 10. Sylvia Plath. 11. They drown. 12. The first fairy. 13. Thomas Gainsborough. 14. Jamaica Inn. 15. Venice.

SESSION 7 QUIZ 8

Pot Luck

1 According to the proverb you should strike while what is hot?

2 In which war did the original 'Backroom Boys' take part?

3 Which bird is traditionally believed to sing before it dies?

4 Which two words, sounding alike, mean the same as these phrases: two of a kind/a fruit?

5 What is 'Welsh rarebit'?

6 How many bottles of wine make up a magnum?

7 What is a 'pied' animal?

8 What is a 'purse' called in the United States?

9 What nationality were the original Hooligans?

10 Under what circumstances would you wear sackcloth and ashes?

11 What are the Palatine, Capitoline, Aventine, Caelia, Esquiline, Viminal and Quirnal?

12 Which French ruler referred to the English as 'a nation of shopkeepers'?

13 'Every day, in every way, I am getting better and better.' Whose formula was this?

14 What does 'antediluvian' mean?

15 How was the Australian and New Zealand Army Corps better known?

ANSWERS

1. The iron. 2. World War II. 3. Swan. 4. Pair/pear. 5. Cheese on toast with seasoning. 6. Two. 7. More than one colour, usually black and white. 8. A handbag (also a boxer's winnings as in England). 9. Irish. 10. When you are sorry. 11. Seven hills of Rome. 12. Napoleon. 13. Emil Coué. 14. Before the flood. 15. ANZACs.

SESSION 8 QUIZ 1

TV, music & entertainment

1. What is Madonna's surname?

2. What is the name of the fictional town where *Neighbours* is set?

3. George Clooney is the son of Rosemary Clooney. True or false?

4. David Jones is the real name of: (a) David Bowie, (b) David Essex or (c) David Cassidy?

5. Who played Arnold Schwarzenegger's twin brother in the film *Twins*?

6. With which band is Cerys Matthews the lead singer?

7. What was the name of the guardian angel in *It's a Wonderful Life*?

8. What is the name of Victor Meldrew's wife in *One Foot in the Grave*?

9. Which famous singer comes from Tiger Bay, Cardiff?

10. Alison Steadman played Abigail in the BBC production of Mike Leigh's play *Abigail's Party*. True or false?

11. Which musical features the songs 'Summer Nights' and 'Hopelessly Devoted to You'?

12. Which US chat-show host finishes each show with the words 'Take care of yourselves ... and each other.'?

13. Name the six singing Osmond brothers.

14. Name the actors who played the part of evil Max Cady in the 1962 version and in the 1991 version of *Cape Fear*.

15. Who shot 'J. R.'?

ANSWERS

1. Ciccone. 2. Erinsborough. 3. False. He is her nephew. 4. (a) David Bowie. 5. Danny De Vito. 6. Catatonia. 7. Clarence. 8. Margaret. 9. Shirley Bassey. 10. False. She played Bev. Abigail does not appear in the play. 11. *Grease*. 12. Jerry Springer. 13. Alan, Wayne, Merrill, Jay, Donny and Little Jimmy. 14. Robert Mitchum in 1962 and Robert De Niro in 1991. 15. Kristin Shepherd, Sue Ellen's sister.

SESSION 8 QUIZ 2

History

1 Which king married Lady Elizabeth Bowes-Lyon?

2 Which fleet was defeated at the Battle of Aboukir Bay?

3 Which famous musician sired 13 children?

4 Who was executed in 1587 by Queen Elizabeth?

5 In what city might one have found a Doge?

6 Which poet wrote the *Morte d'Arthur*?

7 By which name was Giovanni Caboto better known?

8 Was English used for the first time in Parliament in (a) 1178, (b) 1245 or (c) 1362?

9 What was abolished in Britain in 1833?

10 Who was the first Christian martyr in Great Britain?

11 Who did the Republicans fight in the Spanish Civil War?

12 In which country is the Bay of Pigs?

13 Convicts were dumped in Australia for the last time in 1879. True or false?

14 By what other nickname was William the Conqueror known?

15 Who was known as the 'Desert Fox'?

ANSWERS

1. George VI. She is the Queen Mother. 2. French. 3. J. S. Bach. 4. Mary Queen of Scots.
5. Venice. 6. Thomas Malory. 7. John Cabot, the explorer. 8. (c) 1362. 9. Slavery.
10. St Alban. 11. Nationalists. 12. Cuba. 13. False. The last convicts arrived in 1849.
14. The Bastard. 15. Erwin Rommel.

SESSION 8 · QUIZ 3

Sports

1 What sports make up the triathlon?

2 What arena is 6.1 metres square?

3 How many balls are there on a snooker table?

4 Tom Morris Sr. is the oldest winner of what?

5 Which player has scored the most runs in Test Cricket?

6 What was her surname before the tennis star became Mrs Crawley?

7 Mark McNulty was born in 1953 in which country?

8 What sport do the Detroit Tigers play?

9 What did John L. Sullivan use for the first time in 1892?

10 What is John McEnroe's middle name?

11 Bob Willis added 'Dylan' to his name in honour of the musician Bob. True or false?

12 Which footballer has played the most times for England?

13 Vasily Alexeyev represented Russia at which sport?

14 Who painted the picture, 'Going to the Match'?

15 Where is Moor Park golf course?

ANSWERS

1. Running, swimming and cycling. 2. A boxing ring. 3. 22 including the cue ball. 4. The British Open. 5. Don Bradman. 6. Goolagong. 7. Zimbabwe. 8. Baseball. 9. Boxing gloves. 10. Patrick. 11. True. 12. Peter Shilton. 13. Weightlifting. 14. L. S. Lowry. 15. Near Rickmansworth, Herts.

SESSION 8   QUIZ 4

General knowledge

1   What does 'Cantab.' after someone's name mean?

2   What everyday item has the dimensions 17 by 13.5 inches?

3   What do Italians call Sellotape?

4   Who wrote a book called *The Interpretations of Dreams'*?

5   What style of art did Pablo Picasso help to found?

6   What is Maria Montessori famous for?

7   Are there (a) 54, (b) 367 or (c) 862 main acupuncture points on the human body?

8   Jenner developed a vaccine for which disease?

9   By what name are Carreras, Domingo and Pavarotti collectively known?

10   Which Shakespeare character has the most lines?

11   Buena Vista are associated with which film makers?

12   Winston Churchill won the Nobel Prize for peace. True or false?

13   Which was the first country to ban capital punishment?

14   Who is Tenzing Norgay normally associated with?

15   What does the abbreviation 'NB' mean?

ANSWERS

1. A graduate from the university of Cambridge. 2. Foolscap paper. 3. Scotch. 4. Sigmund Freud. 5. Cubism. 6. Education. 7. (b) 367. 8. Smallpox. 9. The Three Tenors. 10. Hamlet. 11. Walt Disney. 12. False. He received it for literature in 1953. 13. Russia in 1826. 14. Edmund Hillary, the man with whom he climbed Everest. 15. Note well (Latin: nota bene).

SESSION 8 — QUIZ 5

Technology & science

1 Which fruit has the Latin name of *Malus pumila*?

2 What type of animal is *Pulex irritans*?

3 *Homo sapiens* is the Latin name for 'human beings'. What is the translation?

4 What is the name given to the substance which speeds up or slows down a chemical reaction?

5 In dyeing, what name is given to the substance used for fixing the colour?

6 What is the connection between emus, cassowaries and kiwis?

7 What is the name given to the lowest temperature theoretically possible?

8 What is the mathematical term used to describe the shape of a cell in a honeycomb?

9 How many degrees are there in a circle?

10 What is the name given to the green pigment in plants?

11 What is the instrument used to measure atmospheric pressure?

12 What colour spots has the common ladybird?

13 What is the gestation period of a giraffe?

14 For which invention of 1852 is Elisha G. Otis credited?

15 What is ESP?

ANSWERS

1. Apple. 2. The human flea. 3. Literally, it translates as 'wise man'. 4. Catalyst.
5. A mordant. 6. All are birds that cannot fly. 7. Absolute Zero. 8. Hexagon.
9. 360 degrees. 10. Chlorophyll. 11. Barometer. 12. Black. 13. 450 days.
14. The mechanical lift. 15. Extrasensory perception.

SESSION 8   QUIZ 6

Geography

1 Which range of hills lies along part of the border of Scotland with England?

2 Ratisbon is the English name for which German city?

3 In which city, separated from Germany by the Rhine, could you see the Palais de l'Europe?

4 Which Canadian province stretches from the St Lawrence Seaway in the east to Hudson Bay in the west?

5 Which English city is situated on the River Irwell?

6 What proportion of the world's fresh water is contained in Lake Baikal in Russia: (a) one fifth, (b) one fiftieth or (c) one five hundreth?

7 What is the capital of Bolivia?

8 Which river flows through Hamburg?

9 Hollywood is in which American city?

10 Which of these towns is outside the M25: (a) Epsom, (b) Esher or (c) Dorking?

11 What are the grasslands of North America called?

12 Aconcagua is the highest peak in which mountain range?

13 What is the name for land which has been reclaimed from the sea?

14 In which country are the remains of the Inca city Machu Picchu?

15 The Seikan railway tunnel is 54 kilometres long; which country is it in?

ANSWERS

1. Cheviot Hills. 2. Regensburg. 3. Strasbourg. 4. Quebec. 5. Manchester. 6. (a) one fifth. 7. La Paz. 8. River Elbe. 9. Los Angeles. 10. (c) Dorking. 11. Prairies. 12. Andes. 13. Polder. 14. Peru. 15. Japan.

70

The Arts

1 Which poet was declared to be 'Mad, bad and dangerous to know'?

2 Where does the phrase 'If music be the food of love, play on' originate?

3 Who wrote *The Great Gatsby*?

4 Which romantic novelist's autobiography is called 'We Danced All Night'?

5 What is Christ carrying in Holman Hunt's painting *The Light of the World*?

6 Which fantastical garden was painted by Hieronymus Bosch?

7 The name of which musical instrument is the Hawaiian word for 'jumping flea'?

8 Whose poems contain no capital letters or punctuation marks?

9 Who was the 'Shropshire Lad'?

10 In Botticelli's *The Birth of Venus*, what is the figure of Venus standing on?

11 'With monstrous head and sickening cry and ears like errant wings', which creature is being described by G. K. Chesterton?

12 Who wrote *The Grapes of Wrath*?

13 In which city are Colin Dexter's *Inspector Morse* novels set?

14 What did Puck place on Bottom's head in *A Midsummer Night's Dream*?

15 Who was Ebenezer Scrooge's deceased partner?

ANSWERS

1. Lord Byron. 2. *Twelfth Night*. 3. F. Scott Fitzgerald. 4. Barbara Cartland. 5. A lantern. 6. *Garden of Earthly Delights*. 7. Ukulele. 8. e e cummings. 9. A. E. Housman. 10. A clam shell. 11. Donkey. 12. John Steinbeck. 13. Oxford. 14. An ass's head. 15. Jacob Marley.

SESSION 8 — QUIZ 8

Pot Luck

1 Who originally wrote, 'the female of the species is more deadly than the male'?

2 What is a 'red letter' day?

3 What did alchemists believe they could turn metals into?

4 Orang-utans are monkeys. True or false?

5 What is the main ingredient of risotto?

6 'If two wrongs don't make a right, try three', was said to be the motto of which US president?

7 Complete this quotation 'Where ignorance is bliss ...'.

8 Who wrote *War and Peace*?

9 In which year were the new towns of Runcorn and Redditch built?

10 Who was the 'Lady with the Lamp'?

11 Which 'Cluedo' character is called 'Oberst von Gatow' in Germany?

12 What fruit is perry made from?

13 What word beginning with 'o' is both a unit of weight and a snow leopard?

14 Who was 'Good Queen Bess'?

15 What colour is cochineal?

ANSWERS

1. Rudyard Kipling. 2. A lucky day. 3. Gold. 4. False, they are apes. 5. Rice. 6. Nixon. 7. ''Tis folly to be wise'. 8. Leo Tolstoy. 9. 1964. 10. Florence Nightingale. 11. 'Colonel Mustard'. 12. Pears. 13. Ounce. 14. Queen Elizabeth I. 15. Red.

SESSION 9

QUIZ 1

TV, music & entertainment

1 Who was the first 'Bond girl'?

2 Which singer was nicknamed 'the Little Sparrow'?

3 Name the two Appleton sisters who are members of the band All Saints?

4 In which film did Sean Connery play Harrison Ford's father?

5 Name the seven children in TV's *The Waltons*.

6 Who is the lead singer with Republica?

7 Who is the presenter of *Animal Hospital*?

8 Linda Hunt won an Academy Award for Best Supporting Actress for her part in *The Year of Living Dangerously* in 1983. What was unusual about this?

9 Which comic opera by Gilbert and Sullivan has a Japanese theme?

10 Who was buried under the patio in *Brookside*?

11 In *Field of Dreams*, Kevin Costner's character hears a voice saying, 'If you build it, he will come.' What is he to build?

12 'Stand by your Man' was a hit for: (a) Dolly Parton, (b) Tammy Wynette or (c) Crystal Gayle?

13 What was the name of the central character in the TV drama serial *Roots*?

14 Who provided the voice of 'the Genie' in Walt Disney's *Aladdin*?

15 Rod Stewart is Scottish. True or false?

ANSWERS

1. Ursula Andress. 2. Edith Piaf. 3. Natalie and Nicole. 4. *Indiana Jones and the Last Crusade*. 5. John Boy, Mary Ellen, Erin, Jason, Ben, Jim Bob and Elizabeth. 6. Saffron. 7. Rolf Harris. 8. She played the part of a man. 9. *The Mikado*. 10. 'Trevor Jordache'. 11. A baseball field. 12. (b) Tammy Wynette. 13. Kunta Kinte. 14. Robin Williams. 15. False. He is English. His father was Scottish.

SESSION 9 QUIZ 2

History

1 Stanley Baldwin was the only prime minister during the reign of which king?

2 Did World War II last: (a) 1,896, (b) 2,174 or (c) 3,052 days?

3 According to Napoleon, England was a nation of what?

4 Who lived at Avignon during the 14th century?

5 What was opened in 80 AD in order to host mock-battles and gladiator fights?

6 In which year did the Panama Canal open?

7 Was Coventry cathedral consecrated in: (a) 1956, (b) 1962 or (c) 1965?

8 What kind of institution was Elizabeth Fry famous for reforming?

9 Who was Henry VIII's second wife?

10 In which year did the massacre at Tiananmen Square take place?

11 How many Tolpuddle Martyrs were there?

12 Who was the apostle of the Gentiles?

13 Zog was the dictator of which country?

14 What nickname was given to American General Thomas Jackson?

15 No British prime minister has ever been assassinated. True or false?

ANSWERS

1. Edward VIII. 2. (b) 2,174. 3. Shopkeepers. 4. The Pope. 5. The Colosseum. 6. 1914. 7. (b) 1962. 8. Prisons. 9. Anne Boleyn. 10. 1989. 11. Six. 12. Paul. 13. Albania. 14. Stonewall. 15. False. Spencer Perceval was killed in 1812.

SESSION 9 QUIZ 3

Sports

1   How many holes are there in a ten-pin bowling ball?

2   Where was the golfer, Nancy Lopez, born?

3   Who won the 1998 Grand National?

4   Which Welshman won Olympic gold in Japan for the long jump?

5   In which year did he win?

6   Which team did Everton beat in the FA Cup Final of 1984?

7   Nat Lofthouse played for which club?

8   What nationality is tennis player Martina Hingis?

9   Who won the Goodwood Cup in 1997 and 1998?

10   To which country do the Springboks belong?

11   Which rugby league star was called the 'Voll'?

12   Is René Arnoux: (a) French, (b) Swiss or (c) Canadian?

13   In the Isle of Man motorcycle races, what do the initials 'TT' stand for?

14   Who devised boxing's rules?

15   Above which wind speed are athletics records invalid?

ANSWERS

1. Three. 2. Torrance, California. 3. Earth Summit. 4. Lynn Davies. 5. 1964. 6. Watford. 7. Bolton. 8. Swiss. 9. Double Trigger. 10. South Africa. 11. Tom von Vollenhoven. 12. (a) French. 13. Tourist Trophy. 14. Marquess of Queensberry. 15. 2 metres per second.

SESSION 9   QUIZ 4

General knowledge

1 Which is the heaviest mammal?

2 How many farthings were there in half a crown?

3 Where is Davy Jones' Locker?

4 What does 'aka' stand for?

5 Who wrote *Roots*?

6 Who succeeded Neil Kinnock as the leader of the Labour party?

7 The sycamore leaf is the national symbol of Canada.
   True or false?

8 Which bone is longer, the radius or the ulna?

9 What is 25 March called in the church calendar?

10 What does 'mammal' mean?

11 What is 'its own reward'?

12 Which metal is known as quicksilver?

13 North Americans call it Rutabaga, what do the English call it?

14 Whose heart was 'strangely warmed'?

15 By what name are the Gospels Matthew, Mark and Luke known?

ANSWERS

1. The Blue Whale. 2. 120. 3. The bottom of the sea. 4. Also known as. 5. Alex Haley. 6. John Smith. 7. False. It is the maple leaf. 8. The radius. 9. Lady Day, when the church remembers the annunciation to Mary. 10. Possessing breasts. 11. Virtue. 12. Mercury. 13. Swede. 14. John Wesley spoke in this way to describe the moment of his conversion to Christianity. 15. The Synoptic Gospels.

76

QUIZ 5

Technology & science

1   The deficiency of which vitamin causes scurvy?

2   How many coloured squares has a Rubik Cube?

3   What type of creature is a sidewinder?

4   To which profession would a person belong if they had FRCVS after their name?

5   What does a palaeontologist study?

6   What is considered to be the least nutritious fruit/vegetable?

7   What is the name given to the short tail of a rabbit?

8   Which pistol took its name from the person who patented it in 1835?

9   What are the names given to the male and female swan?

10 Who discovered X-rays in 1895?

11 Granny Smith, James Grieve and Egremont Russet are all types of which fruit?

12 What is the name of the sugar found in fruit?

13 From which language does the term *eureka* come?

14 What Nobel Prize winner wrote a book called *The Double Helix*?

15 What do Fairbourne, Snowdon and Leighton Buzzard have in common?

ANSWERS

1. Vitamin C. 2. 54. 3. Desert rattlesnake. 4. Veterinary surgeon. 5. Fossils. 6. The cucumber. 7. Scut. 8. Colt. 9. Cob (male) and pen (female). 10. Röntgen. 11. Apple. 12. Fructose. 13. Greek. 14. James D. Watson. 15. All have narrow gauge railways.

SESSION 9 QUIZ 6

Geography

1 Which cathedral town in north west England was important in Roman times because of its proximity to Hadrian's Wall?

2 The Grand Canyon is in: (a) Arizona, (b) Nevada or (c) Utah?

3 The island of Tierra del Fuego is owned by two countries. One is Argentina, what is the other?

4 In which French city could you walk along the 'Promenade des Anglais'?

5 What was the country of Myanmar formerly known as?

6 Which Pacific island, famous for hundreds of stone statues, was annexed by Chile in 1888?

7 A 'barchan' is: (a) a mountain lake, (b) a crescent-shaped sand dune or (c) an underground cave?

8 Which former Olympic city is on the River Isar?

9 Which inland sea is in the countries of Kazakhstan and Uzbekistan?

10 What is the statistical study of population called?

11 Four countries have coastlines on the Gulf of Aqaba; three are Egypt, Israel and Saudi Arabia, what is the fourth?

12 Which sultanate, under British protection, is on the north coast of Borneo?

13 What strait separates the North and South Islands of New Zealand?

14 What republic, south of Rwanda, gained independence from Belgium in 1962?

15 What country is between Honduras and Costa Rica?

ANSWERS

1. Carlisle. 2. (a) Arizona. 3. Chile. 4. Nice. 5. Burma. 6. Easter Island. 7. (b) a crescent-shaped sand dune. 8. Munich. 9. Aral Sea. 10. Demography. 11. Jordan. 12. Brunei. 13. Cook Strait. 14. Burundi. 15. Nicaragua.

SESSION 9 QUIZ 7

The Arts

1 In which novel is Winston Smith watched over by Big Brother?

2 With whom did Laurie Lee drink cider?

3 What is the name of Bertie Wooster's butler?

4 With which artistic movement is Salvador Dali associated?

5 Who wrote an elegy in a country graveyard?

6 What words accompany Magritte's painting of a pipe?

7 Which artist is best known for his paintings of the can-can dancers at the Moulin Rouge?

8 Who wrote *The Pilgrim's Progress*?

9 Which tales feature the Wife of Bath, the Franklin and the Pardoner?

10 What type of bird was shot down by the Ancient Mariner?

11 In which novel does Richard Hannay first appear?

12 What is the origin of the proverb 'The leopard cannot change his spots'?

13 What term describes a painting or sculpture showing the Virgin Mary supporting the body of the dead Christ on her lap?

14 Which Renaissance artist also designed the lock gates used on modern canals?

15 In which town is Brother Cadfael's monastery?

ANSWERS

1. *1984* by George Orwell. 2. Rosie. 3. Jeeves. 4. Surrealist. 5. Thomas Gray. 6. *Ceci n'est pas une pipe* (This is not a pipe). 7. Henri Toulouse-Lautrec. 8. John Bunyan. 9. *The Canterbury Tales*. 10. An albatross. 11. *The Thirty-Nine Steps*. 12. The Bible, Jeremiah chapter 13, verse 23. 13. Pietà. 14. Leonardo da Vinci. 15. Shrewsbury.

SESSION 9   QUIZ 8

Pot Luck

1 What two words which sound the same mean a root vegetable and a measure of purity of gold?

2 What is 'bladderwrack'?

3 In which month is 'the Glorious twelfth'?

4 What is 'fax' an abbreviation of?

5 Who or what is your 'Alma Mater'?

6 In which mountain range is the 'yeti', or 'Abominable Snowman' said to live?

7 Ambrosia was the food of the gods; what did they drink?

8 How many years are there in a chiliad?

9 What name is given to the four weeks before Christmas?

10 In which American state is Mammoth Cave, the longest in the world?

11 Which reclusive American millionaire had a phobia about germs?

12 Which contains the most calories: an avocado or a large potato?

13 Which purplish colour was the first to be produced synthetically as a dye?

14 What was gunpowder used for in Medieval China?

15 Which country's car registration mark is CDN?

ANSWERS

1. Carrot/carat. 2. Seaweed. 3. August, start of grouse shooting season. 4. Facsimile. 5. One's old school or university. 6. Himalayas. 7. Nectar. 8. 1,000. 9. Advent. 10. Kentucky. 11. Howard Hughes. 12. Avocado. 13. Mauve. 14. Fireworks and signals, not guns. 15. Canada.

SESSION 10   QUIZ 1

TV, music & entertainment

1 Who is the lead singer with Blur?

2 In which film did Marlon Brando say, 'I coulda been a contender'?

3 Which character in *Emmerdale* apparently returned from the dead?

4 Ray Charles was born blind. True or false?

5 In which film did Humphrey Bogart and Lauren Bacall first appear together?

6 Which US soap was a spin-off of *Dallas*?

7 What is the name of Bruce Springsteen's backing band?

8 *High Society* was a musical remake of *The Philadelphia Story*. True or false?

9 In *Birds of a Feather*, where did Sharon and Tracy live?

10 What was Elvis Presley's first film?

11 Which real-life brothers played the Kray twins in the film *The Krays*?

12 In which opera does 'Toreador Song' feature?

13 In which country was sports presenter Desmond Lynam born?

14 In which film does Paul Henreid light two cigarettes and give one to Bette Davis?

15 To which rap star was Puff Daddy's 'Every Step You Take' dedicated?

ANSWERS

1. Damon Albarn. 2. *On the Waterfront*. 3. 'Kim Tate'. 4. False. He lost his sight as a child. 5. *To Have and Have Not*. 6. *Knots Landing*. 7. The E Street Band. 8. True. 9. Chigwell. 10. *Love Me Tender*. 11. Martin and Gary Kemp. 12. *Carmen* by Georges Bizet. 13. Ireland. 14. *Now Voyager*. 15. Notorious B.I.G.

SESSION 10 QUIZ 2

History

1   Who was known as 'Il Duce'?

2   Where was Napoleon born?

3   On which side did W. T. Sherman fight in the US Civil War?

4   What did Gavrilo Princip do?

5   In what year did the Berlin airlift begin?

6   What was the consequence of the 1801 Act of Union?

7   Before becoming a missionary, what was Albert Schweitzer famous for?

8   Which Babylonian emperor is famous for the code of laws he devised?

9   Who painted the Sistine Chapel ceiling?

10   Which English king was killed at the battle of Bosworth Field?

11   Who are the descendants of Dutch settlers in South Africa?

12   How many theses did Martin Luther pin to the church door?

13   What nationality were the Ottomans?

14   What was the hot news of 1666?

15   Who began the Order of the Garter in 1340; was it: (a) Edward I, (b) Edward II or (c) Edward III?

ANSWERS

1. Benito Mussolini. 2. Corsica. 3. Union. 4. He shot Archduke Franz Ferdinand, precipitating World War I. 5. 1948. 6. The union of Great Britain with Ireland. 7. He was a famous organist. 8. Hammurabi. 9. Michelangelo. 10. Richard III. 11. The Boers. 12. 95. 13. Turkish. 14. The Great Fire of London. 15. (c) Edward III.

SESSION 10 | QUIZ 3

Sports

1   What is the diameter of a golf hole?

2   What looms above the skyline at the Oval?

3   What nationality is Said Aouita?

4   What are the stumps in cricket traditionally made from?

5   At the 1948 Olympics who won gold in the 400 metres and silver in the 800 metres?

6   Where would you feel a foil?

7   What was Eusebio's nickname?

8   Who was 'Little Mo'?

9   What sport is Neil Adams known for?

10 Nottingham Forest were promoted as champions of Division 1 in 1998. True or false?

11 The American Bonnie Blair competes at which sport?

12 Who plays at the San Paolo stadium in Italy?

13 Which British runner won the women's London marathon in 1996?

14 Where was the first football World Cup held?

15 Where were Manchester United when Eric Cantona kicked a member of the crowd?

ANSWERS

1. Four inches. 2. A gasometer. 3. Moroccan. 4. Ash. 5. Arthur Wint. 6. Fencing. 7. The 'black pearl'. 8. Maureen Connolly. 9. Judo. 10. True. 11. Speed Skating. 12. Napoli. 13. Liz McColgan. 14. Uruguay. 15. Crystal Palace.

SESSION 10 QUIZ 4

General knowledge

1   What are dried plums called?

2   What Muslim fundamentalist group took over Kabul in 1996?

3   According to Greek mythology, whose look would turn a person to stone?

4   What is a prime number?

5   What would be a suitable present to give to a couple celebrating their sixtieth wedding anniversary?

6   What is a reticule?

7   What do hydrophobics fear?

8   What is the first letter of the Greek alphabet?

9   Where was the temple of Diana located?

10 Kine is the old plural for which word?

11 What is semaphore?

12 Was Canary Wharf completed in: (a) 1990, (b) 1991 or (c) 1992?

13 What is MGM's symbol?

14 The supermarket Waitrose belongs to which company?

15 What was the first programme to be shown on Channel Four?

ANSWERS

13. A roaring lion. 14. The John Lewis Partnership. 15. Countdown.
7. Water. 8. Alpha. 9. Ephesus. 10. Cow. 11. Signalling with flags. 12. (b) 1991.
5. A diamond, because that is the name of the anniversary. 6. A woman's bag or purse.
1. Prunes. 2. The Taleban. 3. 'Medusa'. 4. A number divisible only by itself or 1.

SESSION 10 — QUIZ 5

Technology & science

1 What is the lightest known substance?

2 What is the unit used to measure supersonic speed?

3 What do the initials NASA of the US government agency for space flight represent?

4 What is a chuckwalla?

5 How many pockets has a snooker table?

6 What first appeared beside the roads outside the Houses of Parliament in 1868?

7 What are Romney Marsh, Suffolk and Swaledale?

8 What is a death cap?

9 What is the literal translation of the Latin term *compos mentis*?

10 What are animals called if they are able to live on land or in water?

11 What are the larvae of flies called?

12 What is the gestation period of a cow?

13 What is the name of the minute organisms found drifting near the surface of seas and lakes?

14 What is the name of the instrument used for measuring humidity in the air?

15 What is considered to be the most nutritious fruit?

ANSWERS

1. Hydrogen gas. 2. Mach. 3. National Aeronautics and Space Administration. 4. A lizard. 5. Six. 6. Traffic lights. 7. All are breeds of sheep. 8. A poisonous toadstool. 9. 'Having control of the mind'. 10. Amphibians. 11. Maggots. 12. Nine months. 13. Plankton. 14. Hygrometer. 15. Avocado pear.

SESSION 10 QUIZ 6

Geography

1 Which mountain range forms the eastern boundary of the North European Plain?

2 Which country lies between Ghana and Benin?

3 Which is the highest market town in England?

4 In which American state would you find the old London Bridge?

5 Which of these continents consumes most energy per year: (a) Asia, (b) North America or (c) Europe?

6 Which canal cuts through the strip of land that joins the Peloponnese peninsula to the Greek mainland?

7 What is the capital of Bulgaria?

8 In which country is the Grossglockner mountain?

9 In which country could you ride on the longest straight section of railway track, stretching for 478 kilometres?

10 Is Baku the capital of: (a) Uzbekistan, (b) Azerbaijan or (c) Armenia?

11 Which country has the capital Tirana?

12 What is the alternative name for the River Zaïre?

13 Which Australian city was the scene of a gold rush in 1815?

14 What sea is the Italian port of Ancona on?

15 Which desert state has the capital Windhoek?

ANSWERS

1. Ural mountains. 2. Togo. 3. Alston. 4. Arizona. 5. (b) North America. 6. Corinth Canal.
7. Sofia. 8. Austria. 9. Australia. 10. (b) Azerbaijan. 11. Albania. 12. River Congo.
13. Bathurst. 14. Adriatic. 15. Namibia.

SESSION 10 QUIZ 7

The Arts

1 Which romantic poet drowned in a storm off the coast of Italy?

2 Whom did William Shakespeare marry?

3 According to John Donne, for whom does the bell toll?

4 'Reader, I married him'. Who married whom?

5 'Air on the G string' is an arrangement of an air from an orchestral suite by which composer?

6 What is the main colour in a grisaille painting?

7 Who killed the monster Grendel?

8 What creature did William Blake describe as 'burning bright, in the forests of the night'?

9 Which British artist was the subject of the film *Love is the Devil* in which he was played by Derek Jacobi?

10 Which jeweller created fabulously decorated eggs for the Russian Tsar and his family?

11 Which perpetual dreamer was created by Keith Waterhouse?

12 Which German brothers collected many of the fairy tales known today?

13 Miss Havisham, who was jilted on her wedding night, appears in which novel by Charles Dickens?

14 Who wrote the *Swallows and Amazons* stories?

15 Which war poet wrote 'Anthem for Doomed Youth'?

ANSWERS

1. Percy Bysshe Shelley. 2. Anne Hathaway. 3. 'It tolls for thee'. 4. Jane Eyre married Mr Rochester. 5. J. S. Bach. 6. Grey. 7. Beowulf. 8. The tiger. 9. Francis Bacon. 10. Fabergé. 11. Billy Liar. 12. The Brothers Grimm. 13. *Great Expectations*. 14. Arthur Ransome. 15. Wilfred Owen.

SESSION 10 | QUIZ 8

Pot Luck

1 The Mazateco Indians of Mexico can hold complete conversations by: (a) whistling, (b) sneezing or (c) humming?

2 Which is the world's smallest independent country?

3 What disease was also known as consumption or the 'White Death'?

4 What is the human body's largest organ?

5 Who originally wrote, 'Gather ye rosebuds while ye may'?

6 After which American president are 'Teddy bears' named?

7 Where would you wear a snood?

8 The title of duke of which city was offered to Winston Churchill when he retired in 1955?

9 What is a palindrome?

10 What is ricotta?

11 Who rode naked through the streets of Coventry?

12 What type of nymph is a dryad?

13 In what country was the game 'Trivial Pursuit' invented?

14 Aspirin was originally obtained from the bark of which tree?

15 A parsimonious man is generous with his money. True or false?

ANSWERS

1. (a) whistling. 2. Vatican City State. 3. Tuberculosis. 4. Skin. 5. Robert Herrick.
6. Theodore 'Teddy' Roosevelt. 7. On your head. 8. Duke of London. 9. A word that reads the same backwards and forwards. 10. A soft cheese. 11. Lady Godiva. 12. A tree nymph.
13. Canada. 14. Willow. 15. False, he is particularly mean.

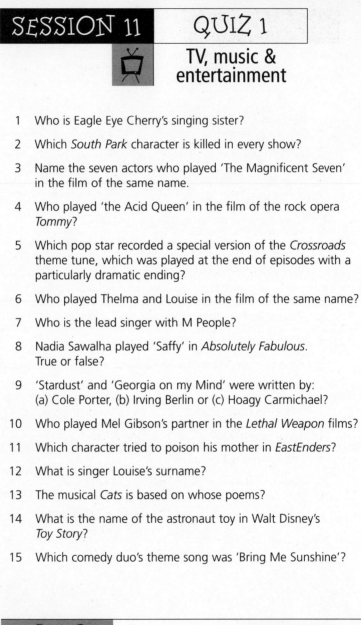

SESSION 11   QUIZ 1

TV, music & entertainment

1   Who is Eagle Eye Cherry's singing sister?

2   Which *South Park* character is killed in every show?

3   Name the seven actors who played 'The Magnificent Seven' in the film of the same name.

4   Who played 'the Acid Queen' in the film of the rock opera *Tommy*?

5   Which pop star recorded a special version of the *Crossroads* theme tune, which was played at the end of episodes with a particularly dramatic ending?

6   Who played Thelma and Louise in the film of the same name?

7   Who is the lead singer with M People?

8   Nadia Sawalha played 'Saffy' in *Absolutely Fabulous*. True or false?

9   'Stardust' and 'Georgia on my Mind' were written by: (a) Cole Porter, (b) Irving Berlin or (c) Hoagy Carmichael?

10   Who played Mel Gibson's partner in the *Lethal Weapon* films?

11   Which character tried to poison his mother in *EastEnders*?

12   What is singer Louise's surname?

13   The musical *Cats* is based on whose poems?

14   What is the name of the astronaut toy in Walt Disney's *Toy Story*?

15   Which comedy duo's theme song was 'Bring Me Sunshine'?

ANSWERS

1. Neneh Cherry. 2. Kenny. 3. Yul Brynner, Steve McQueen, James Coburn, Charles Bronson, Robert Vaughn, Horst Buchholz, and Brad Dexter. 4. Tina Turner. 5. Paul McCartney. 6. Geena Davis and Susan Sarandon. 7. Heather Small. 8. False. It was her sister, Julia Sawalha. 9. (c) Hoagy Carmichael. 10. Danny Glover. 11. Nick Cotton. 12. Nurding. 13. T. S. Eliot. 14. 'Buzz Lightyear'. 15. Morecambe and Wise.

SESSION 11   QUIZ 2

History

1 Who used the Santa Maria, the Nina and the Pinta?

2 Who was killed in the battle at Kappel in 1531?

3 How did the prime minister Viscount Castlereagh die?

4 What was the codename for the planned German invasion of Great Britain during World War II?

5 Who built Machu Picchu?

6 When did India become a Crown colony? Was it: (a) 1803, (b) 1858 or (c) 1906?

7 On what day did 'England expect every man to do his duty'?

8 Where did Napoleon die?

9 What did Romulus and Remus found?

10 Who was the last British prime minister of the 19th century?

11 Who lost the battle of Austerlitz?

12 Which king was born 19 June 1566 in Edinburgh castle?

13 What year did Julius Caesar invade Britain?

14 Where are the Killing Fields?

15 What did the volunteer soldiers of 1914 form?

ANSWERS

1. Columbus on his voyage to America. 2. Zwingli the Swiss reformer. 3. He committed suicide. 4. Sealion. 5. The Incas. 6. (b) 1858. 7. 21 October 1805. 8. St Helena. 9. Rome. 10. The Marquess of Salisbury. 11. The Austrians and the Russians. 12. James I. 13. 55 BC. 14. Cambodia. 15. Kitchener's Armies.

SESSION 11 QUIZ 3

Sports

1 What is an alternative name for the sport of motocross?

2 Who was England's winner at the 1968 Olympics 400-metre hurdles?

3 Where is Longchamps race track?

4 What number was Gareth Southgate wearing when he missed a penalty in Euro '96?

5 Where was golfer Christy O'Connor born?

6 Which 'odd' golfer was born in 1955 in Virginia, USA?

7 Which country won the most gold medals at the 1998 Winter Olympics?

8 Ian Botham has never captained England. True or false?

9 Which team does rugby's Adedayo Adebayo play for?

10 What is the longest track race in athletics?

11 Who won the 1998 Scottish First Division title?

12 Who is the British men's 400-metre hurdle record holder?

13 Who was the first European Footballer of the year?

14 In what film did O. J. Simpson take to the skies?

15 Graham Hill is commemorated on which race circuit?

ANSWERS

1. Scrambling. 2. David Hemery. 3. Paris. 4. Six. 5. Galway. 6. Curtis Strange. 7. Germany with 12. 8. False. He was captain from 1980-81. 9. Bath. 10. 10,000 metres. 11. Dundee. 12. Kriss Akabusi. 13. Stanley Matthews. 14. *Airplane*. 15. Brands Hatch.

SESSION 11   QUIZ 4

General knowledge

1. What does LLD stand for?

2. What did the 'City of Truro' do in 1904?

3. Orly is to the south of which European city?

4. What did the visionary Salvino degli Armati invent in 1280?

5. What is arctophily more commonly known as?

6. What would you do with anthracite?

7. Which country is known as the Bread Basket of Europe?

8. Are there: (a) 3, (b) 6 or (c) 8 electron beams in a colour television?

9. What is architect John Utzon's most famous creation?

10. The Greeks called him Zeus, what did the Romans call him?

11. What is the name given to the French national anthem?

12. Who founded a waxworks exhibition in Baker Street, London, in 1835?

13. If twins were born within twenty minutes of each other and one of them was Gemini and the other was Taurus, on what days would they have been born?

14. Which animal is reckoned to have the longest life span?

15. According to the saying, whose son always goes barefoot?

ANSWERS

1. Doctor of Laws, from the Latin 'Legum Doctor'. 2. Travel at a speed above 100 mph for the first time. 3. Paris. 4. Spectacles. 5. Teddy bear collecting. 6. Burn it. It is coal. 7. The Ukraine. 8. (a) 3. One for each primary colour. 9. The Sydney Opera House. 10. Jupiter. 11. The Marseillaise. 12. Madame Tussaud. 13. 20 and 21 May. 14. Tortoise. 15. The shoemaker's. In other words, children are the last to benefit from their parents' expertise.

SESSION 11

QUIZ 5

Technology & science

1   What is the nickname given to the crane-fly?

2   What name was given to the underwater explosive missile first developed by Robert Whitehead in 1866?

3   How many tentacles does a cuttlefish have?

4   What is the name of the clear fluid that forms a large proportion of blood?

5   On the Internet, what would the abbreviation 'Y2K' stand for?

6   What is the difference between the terms *in vitro* and *in vivo*?

7   Which edible nut of the American hickory tree is similar to a walnut?

8   Neil Armstrong was the first man to set foot on the Moon, but who was the second person to do so?

9   What instrument measures current flowing in an electric circuit?

10   What are the Northern Lights otherwise known as?

11   What do the initials PVC stand for?

12   What name is given to the study of paths taken by projectiles such as bullets and rockets?

13   Who invented the flush toilet in 1778?

14   What is the name given to an alloy of mercury?

15   What is the national emblem that appears on the Canadian flag?

ANSWERS

1. Daddy-long-legs. 2. Torpedo. 3. Ten. 4. Plasma. 5. Year 2000. 6. In science, *in vitro* refers to experiments in a 'test tube', and *in vivo* to those in a living organism. 7. Pecan nut. 8. Buzz (Edwin) Aldrin. 9. Ammeter. 10. Aurora borealis. 11. Polyvinyl chloride. 12. Ballistics. 13. Joseph Bramah. 14. Amalgam. 15. The maple leaf.

SESSION 11 QUIZ 6

Geography

1 Which one of these lakes is in Switzerland: (a) Lake Como, (b) Lake Lugano or (c) Lake Garda?

2 What is the capital of the Philippines?

3 In which country is Mount Fuji?

4 Which long-distance footpath goes from Edale in the Peak District to Kirk Yetholm in the Scottish Borders?

5 In which group of volcanic islands in the Pacific are Viti Levu and Vanua Levu: (a) Samoa, (b) Tonga or (c) Fiji?

6 In which English county is Winchester?

7 Is a 'lahar': (a) a volcanic mud flow, (b) an Asian climatic zone or (c) an African wind?

8 In which Canadian city is the CN Tower?

9 The Tropic of Capricorn passes through Australia. True or false?

10 In what country is the Yucatán peninsula?

11 What country was formerly known as Southern Rhodesia?

12 In which American state is Las Vegas?

13 Bratislava is the capital of Slovenia. True or false?

14 Which of these is not the name of an ocean current: (a) Peru current, (b) Gulf Stream or (c) South Atlantic Drift?

15 In which country is the Lüneburg Heath?

ANSWERS

1. (b) Lake Lugano. 2. Manila. 3. Japan. 4. The Pennine Way. 5. (c) Fiji. 6. Hampshire. 7. (a) a volcanic mud flow. 8. Toronto. 9. True. 10. Mexico. 11. Zimbabwe. 12. Nevada. 13. False, it is the capital of Slovakia. 14. (c) South Atlantic Drift. 15. Germany.

SESSION 11 QUIZ 7

The Arts

1 What was Richmal Crompton's original surname?

2 Which king was the subject of Tennyson's 'Idylls of the King'?

3 What type of picture is made by sticking pieces of paper, cloth and other objects onto a flat surface?

4 Which pop artist's paintings include a tin of soup and a banana?

5 Who wrote a Fireworks suite for a firework display at Green Park in London in 1749?

6 Who wrote *Paradise Lost*?

7 J.M.W. Turner's paintings were mainly: (a) portraits, (b) seascapes or (c) still lifes?

8 *The Rake's Progress* and *Marriage à la mode* are works by which artist?

9 Which of Charles Dickens' characters attended Mr Wackford Squeers' Academy at Dotheboys Hall?

10 What did William Wordsworth find when he was wandering lonely as a cloud?

11 Who was Bilbo Baggins?

12 Who in 1892 started his own twopenny weekly publication called *To-Day*?

13 What did Walter de la Mare's 'Traveller' ask when he knocked on the door?

14 According to Keats, which is the season 'of mists and mellow fruitfulness'?

15 Who wrote *Peter Pan*?

ANSWERS

1. Lamburn. 2. King Arthur. 3. Collage. 4. Andy Warhol. 5. George Frederick Handel. 6. John Milton. 7. (b) seascapes. 8. William Hogarth. 9. Nicholas Nickleby. 10. A host of golden daffodils. 11. The Hobbit from the book of the same name. 12. Jerome K. Jerome. 13. 'Is there anybody there?' 14. Autumn. 15. J. M. Barrie.

SESSION 11 QUIZ 8

Pot Luck

1 On what night is Hallowe'en?

2 Which official residence did Winston Churchill describe as 'shaky and lightly built'?

3 What did President Harry S. Truman's middle initial stand for?

4 In what substance was Nelson's body preserved after his death at the Battle of Trafalgar?

5 Which Antarctic animals gather in colonies or rookeries?

6 In 1908 the king of which European country reigned for only 20 minutes?

7 Does sound travel faster through water or through air?

8 Which famous train used to run between Paris and Istanbul?

9 What percentage of the Earth's surface is covered with water?

10 In which British town is Squeeze-belly Alley, the narrowest street in the world?

11 According to the proverb what does 'pride come before'?

12 What is 'sauerkraut'?

13 What word beginning with 'j' means a lively dance?

14 Who was Mata Hari?

15 Cordelia, Ophelia, Desdemona and Portia are all satellites of which planet?

ANSWERS

1. 31 October. 2. 10 Downing Street. 3. Nothing, it was just an initial. 4. Brandy. 5. Penguins. 6. Portugal, he died 20 minutes after his father. 7. Water. 8. *The Orient Express*. 9. 70 per cent. 10. Port Isaac. 11. A fall. 12. Pickled cabbage. 13. Jig. 14. An exotic dancer accused of being a Nazi spy. 15. Uranus.

SESSION 12 QUIZ 1

TV, music & entertainment

1 Which film director made a fleeting appearance in each of his films?

2 Who recorded the theme song for the James Bond film *A View to a Kill*?

3 In *Thunderbirds*, what was the registration number of Lady Penelope's car?

4 Which German composer wrote *The Ring Cycle*?

5 In *Coronation Street*, how did Ken Barlow's first wife, Val, die?

6 The song 'To All the Girls I've Loved Before' was written by: (a) Sacha Distel, (b) Julio Iglesias or (c) Willie Nelson?

7 Which TV drama serial featured five young lawyers who shared a house?

8 Which singer/actress played Billie Holiday in the film *Lady Sings the Blues*?

9 Greta Garbo's debut in talkies was hailed with the slogan 'Garbo Talks!' What was the name of the film?

10 Which singer used to be a member of the Sugarcubes?

11 Who was the star of the sitcom *The Fresh Prince of Bel Air*?

12 What is the nationality of the actress Nicole Kidman?

13 What was the date of the Live Aid concert?

14 Who is comedian Lenny Henry's wife?

15 What was Rocky's surname in the *Rocky* films?

ANSWERS

1. Alfred Hitchcock. 2. Duran Duran. 3. FAB 1. 4. Richard Wagner. 5. She was electrocuted by a faulty hairdrier. 6. (c) Willie Nelson. 7. *This Life*. 8. Diana Ross. 9. *Anna Christie*. 10. Björk. 11. Will Smith. 12. Australian. 13. 13 July 1985. 14. Dawn French. 15. Balboa.

SESSION 12   QUIZ 2

History

1   Who was the American president during the Gulf War?

2   By what name was Agnes Bojaxhiu better known?

3   Which scientist proposed the theory that animals evolve during their own lifetime?

4   Gladys Aylwood was a missionary to which country?

5   What did Napoleon sell the US in 1803?

6   Which war lasted from 1808-14?

7   Who first walked along the Via Dolorosa?

8   Which book did Edmund Spenser begin in 1590?

9   'Reason' ushered in which age?

10   What did Samuel Pepys keep?

11   Which king began work on the Tower of London?

12   Which famous political document was published in 1834?

13   Was Pearl Harbor attacked on the: (a) 7, (b) 8 or (c) 9 December 1941?

14   Which monarch was said not to have been amused?

15   Where were tanks used on a large scale for the first time in 1917?

ANSWERS

1. George Bush. 2. Mother Theresa of Calcutta. 3. Jean-Baptiste Lamarck. 4. China. 5. Louisiana. 6. The Peninsular War. 7. Jesus, on his way to be crucified. 8. *The Faerie Queene.* 9. The Enlightenment. 10. A diary. 11. William the Conqueror. 12. *The Tamworth Manifesto.* 13. (a) 7 December 1941. 14. Queen Victoria. 15. Cambrai.

SESSION 12 QUIZ 3

Sports

1 Which club did Mark Lawrenson leave to join Liverpool?

2 Which golfer was born at Oswestry in 1958?

3 Which county won the Benson and Hedges Cricket Final in 1998?

4 Over what distance is the steeplechase run in athletics?

5 How old was Dino Zoff when he captained Italy in the 1982 World Cup Final?

6 On what racecourse would you find Tattenham Corner?

7 Australia won the most gold medals at the 1998 Commonwealth Games. True or false?

8 Where is the Lincoln Handicap run?

9 Who scored Everton's goals in their 3-2 defeat by Liverpool in the FA Cup Final of 1989?

10 Which player scored 100 tries for both Humberside rugby league clubs?

11 What nationality is Carlos Reutemann?

12 Which club does international Jeremy Guscott play for?

13 Who is the chairman of Blackburn Rovers?

14 What part of the anatomy is Mike Tyson partial to?

15 Who is the sponsor of English soccer's first division?

ANSWERS

1. Brighton and Hove Albion. 2. Ian Woosnam. 3. Essex. 4. 3,000 metres. 5. 40. 6. Epsom. 7. True. 8. Doncaster. 9. McCall. 10. Clive Sullivan. 11. Argentinian. 12. Bath. 13. Jack Walker. 14. The ear. He bit off a piece of Evander Holyfield's ear in a fight in 1997. 15. Nationwide.

SESSION 12   QUIZ 4

General knowledge

1   Who abandoned architecture for writing in 1874?

2   What is the chemical symbol for silver?

3   What is the nearest star to Earth?

4   What are the most numerous members of the animal kingdom?

5   Which is the second largest of the Great Lakes?

6   What would you do with a Sopwith Camel?

7   What was the name of the prostitute caught committing a lewd act with Hugh Grant?

8   Who was Abraham's first-born son?

9   According to the Egyptians what was the name of the sun-god?

10   How many furlongs are there in a mile?

11   Surinam is in Africa. True or false?

12   What lies at the centre of the Japanese flag?

13   Who is the most quoted author in the *Oxford English Dictionary*?

14   What controversial product is one of the mainstays of BAT industries?

15   Which is Europe's second busiest airport?

ANSWERS

1. Thomas Hardy. 2. Ag. 3. Proxima Centauri which is approximately 4.22 light-years away.
4. Insects. 5. Lake Huron. 6. Fly it. It is an early airplane, used in World War I. 7. Divine Brown.
8. Ishmael. 9. Ra. 10. Eight. 11. False. It is in South America. 12. A red circle.
13. William Shakespeare. 14. Tobacco. 15. Frankfurt.

SESSION 12 QUIZ 5

Technology & science

1 Who was the English naturalist who accompanied Cook on his expedition around the world?

2 From what kind of animal is cat gut obtained?

3 What was the name of the man who invented the Kodak camera in 1888?

4 How often does Halley's comet orbit the Sun?

5 What is a female donkey called?

6 What is the name given to the study of water on the Earth's surface?

7 What is the name of the the acid found in oranges, limes and lemons?

8 In the field of space science, what is TIROS?

9 Which planet has a great red spot?

10 What is the translation of the Greek word 'chrysanthemum'?

11 In which year was the felt-tip pen first used?

12 The computer language BASIC is an acronym used in computing; what is its full form?

13 What is the SI unit of illumination?

14 What name is given to the acid in vinegar?

15 How many carats has pure gold?

ANSWERS

1. Joseph Banks. 2. Usually sheep, but also horse or ass. 3. George Eastman. 4. Every 76 years. 5. A jenny. 6. Hydrology. 7. Citric acid. 8. Television and Infra-red Observation Satellite. 9. Jupiter. 10. 'Gold flower'. 11. 1955. 12. Beginner's all-purpose symbolic instruction code. 13. The lux. 14. Acetic acid. 15. 24.

SESSION 12   QUIZ 6

Geography

1   The Simplon Pass joins Switzerland to which other country?

2   In which American state are the cities of Duluth, St Paul and Minneapolis?

3   Which of these countries does not have a border on Lake Chad: (a) Nigeria, (b) Cameroon or (c) Sudan?

4   Where is Mount Etna?

5   The Denmark Strait separates Greenland and Iceland. True or false?

6   Is Wellington on New Zealand's North or South Island?

7   Which is the longest canal for ocean-going vessels?

8   Which county is sandwiched between Oxfordshire and Hampshire?

9   Papeete is the chief town of which island?

10   What is the capital of Croatia?

11   Which is the most industrialized and urbanized country in Africa?

12   What are the high tides called, when the Sun, Moon and Earth are ranged in a straight line?

13   Which of these cities has a desert climate: (a) Lima, (b) Santiago or (c) Buenos Aires?

14   Which volcanic island, with its capital at Castries, became independent in 1979?

15   If you flew into Faro airport, which country would you be in?

ANSWERS

1. Italy. 2. Minnesota. 3. (c) Sudan. 4. Sicily. 5. True. 6. North Island. 7. Suez canal. 8. Berkshire. 9. Tahiti. 10. Zagreb. 11. South Africa. 12. Spring tides. 13. (a) Lima. 14. St Lucia. 15. Portugal.

SESSION 12 QUIZ 7

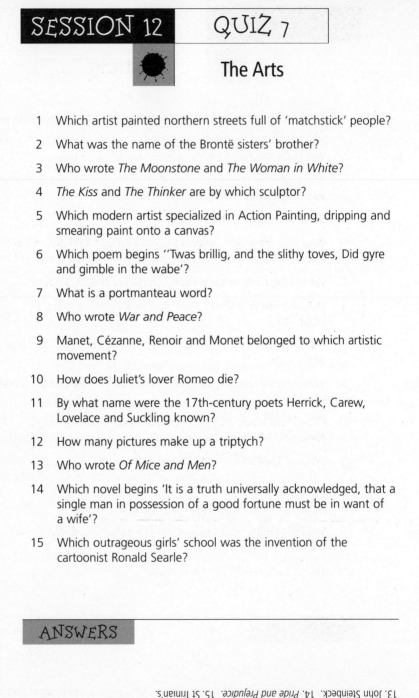

The Arts

1 Which artist painted northern streets full of 'matchstick' people?

2 What was the name of the Brontë sisters' brother?

3 Who wrote *The Moonstone* and *The Woman in White*?

4 *The Kiss* and *The Thinker* are by which sculptor?

5 Which modern artist specialized in Action Painting, dripping and smearing paint onto a canvas?

6 Which poem begins ''Twas brillig, and the slithy toves, Did gyre and gimble in the wabe'?

7 What is a portmanteau word?

8 Who wrote *War and Peace*?

9 Manet, Cézanne, Renoir and Monet belonged to which artistic movement?

10 How does Juliet's lover Romeo die?

11 By what name were the 17th-century poets Herrick, Carew, Lovelace and Suckling known?

12 How many pictures make up a triptych?

13 Who wrote *Of Mice and Men*?

14 Which novel begins 'It is a truth universally acknowledged, that a single man in possession of a good fortune must be in want of a wife'?

15 Which outrageous girls' school was the invention of the cartoonist Ronald Searle?

ANSWERS

1. L. S. Lowry. 2. (Patrick) Branwell. 3. Wilkie Collins. 4. Auguste Rodin. 5. Jackson Pollock.
6. 'Jabberwocky'. 7. One that combines the sound and meaning of two others, e.g., *motel*.
8. Leo Tolstoy. 9. Impressionism. 10. He poisons himself. 11. Cavalier poets. 12. Three.
13. John Steinbeck. 14. *Pride and Prejudice*. 15. St Trinian's.

SESSION 12 QUIZ 8

Pot Luck

1 A new born baby has: (a) 94 more bones or (b) 94 fewer bones than an adult?

2 Who was the first Roman Catholic president of the United States?

3 Which king turned everything he touched into gold?

4 What does *Glasnost* mean?

5 Which of these was never a king of England: (a) Edward the Confessor, (b) Edward the Worthy or (c) Edward the Martyr?

6 What type of weather is expected during the 'dog days'?

7 In Puritan New England who were branded with a scarlet letter 'A'?

8 Which garden flower tends to be pink in alkaline soil and blue in acidic soil?

9 Which contains more caffeine, a teaspoon of tea or a teaspoon of coffee?

10 Henry Ford made nineteen cars, Models A–T, before his successful Model T. True or false?

11 What did sailors call rum diluted with water?

12 Where are the Doldrums?

13 What does the name Stalin mean literally?

14 In 1957, which British prime minister said, 'Our people have never had it so good'?

15 Which herb is used to make pesto?

ANSWERS

SESSION 13

QUIZ 1

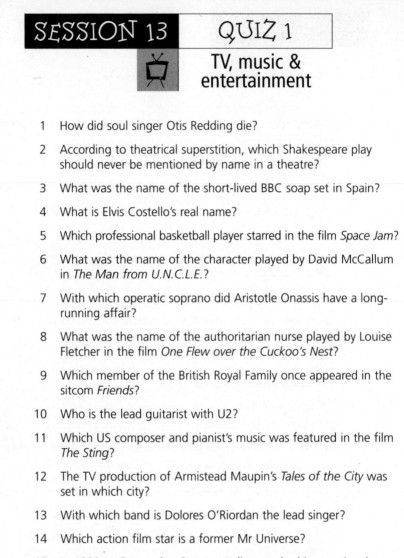

TV, music & entertainment

1   How did soul singer Otis Redding die?

2   According to theatrical superstition, which Shakespeare play should never be mentioned by name in a theatre?

3   What was the name of the short-lived BBC soap set in Spain?

4   What is Elvis Costello's real name?

5   Which professional basketball player starred in the film *Space Jam*?

6   What was the name of the character played by David McCallum in *The Man from U.N.C.L.E.*?

7   With which operatic soprano did Aristotle Onassis have a long-running affair?

8   What was the name of the authoritarian nurse played by Louise Fletcher in the film *One Flew over the Cuckoo's Nest*?

9   Which member of the British Royal Family once appeared in the sitcom *Friends*?

10 Who is the lead guitarist with U2?

11 Which US composer and pianist's music was featured in the film *The Sting*?

12 The TV production of Armistead Maupin's *Tales of the City* was set in which city?

13 With which band is Dolores O'Riordan the lead singer?

14 Which action film star is a former Mr Universe?

15 In 1998, a *Coronation Street* storyline resulted in a national 'Free the Weatherfield One' campaign. Who was 'the Weatherfield One'?

ANSWERS

1. He was killed in a plane crash. 2. *Macbeth*. 3. *Eldorado*. 4. Declan McManus. 5. Michael Jordan. 6. 'Ilya Kuriakin'. 7. Maria Callas. 8. 'Miss Ratched'. 9. Sarah Ferguson, Duchess of York. 10. 'The Edge'. 11. Scott Joplin. 12. San Francisco. 13. The Cranberries. 14. Arnold Schwarzenegger. 15. Deirdre Rachid.

SESSION 13   QUIZ 2

History

1   Which book on economic theory by Adam Smith was published in 1776?

2   What was the last town in Palestine to be held by the Crusaders?

3   For what reason is Caxton's *The Histories of Troy* a famous book?

4   What did Chamberlain bring back from Munich in 1938?

5   Which school of philosophy did Zeno found?

6   What is the name given to the uprisings in Scotland in the 17th century?

7   In which year was 'Custer's Last Stand'?

8   What age was Palmerston when he became prime minister for the first time?

9   Who attacked the British army at the battle of Rorke's Drift?

10   What happened on 22 November 1963?

11   What female aviator disappeared while flying over the Pacific Ocean?

12   Who is the youngest monarch to succeed to the British crown?

13   Who established France's 'Reign of Terror'?

14   What did Albert Pinkerton establish for the first time in America?

15   Which political party did Kier Hardie found in 1893?

ANSWERS

1. *The Wealth of Nations.* 2. Acre. 3. The first book to be printed by Caxton in English in 1474. 4. A piece of paper. 5. The stoic school. 6. The Jacobite rebellions. 7. 1876. 8. 70 years old. 9. The Zulus. 10. John Kennedy was assassinated. 11. Amelia Earhart. 12. Henry VI aged 8 months. 13. Maximillien Robespierre. 14. A detective agency. 15. The Independent Labour Party.

SESSION 13 · QUIZ 3

Sports

1 What American sport do the Baltimore Orioles play?

2 Who trained the horse Aldaniti?

3 What do the New Zealand Rugby team do before their matches?

4 By what score did France beat Croatia in the semi-final of the 1998 World Cup?

5 What is a powered hang-glider called?

6 Which course is known as the 'Course that Jack built'?

7 Which part of the anatomy is all important for the finish of athletics races?

8 Which sport uses an épée?

9 Who holds the record for the most wickets in a Test Match?

10 How many players are there in a baseball team?

11 Which country beat England in the third and fourth place play-off in Italia '90?

12 Did Ann Packer win Olympic gold at: (a) long jump, (b) 100 metres or (c) 800 metres?

13 Who was stabbed by a Steffi Graf fan in April 1993?

14. For which club was Peter Shilton playing when he made his 1,000th league appearance?

15 Where do rugby club Saracens play?

ANSWERS

1. Baseball. 2. Josh Gifford. 3. A Maori war dance, called the haka. 4. 2-1. 5. A microlight. 6. Muirfield Village, Ohio. 7. The torso. 8. Fencing. 9. Jim Laker. 10. Nine. 11. Italy. 12. (c) 800 metres in 1964. 13. Monica Seles. 14. Leyton Orient. 15. Vicarage Road, home of Watford football club.

SESSION 13 QUIZ 4

General knowledge

1   'Turtle' was the appropriate name given to which object built by David Bushnell in 1775?

2   How quickly did Michael Palin travel around the world?

3   What is Britain's oldest weekly publication that deals with medical matters?

4   *Hudson Hawk* was a flop for which Hollywood die-hard?

5   In which country was T. S. Eliot born?

6   What is the commonest name for the pope?

7   What is the cassowary?

8   By what name is Peter Sutcliffe better known?

9   What is the largest flightless bird?

10   What feat did Matthew Webb accomplish in 1875?

11   What nationality was Marie Curie?

12   Who fell in love with himself?

13   The name Hindu derives from the Indian river the Indus. True or false?

14   What is the Monroe doctrine?

15   What is foliation?

ANSWERS

1. A submarine. 2. 80 days. 3. *The Lancet*. 4. Bruce Willis. 5. USA. 6. John. This name has been used on 23 occasions. 7. A bird. 8. 'The Yorkshire Ripper'. 9. The ostrich. 10. He became the first man to swim across the Channel. 11. Polish. 12. Narcissus. 13. True. 14. American policy opposing the involvement of foreign powers on the continent of America. 15. The process of producing leaves.

SESSION 13 QUIZ 5

Technology & science

1   What do the initials TNT stand for?

2   Who devised the first ball-point pen in 1938?

3   What name is given to the science that studies the flow of fluids?

4   In computing, what does USB stand for?

5   What is the name of the only armoured mammal?

6   When was the ultrasound first used in obstetrics?

7   What is the derivation of the name of the flower 'daisy' thought to be?

8   What was the former name of the element tungsten?

9   What is the collective name for birds' feathers?

10   What is remarkable about the direction of a comet's tail?

11   What were the names of the first Russian and first American satellites in space?

12   Which major planet was discovered in 1846?

13   What is the SI unit for resistance?

14   What are Chinese gooseberries?

15   What term is used to describe the lines on a chart that join points of equal temperature?

ANSWERS

1. Trinitrotoluene. 2. Laszlo Biró. 3. Hydraulics. 4. Universal serial bus. 5. Armadillo. 6. 1958. 7. From 'day's eye' because the flower opens in the morning and closes at night. 8. Wolfram. 9. Plumage. 10. It always points away from the Sun. 11. 'Sputnik 1' and 'Explorer 1'. 12. Neptune. 13. Ohm. 14. Kiwi fruit. 15. Isotherms.

SESSION 13 — QUIZ 6

Geography

1. In which country is the River Po?

2. Cologne is the English name for which German city?

3. Which is closer to London: Paris or Edinburgh?

4. Which American state has the largest population?

5. Is an 'isthmus' a strip of land or a stretch of water?

6. Where is the seat of government in the Netherlands?

7. Which river flows through York?

8. Pillow lava is formed under the sea. True or false?

9. Which country, with its capital at Kiev, achieved independence from the USSR in 1991?

10. Which country, with a strong economy based on coffee, bananas and tourism, has the highest life expectancy in Central America?

11. What is the aboriginal name for Ayers Rock?

12. Kilbrannan Sound lies between Kintyre and which island?

13. Which of these countries has a scientific station on Antarctica: (a) Italy, (b) Korea or (c) South Africa?

14. In which country is the Deccan plateau?

15. In which country are the Coromandel hills, on the Coromandel peninsula?

ANSWERS

1. Italy. 2. Köln. 3. Paris. 4. California. 5. A strip of land. 6. The Hague. 7. Ouse. 8. True. 9. Ukraine. 10. Costa Rica. 11. Uluru. 12. Arran. 13. (b) Korea. 14. India. 15. New Zealand.

SESSION 13   QUIZ 7

The Arts

1   Who wrote the lengthy poem 'The Waste Land'?

2   Which hill in Paris is a gathering point for artists and portrait painters?

3   What are 'gothic novels'?

4   Who wrote *The Wings of the Dove* and *The Golden Bowl*?

5   Who created the elderly detective Miss Marple?

6   The Clore Gallery in the Tate houses works by which British landscape artist?

7   In Alice in Wonderland what did the sneezing baby turn into?

8   What did people find scandalous about Manet's painting *Déjeuner sur l'herbe*?

9   In which of Shakespeare's plays do Sir Andrew Aguecheek and Sir Toby Belch appear?

10 Which composer's works include a 'New World' symphony?

11 According to Keats 'A thing of beauty' is what?

12 Who wrote *The Little Mermaid* and *The Little Match Girl*?

13 Whose marriage is an opera by Mozart?

14 Who declared that 'Marriage has many pains, but celibacy has no pleasures'?

15 'If I should die think only this of me...' What line follows?

ANSWERS

1. T. S. Eliot. 2. Montmartre. 3. Horror stories. 4. Henry James. 5. Agatha Christie. 6. J. M. W. Turner. 7. A pig. 8. A naked woman is sat amongst clothed men. 9. *Twelfth Night*. 10. Antonin Dvořák. 11. 'A joy for ever'. 12. Hans Christian Andersen. 13. Figaro. 14. Samuel Johnson. 15. 'That there's some corner of a foreign field, That is for ever England'.

SESSION 13   QUIZ 8

Pot Luck

1   What are *billet-doux*?

2   What is a female fox called?

3   Who was the sixth American president, who was also the son of the second president?

4   Who was the British defence minister during the Falklands War?

5   A gathering of ravens is called: (a) a cruelty or (b) an unkindness?

6   Mandrill, Howler and Capuchin are all types of what animal?

7   Which king of Christmas carol fame was a 10th-century ruler of Bohemia?

8   What invention was first demonstrated by John Logie Baird in 1926?

9   In which ocean is the Marianas Trench, the deepest point on Earth?

10   Which animal makes a loud noise like hysterical laughter?

11   St Jerome is the patron saint of: (a) librarians, (b) teachers or (c) scrap merchants?

12   What is 'pumpernickel'?

13   The 'pound of flesh' features in which of Shakespeare's plays?

14   Mohair is wool from a: (a) goat, (b) Highland sheep or (c) llama?

15   What is a 'tam o' shanter'?

ANSWERS

1. Love letters. 2. Vixen. 3. John Quincy Adams, son of John Adams. 4. John Nott. 5. (b) unkindness. 6. Monkey. 7. King Wenceslas. 8. Television. 9. Pacific. 10. Hyena. 11. (a) librarians. 12. Bread. 13. *The Merchant of Venice*. 14. (a) goat. 15. A hat or woollen cap.

SESSION 14

QUIZ 1

TV, music & entertainment

1. What is Sting's real name?

2. Which *Brookside* character was nicknamed 'Rod the Plod'?

3. Who was Dean Martin's comedy partner from 1946 till 1956?

4. Who provided the vocals on the *South Park* single 'Chef's Chocolate Salty Balls'?

5. What was the name of the Cartwrights' ranch in *Bonanza*?

6. Which character did not survive the shark hunt in *Jaws*?

7. Who duetted with Bing Crosby on 'Little Drummer Boy'?

8. In *The Cosby Show*, Bill Cosby played himself. True or false?

9. Drew Barrymore is the granddaughter of Lionel Barrymore. True or false?

10. Iggy Pop's 'Lust for Life' was used as the theme song for which 1996 feature film?

11. In which city is teen soap *Hollyoaks* set?

12. What was the first major film with synchronized sound?

13. By what name is singer Anthony Benedetto better known?

14. What was the name of the postman who regularly propped up the bar in *Cheers*?

15. Which of the stars of *Jurassic Park* also appeared in the sequel, *The Lost World*?

ANSWERS

1. Gordon Sumner. 2. Rod Corkhill. 3. Jerry Lewis. 4. Isaac Hayes. 5. The Ponderosa. 6. Quint. 7. David Bowie. 8. False. He played 'Dr Cliff Huxtable'. 9. False. She is John Barrymore's granddaughter. 10. *Trainspotting*. 11. Chester. 12. *The Jazz Singer* in 1927. 13. Tony Bennett. 14. 'Cliff'. 15. Jeff Goldblum and Richard Attenborough.

SESSION 14   QUIZ 2

History

1   What did Mary Baker Eddy first propound in 1866?

2   Who was the first British prime minister?

3   Did: (a) 500,000 (b) 750,000 or (c) 1,000,000 men die in the American Civil War?

4   What illuminating device did Sir Humphry Davy invent?

5   Which politician succeeded Lenin?

6   In which year was there an army coup in Portugal?

7   By what name is Ivan IV of Russia better known?

8   Who said, 'Here I stand, I can do no other'?

9   What name is given to the wars between Rome and Carthage?

10   Which king was nearly killed in the Gunpowder Plot?

11   What was the name of Hitler's Bavarian retreat?

12   Who were expelled from England in 1290?

13   In what way has Amerigo Vespucci gone down in history?

14   In what year did the Jarrow March take place?

15   Who settled on the Italian mainland for the first time at Cumae?

ANSWERS

1. Christian Science. 2. Robert Walpole in 1727. 3. (a) 500,000. 4. The miner's safety lamp. 5. Stalin. 6. 1974. 7. Ivan The Terrible. 8. Martin Luther replying to requests for him to recant. 9. The Punic Wars. 10. King James I. 11. Berchtesgaden. 12. The Jews. 13. He gave his name to America. 14. 1936. 15. The Greeks.

SESSION 14 | QUIZ 3

Sports

1 What colour socks do the rugby team the Barbarians wear?

2 Who was the favourite for the Olympic 800-metre men's title in Moscow 1980?

3 What number did Dean Richards play for his club, Leicester?

4 What city is host to FIFA?

5 What is the name of the New Zealand Rugby League team?

6 Colin Chapman was associated with which Formula 1 racing team?

7 In which sport would you find a 'brakeman'?

8 When Scotland played Wales at rugby in 1998 which team won?

9 Who owned 'Nedawi', the winner of the 1998 St Leger?

10 Which football team won the Charity Shield each year from 1984–87?

11 In what year was Jack Nicklaus born? Was it (a) 1940, (b) 1945 or (c) 1950?

12 If you knock down all ten bowling pins with two balls in one frame what is it called?

13 At what sport might you see a 'jerk'?

14 Who said, 'That's cricket, Harry, you get those sorts of things in boxing'?

15 In which year were the Jesse Owens' games?

ANSWERS

1. It depends. Each player wears his club socks. 2. Sebastian Coe. 3. He didn't - they wear letters. 4. Zurich. 5. The Kiwis. 6. Lotus. 7. Bobsleigh. 8. Wales. 9. Godolphin. 10. Everton. 11. (a) 1940. 12. A spare. 13. Weightlifting. 14. Frank Bruno. 15. 1936.

SESSION 14   QUIZ 4

General knowledge

1   Who suffers when someone has halitosis?

2   What does 'perorate' mean?

3   Who was Rodney King?

4   By what name is the medical condition talipes, better known?

5   Who is Mrs Tiggywinkle?

6   What is the maximum score allowed in the card game pontoon?

7   Lack of vitamin B1 in the body can cause which disease?

8   What does 'Kamikaze' mean?

9   Indians call their country by what name?

10   Shabat, Adar and Nisan are Jewish festivals. True or false?

11   How many bundles make one bale of printing paper?

12   In which country would you expect to see a 'gaucho'?

13   By what name is the writer Jean-Baptiste Poquelin better known?

14   'What A Wonderful World' was whose signature tune?

15   Who proved that Copernicus had been right?

ANSWERS

1. People near them. It is bad breath. 2. To speak at length. 3. The black driver beaten by LA police in 1991. 4. Club foot. 5. A hedgehog created by Beatrix Potter. 6. 21. 7. Beriberi. 8. Divine Wind. 9. Bharat, after a legendary monarch. 10. True. 11. Five. 12. Argentina. They are cowboys. 13. Molière. 14. Louis Armstrong. 15. Galileo Galilei, who proved that the Earth moved round the Sun and not the other way round.

SESSION 14

QUIZ 5

Technology & science

1 What was the invention of Charles Goodyear in 1839?

2 By what abbreviation is trichlorophenylmethyliodisalicyl better known?

3 What is the popular name for the baby kangaroo?

4 In which year was the AIDS virus isolated?

5 What was the name of the first communications satellite to orbit the Earth?

6 If you suffer from agoraphobia, what would you fear?

7 How many arms does a starfish usually have?

8 Which plant derives its name from the Latin *dens leonis*?

9 What is the name for the study of children's diseases?

10 What do the initials VHF stand for?

11 Which star is also known as the Pole Star or North Star?

12 Which chemical element has the symbol Cu?

13 Which vegetable is also know as leaf beet or seakale beet?

14 Who was the scientist who invented the kaleidoscope?

15 What is the average human body temperature?

ANSWERS

1. Vulcanized rubber. 2. TCP. 3. Joey. 4. 1983. 5. 'Early Bird'. 6. Open spaces. 7. Five. 8. Dandelion, because of the jagged shape of its leaves. 9. Paediatrics. 10. Very high frequency. 11. Polaris. 12. Copper. 13. Swiss chard. 14. David Brewster. 15. 37 degrees Celsius.

SESSION 14

QUIZ 6

Geography

1 What is the name of the wooded hill region in southern Belgium, Luxembourg and north-east France?

2 Which volcano dominates Naples in Italy?

3 Which island lies immediately west of Anglesey?

4 Which is further south, Boston in England or Boston in America?

5 Which inhospitable area in Russia is rich in fuel and minerals?

6 On the northern bank of which river does Lisbon stand?

7 The Aran Islands lie at the mouth of which Irish bay?

8 Which of these African countries has a coastline on the Atlantic Ocean: (a) Chad, (b) Niger or (c) Cameroon?

9 What city was formerly known as Constantinople?

10 Through which country does the Indus flow to the sea?

11 Which country has Algeria to the west and Libya to the southeast?

12 Which county do Whitstable oysters come from?

13 What is the state capital of Colorado?

14 The Franz Josef Glacier is a popular tourist destination in which country: (a) New Zealand, (b) Canada or (c) Austria?

15 Patagonia is a region of which South American country?

ANSWERS

1. Ardennes. 2. Vesuvius. 3. Holy Island. 4. Boston in America. 5. Siberia. 6. River Tagus. 7. Galway Bay. 8. (c) Cameroon. 9. Istanbul. 10. Pakistan. 11. Tunisia. 12. Kent. 13. Denver. 14. (a) New Zealand. 15. Argentina.

SESSION 14 · QUIZ 7

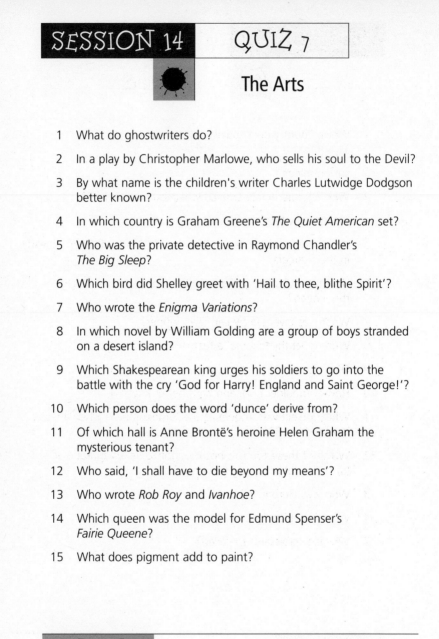

The Arts

1 What do ghostwriters do?

2 In a play by Christopher Marlowe, who sells his soul to the Devil?

3 By what name is the children's writer Charles Lutwidge Dodgson better known?

4 In which country is Graham Greene's *The Quiet American* set?

5 Who was the private detective in Raymond Chandler's *The Big Sleep*?

6 Which bird did Shelley greet with 'Hail to thee, blithe Spirit'?

7 Who wrote the *Enigma Variations*?

8 In which novel by William Golding are a group of boys stranded on a desert island?

9 Which Shakespearean king urges his soldiers to go into the battle with the cry 'God for Harry! England and Saint George!'?

10 Which person does the word 'dunce' derive from?

11 Of which hall is Anne Brontë's heroine Helen Graham the mysterious tenant?

12 Who said, 'I shall have to die beyond my means'?

13 Who wrote *Rob Roy* and *Ivanhoe*?

14 Which queen was the model for Edmund Spenser's *Fairie Queene*?

15 What does pigment add to paint?

ANSWERS

SESSION 14 QUIZ 8

Pot Luck

1 Which country does 'paella' come from?

2 Which animal changes its colour to blend in with its surroundings?

3 Which former Radio One DJ was nicknamed 'Fluff'?

4 What is a 'white elephant'?

5 What job did both Marlon Brando and Dr David Owen do early in their careers?

6 How many Secretary-General of the United Nations have there been?

7 What was invented by Earl Silas Tupper?

8 What is 'ichthyophobia' a fear of?

9 Of which country is the dong a unit of currency?

10 How is shoulder pork and ham better known?

11 Which object was known as the 'drunkometer' when it was invented in 1938?

12 Which of these foods is not thought to be an aphrodisiac: (a) celery, (b) prunes or (c) cucumber?

13 Who was Geronimo?

14 What is a 'Blue Peter'?

15 Why is a 'croissant' so called?

ANSWERS

1. Spain. 2. Chameleon. 3. Alan Freeman. 4. An unwanted item. 5. Sewage workers. 6. Seven. 7. Tupperware. 8. Fish. 9. Vietnam. 10. Spam. 11. Breathalyser 12. (c) cucumber. 13. An Apache Indian chief. 14. A flag (raised as ship leaves port). 15. It is crescent shaped.

SESSION 15   QUIZ 1

TV, music & entertainment

1. When asked by an interviewer what she wore in bed, what did Marilyn Monroe reply?

2. Who was Burt Bacharach's songwriting partner on hits such as 'What the World Needs Now is Love', 'Alfie', and 'I'll Never Fall in Love Again'?

3. In which TV comedy-drama does Calista Flockhart star?

4. In *Taxi Driver*, when Robert De Niro's character repeatedly said, 'Are you talking to me?', who was he addressing?

5. Who married and divorced Motley Crue's drummer, Tommy Lee?

6. Who is the principal of Summer Bay High in *Home and Away*?

7. What was the name of the character played by Marlon Brando in *Apocalypse Now*?

8. What was the name of Ian Dury's backing band from 1978 till 1981?

9. Was Gene Roddenberry the creator of: (a) *Blake's Seven*, (b) *Dr Who* or (c) *Star Trek*?

10. Which film director said, 'Actors are cattle'?

11. Who are the Three Tenors?

12. Larry Hagman of *Dallas* fame is the son of musical comedy star Mary Martin. True or false?

13. What was the name of the family featured in *The Sound of Music*?

14. Which country singer is known as 'The Man in Black'?

15. Who was Captain Scarlet's arch-enemy?

ANSWERS

1. Chanel No. 5. 2. Hal David. 3. *Ally McBeal*. 4. His own reflection in the mirror. 5. Pamela Anderson. 6. Donald Fisher. 7. Colonel Kurtz. 8. The Blockheads. 9. (c) *Star Trek*. 10. Alfred Hitchcock. 11. Luciano Pavarotti, Placido Domingo and José Carreras. 12. True. 13. The Von Trapp family. 14. Johnny Cash. 15. 'Captain Black'.

SESSION 15   QUIZ 2

History

1 Where did the Marie Celeste disappear?

2 Florence Nightingale was a nurse in which war?

3 753 BC is the traditional date for the founding of which ancient city?

4 Which classic history book's first volume was published in 1776?

5 What is the Rococo style of architecture?

6 William III was also known as what?

7 Who was the second president of America?

8 What was Alfred Dreyfus accused of doing?

9 What alliance was formed in 1949?

10 Who did Mark Anthony defeat in battle at Philippi?

11 Who seized power in Uganda in 1971?

12 Who was the Lord Protector of England?

13 Who ran the Nazi Propaganda ministry during World War II?

14 Who was the first Christian Roman Emperor?

15 Ireland's independence from Britain was negotiated by who?

ANSWERS

1. It didn't - the crew disappeared inside the Bermuda Triangle. 2. The Crimean. 3. Rome.
4. *The History of the Decline and Fall of the Roman Empire.* 5. A lighter form of Baroque.
6. William of Orange. 7. John Adams. 8. Selling French secrets to the Germans. 9. NATO.
10. Brutus and Cassius. 11. Idi Amin. 12. Cromwell. 13. Joseph Goebbels. 14. Constantine.
15. Michael Collins.

122

SESSION 15 QUIZ 3

Sports

1 Who rode Foxhunter?

2 How old was Rod Laver when he won Wimbledon in 1969?

3 Is Björn Borg (a) Gemini, (b) Cancer or (c) Leo?

4 How old is a filly when it becomes a mare?

5 In which year did rower Steve Redgrave win his first gold medal at the Olympics?

6 Who won the light heavyweight class at the 1960 Olympics?

7 What is a cleek?

8 What animal discovered the World Cup when it disappeared in 1966?

9 What is the name of Real Madrid's stadium?

10 Which racehorse would murder any backward member of the opposition at Aintree?

11 What is golfer Mr Zoeller called?

12 What was the name of Ted Heath's famous yacht?

13 Manchester United were the first English club to win the European Cup. True or false?

14 Which royal opened Wimbledon in 1922?

15 Where are the 2000 Olympics to be held?

ANSWERS

1. Colonel Harry Llewellyn in the 1956 Olympics. 2. 30. 3. (a) Gemini. 4. Five years old. 5. 1984. 6. Cassius Clay. 7. A Scottish term for a golf iron. 8. A dog called Pickles. 9. Bernabau. 10. Red Rum. It spells 'murder' backwards. 11. Fuzzy. 12. Morning Cloud. 13. True. 14. King George V. 15. Sydney.

SESSION 15 QUIZ 4

General knowledge

1   What rank is above an admiral in the Royal Navy?

2   Which country borders on the greatest number of other countries?

3   Where does a riparian live?

4   What are Comanche, Navajo and Creek?

5   What name is given to Viking longboats?

6   ECG is short for what?

7   How do scorpions move their young?

8   Are there: (a) 1,403, (b) 1,609 or (c) 1,954 kilometres to a mile?

9   Which part of the body does myelitis affect?

10   What is the Tellytubby Po's favourite toy?

11   What name was given to the fortified line built by the French after World War I?

12   Which biblical king ordered a baby to be cut in two?

13   The dish chile con carne originates from Mexico. True or false?

14   What number is opposite four on a dice?

15   Who is the 'patron saint' of Marks and Spencer?

ANSWERS

1. Admiral of the Fleet. 2. China, which has 16 neighbours. 3. On the bank of a river. 4. North American Indian peoples. 5. Longships. 6. Electrocardiogram or electrocardiograph. 7. They carry them on their backs. 8. (b) 1,609 km. 9. The spinal cord. 10. A scooter. 11. The Maginot line. 12. Solomon. When there was a dispute of ownership over a child, he made this suggestion. The real mother offered it to the other, whilst the fraud was indifferent to its fate. 13. True. 14. Three. All opposite faces add up to seven. 15. St Michael.

SESSION 15

QUIZ 5

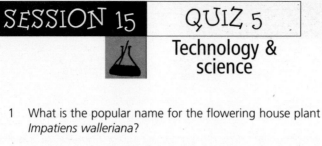

Technology & science

1 What is the popular name for the flowering house plant *Impatiens walleriana*?

2 A URL specifies the location of a document on the Internet; what do the letters stand for?

3 Cork is obtained from the bark of which tree?

4 Who established the first English printing press?

5 Which group of mammals are the only ones able to fly?

6 The 'Lent Lily' refers to which plant?

7 Of which country is the dahlia the national flower?

8 What was the name of the spacecraft that took the first human (Yuri Gagarin) into space in 1961?

9 Name the fruit that is a cross between a peach and a plum.

10 Copra is used to make margarine and candles; from which plant does it come?

11 Kale is a variety of which winter vegetable?

12 What is the Mercalli scale used for measuring?

13 From what animals' skin does Morocco leather come?

14 What do the initials UHF stand for?

15 What has the chemical symbol Fe?

ANSWERS

1. Busy Lizzie. 2. Uniform (or Universal) Resource Locator. 3. Oak. 4. William Caxton. 5. Bats. 6. Daffodil. 7. Mexico. 8. *Vostock*. 9. Nectarine. 10. Coconut plant. 11. Cabbage. 12. The intensity of earthquakes. 13. Goats. 14. Ultra High Frequency. 15. Iron.

SESSION 15   QUIZ 6

Geography

1 Which river forms the boundary between Texas and Mexico?

2 The Tropic of Capricorn runs through the Red Sea. True or false?

3 What is the name of the mountain range which runs through Morocco and Algeria?

4 Which is the largest lake in Australia: (a) Lake Eyre, (b) Lake Gairdner or (c) Lake Torrens?

5 Which headland is the most westerly point in Wales?

6 Which republic, to the north of Ukraine, has the capital Minsk?

7 In which country are the Taurus mountains?

8 Which country owns the Andaman and Nicobar Islands?

9 Which of these African countries has the largest population: (a) The Gambia, (b) Guinea or (c) Ghana?

10 In which ocean is the island of South Georgia?

11 What distance separates Ireland from Scotland: (a) 20 km, (b) 30 km or (c) 40 km?

12 In which country is the Mato Grosso plateau?

13 In which English county are the rivers Alde, Deben and Orwell?

14 What is the capital of Cuba?

15 Which South American country was called British Guiana before it gained independence in 1966?

ANSWERS

1. The Rio Grande. 2. False, it is the Tropic of Cancer. 3. Atlas mountains. 4. (a) Lake Eyre. 5. St David's Head. 6. Belarus. 7. Turkey. 8. India. 9. (c) Ghana. 10. Atlantic. 11. (a) 20 km. 12. Brazil. 13. Suffolk. 14. Havana. 15. Guyana.

SESSION 15   QUIZ 7

The Arts

1   Which creature of the deep was created by Peter Benchley?

2   How many ages of man does Jaques describe in *As You Like It*?

3   Who wrote the ballets *Swan Lake* and *Nutcracker*?

4   Which city do the poets Roger McGough and Adrian Henry come from?

5   In which gaol was Oscar Wilde imprisoned in 1895?

6   Who wrote *Women in Love* and *Sons and Lovers*?

7   Whose diaries include an account of the Great Fire of London?

8   Which schoolboy was led astray by a fox and a cat?

9   Who wrote *Under Milk Wood*?

10   In which city is James Joyce's *Ulysses* set?

11   Which artist reputedly cut off his own ear?

12   What is the meaning of this line from a poem by Wilfred Owen: '*Dulce et decorum est pro patria mori*'?

13   In which country was Mervyn Peake born?

14   Who wrote *Far From the Madding Crowd*?

15   What genre of books are written by Stephen King?

ANSWERS

1. *Jaws.* 2. Seven. 3. Tchaikovsky. 4. Liverpool. 5. Reading. 6. D. H. Lawrence. 7. Samuel Pepys. 8. Pinocchio. 9. Dylan Thomas. 10. Dublin. 11. Van Gogh. 12. 'It is sweet and right to die for one's country'. 13. China. 14. Thomas Hardy. 15. Horror.

SESSION 15   QUIZ 8

Pot Luck

1   Who wrote *The Strange Case of Dr Jekyll and Mr Hyde*?

2   What is ecclesiaphobia a fear of?

3   Which city was the first destination of Thomas Cook's tours in 1855?

4   The name Wayne means: (a) jewel, (b) star-gazer or (c) wagon-maker?

5   In which country was the umbrella invented in the second century BC?

6   From which story does the phrase 'kill the fatted calf' originally come?

7   What object is 150 million kilometres (93 million miles) from the Earth?

8   Which king of England was unable to speak English?

9   In which prison was the former Nazi, Rudolf Hess held until his death?

10   Which mammal has the heaviest brain?

11   Which expensive perfume oil is extracted from male deer?

12   At what time of day is 'reveille' called?

13   Who survived assassination by poisoning and shooting before being shot and drowned?

14   The words 'caviar', 'coffee', 'kiosk' and 'tulip' originated in which language: (a) Spanish, (b) Dutch or (c) Turkish?

15   Where would you be if you were doing 'bird-lime'?

ANSWERS

1. Robert Louis Stevenson. 2. Churches. 3. Paris. 4. (c) wagon-maker. 5. China. 6. The prodigal son, in the Bible (Luke chapter 15). 7. The Sun. 8. George I. 9. Spandau. 10. Sperm whale, six times heavier than a human's. 11. Musk. 12. First thing in the morning. 13. Rasputin. 14. (c) Turkish. 15. Prison, rhyming slang for 'doing time'.

SESSION 16   QUIZ 1

TV, music & entertainment

1. Crispian Mills of the band Kula Shaker is the son of actress Hayley Mills. True or false?

2. In *Thunderbirds*, who was Lady Penelope's chauffeur?

3. Who played 'Elliot Ness' in the film *The Untouchables*?

4. Who played at both Wembley Stadium, London and J FK Stadium, Philadelphia during Live Aid in 1985?

5. Which US sitcom features three 'Cranes' and a 'Bulldog'?

6. Who played Robert De Niro's stepson in the film *This Boy's Life*?

7. Name the members of the Jackson 5.

8. Mike Reid, who plays 'Frank Butcher' in *EastEnders*, is also a stand-up comedian. True or false?

9. Who played the title role in the 1996 version of *The Nutty Professor*?

10. What was the first record ever played on Radio 1?

11. Who played Hari Kumar in the TV serialization of *The Jewel in the Crown*?

12. Which *Star Wars* character was the father of Luke Skywalker?

13. Which Spice Girl duetted with Bryan Adams on 'When You're Gone'?

14. What is the name of the police station featured in TV's *The Bill*?

15. In which film did love mean never having to say you're sorry?

ANSWERS

1. True. 2. Parker. 3. Kevin Costner. 4. Phil Collins. 5. *Frasier* (Niles, Frasier and Martin Crane and bulldog). 6. Leonardo DiCaprio. 7. Jackie, Tito, Jermaine, Marlon and Michael Jackson. 8. True. 9. Eddie Murphy. 10. 'Flowers in the Rain' by the Move. 11. Art Malik. 12. 'Darth Vader'. 13. Mel C. 14. Sun Hill. 15. *Love Story*.

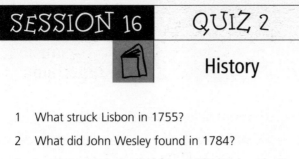

SESSION 16 — QUIZ 2

History

1 What struck Lisbon in 1755?

2 What did John Wesley found in 1784?

3 London was decimated from 1664–65 by what?

4 AD 886 saw the establishment of what in England?

5 The Alps were crossed by a most unusual army in 218BC. Who was in charge of it?

6 What everyday item was invented by Edison in 1879?

7 In 1836 a battle took place that Texans were asked to remember. Where was it?

8 What was built in England in the period from about 2200–1600BC?

9 What was the name given to the revolution that culminated in the ousting of James II?

10 Who led the Peasants' Revolt of 1381?

11 What was the name of Nelson's flagship?

12 Who was the first Englishman to sail around the globe in the late 1570s?

13 Which building project was begun in northern England in AD 122?

14 What began in America in 1861 and ended 4 years later?

15 Which country rebelled in 1857?

ANSWERS

1. An earthquake. 2. The Methodist Church. 3. The Great Plague. 4. Danelaw. 5. Hannibal. His army included elephants. 6. The electric light. 7. The Alamo. 8. Stonehenge. 9. The Glorious Revolution. 10. Wat Tyler. 11. The Victory. 12. Sir Francis Drake. 13. Hadrian's Wall. 14. The American Civil War. 15. India. It was the year of the Indian Mutiny.

SESSION 16

QUIZ 3

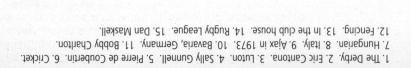

Sports

1 What classic race is run at Epsom?

2 'The Red and The Black' is a book about which French footballer?

3 Which football team did Eric Morecombe support?

4 Who won the women's 400–metre hurdles in the 1996 Atlanta Olympics?

5 Who founded the modern Olympics?

6 In which sport would you find a popping crease?

7 What nationality was Ferenc Puskas?

8 Which country is set to join the Five Nations rugby tournament?

9 Who were the first winners of the European Super Cup for Football?

10 Where was golfer Bernard Langer born?

11 Who has scored the most goals for England?

12 If you were using a sabre, what sport would you be playing?

13 Where is the 19th hole of a golf course?

14 With which sport is Peter Stirling associated?

15 Who was the voice of Wimbledon?

ANSWERS

1. The Derby. 2. Eric Cantona. 3. Luton. 4. Sally Gunnell. 5. Pierre de Coubertin. 6. Cricket. 7. Hungarian. 8. Italy. 9. Ajax in 1973. 10. Bavaria, Germany. 11. Bobby Charlton. 12. Fencing. 13. In the club house. 14. Rugby League. 15. Dan Maskell.

SESSION 16   QUIZ 4

General knowledge

1. What is an 'Indian summer'?

2. What does 'kismet' mean?

3. Who had the head of a man and the body of a bull?

4. What was the name of Gulliver's boat in his famous travels?

5. Anything 'nano-' is very small. What is the origin of the word?

6. What does TNT stand for?

7. In which town was Michael Parkinson born?

8. What is a polder?

9. Who wrote *The Hitchhiker's Guide to the Galaxy*?

10. In which film series did Arnold Schwarzenegger change sides?

11. What was Linda McCartney's surname before she married Paul?

12. What nationality was the inventor of the ballpoint, Laszlo Bíró?

13. Japan, Britain and Australia all drive on the left. True or false?

14. Who were the first men to fly in a 'heavier than air' machine?

15. Which company created Sonic the Hedgehog?

ANSWERS

1. An unusually warm spell after the end of summer. 2. The will of Allah. 3. The minotaur. 4. 'Antelope'. 5. From the Latin for 'dwarf'. 6. Trinitrotoluene. 7. Barnsley. 8. A stretch of land reclaimed from the sea. 9. Douglas Adams. 10. *Terminator*. He was a 'baddie' in the first one and a 'goodie' in the second. 11. Eastman. 12. Hungarian. 13. True. 14. Orville and Wilbur Wright in 1903. 15. Sega.

SESSION 16  QUIZ 5

Technology & science

1 By which initals is dichlorodiphenyltrichlororethane known?

2 What is another name for vitamin B2?

3 What is the meaning of the abbreviation UHT?

4 What is the scientific name for the star *Hadar*?

5 The unit of energy used to be the calorie, what is it now?

6 How many sides does a snowflake have?

7 What is the chemical symbol for chlorine?

8 Which hydrocarbon do the letters LPG represent?

9 Originally used to describe a solvent, what term is now used for waste oily liquid?

10 In which year was Morse code abolished?

11 What is the name of the comet that crashed into Jupiter in 1994?

12 In February 1997, the Roslin Institute in Edinburgh announced a technological breakthrough, what was it?

13 What is the popular name for the constellation *Crux*?

14 Which mineral is the major source of uranium ore?

15 What is the Greek term meaning 'nature'?

ANSWERS

1. DDT. 2. Riboflavin. 3. Ultra Heat Treated. 4. Beta Centauri. 5. Joule. 6. Six. 7. Cl. 8. Liquefied Petroleum Gas. 9. Gunk. 10. 1998. 11. Comet Shoemaker-Levy 9. 12. The first cloned sheep, which they called Dolly. 13. Southern Cross. 14. Pitchblende. 15. Ethos.

SESSION 16 QUIZ 6

Geography

1   Which is the largest lake in Africa: (a) Lake Chad,
    (b) Lake Victoria or (c) Lake Tanganyika?

2   What is the name of the hills in Somerset to the north
    of Taunton?

3   Which of these is not on the Greek mainland: (a) Athens,
    (b) Thessalonika or (c) Rhodes?

4   What is the main manufacturing industry in Detroit, USA?

5   The Estonian flag is black, white and what other colour?

6   Tallahassee is the capital of which American state?

7   Where is the 'Giant's Causeway'?

8   What are the lowest tides called, when the Moon and Sun are at
    right angles relative to the Earth?

9   The Swiss call it Lac Leman, but what is the English name?

10 Which European country granted independence to Benin,
    Niger and Togo in 1960?

11 The Cerne Abbas Giant is cut into a chalk hillside in
    which county?

12 The South Shetland Islands belong to the United Kingdom, but in
    which continent are they?

13 Which of these South American cities has the largest population:
    (a) São Paulo, (b) Buenos Aires or (c) Rio de Janeiro?

14 What is the capital of Syria?

15 Which country has large oil reserves in Lake Maracaibo and the
    Orinoco delta?

ANSWERS

1. (b) Lake Victoria. 2. Quantock hills. 3. (c) Rhodes. 4. Car manufacturing. 5. Blue.
6. Florida. 7. County Antrim, Northern Ireland. 8. Neap tides. 9. Lake Geneva. 10. France.
11. Dorset. 12. Antarctica. 13. (a) São Paulo. 14. Damascus. 15. Venezuela.

134

The Arts

1 What does 'PLR' stand for?

2 What was the name of Margaret Mitchell's only novel, later made into a successful film?

3 Who wrote *Brave New World*?

4 Which operatic hero claimed to have 1,003 lovers in Spain?

5 Which gothic horror story was written by Mary Shelley?

6 Which dangerously split personality was the creation of Robert Louis Stevenson?

7 Which Russian ballet company was founded by Sergei Diaghiliev?

8 In musical notation, what does 'largo' mean?

9 In which artistic field is Bernard Leach famous?

10 Who wrote *The Hunchback of Notre Dame*?

11 What is the name of Shakespeare's 'Moor of Venice'?

12 In *Pygmalion* who declares 'I want to speak like a lady'?

13 In what year was *Lady Chatterley's Lover* brought before the courts under the Obscene Publications Act?

14 In Kipling's 'Smuggler's Song', there is brandy for the Parson, and what for the Clerk?

15 Who wrote *Crime and Punishment*?

ANSWERS

1. Public Lending Right. 2. *Gone With The Wind*. 3. Aldous Huxley. 4. Don Giovanni. 5. *Frankenstein*. 6. *Dr Jekyll and Mr Hyde*. 7. Ballet Russe. 8. Slow. 9. Pottery. 10. Victor Hugo. 11. *Othello*. 12. Eliza Doolittle. 13. 1960. 14. 'Baccy for the Clerk'. (Tobacco). 15. Fyodor Dostoevsky.

SESSION 16   QUIZ 8

Pot Luck

1   Who brought the words 'enthral', 'husband', 'ransack' and 'fog' to England?

2   What is the popular name for St Stephen's Day?

3   Which metal was used from early times in white face powder?

4   Which Chinese philosopher said, 'Do unto others as you would be done by'?

5   What did Hippocrates, 'the father of medicine', believe was carried in the veins?

6   Which boy's name means 'God is my judge'?

7   How do kangaroos keep cool?

8   Which method of transport started life as a hobbyhorse, a walk-along and a velocipede?

9   What do you do to something if you 'efface' it?

10 Which marine animal communicates with squeaks, clicks, barks and whistles?

11 Which Roman emperor made his horse a consul of Rome?

12 Who wrote *The Thirty-Nine Steps*?

13 Who was president of the United States for three years, but never won a national election?

14 Who is the only British prime minister to have fought a duel while in office?

15 Which language is spoken by the largest number of people as their first language?

ANSWERS

1. The Vikings. 2. Boxing Day. 3. Lead. 4. Confucius. 5. Air. 6. Daniel. 7. They lick themselves. 8. Bicycle. 9. Remove it completely. 10. Dolphin. 11. Caligula. 12. John Buchan. 13. Gerald Ford. 14. Duke of Wellington. 15. (Mandarin) Chinese.

SESSION 17   QUIZ 1

TV, music & entertainment

1 Which TV cop show starred John Thaw and Dennis Waterman?

2 Which pop star accidentally set his hair on fire during the filming of a Pepsi commercial?

3 Which film had the advertising slogan, 'Just when you thought it was safe to go back in the water!'?

4 Who is the presenter of the magazine show *Eurotrash*?

5 Which instrument did jazzman Miles Davis play?

6 What kind of creatures is Indiana Jones afraid of?

7 In *Fawlty Towers*, where did Manuel come from?

8 Who is the lead singer with Simply Red?

9 In which film did James Bond get married?

10 In the TV series *Flipper*, what kind of creature was 'Flipper'?

11 After Brian Jones died, who took his place in the Rolling Stones?

12 Which cartoon character did Gene Kelly dance with in *Anchors Aweigh*?

13 In *EastEnders*, what is the name of Phil and Grant Mitchell's sister?

14 Who was Morrissey's songwriting partner in the Smiths?

15 In Mel Brooks' film, *Silent Movie*, there is only one word spoken. What is the word, and who utters it?

ANSWERS

1. *The Sweeney.* 2. Michael Jackson. 3. *Jaws* 2. 4. Antoine de Caunes. 5. Trumpet.
6. Snakes. 7. Barcelona. 8. Mick Hucknall. 9. *On Her Majesty's Secret Service.*
10. A dolphin. 11. Mick Taylor. 12. Jerry Mouse. 13. 'Sam'. 14. Johnny Marr.
15. The word is 'Non', and it is uttered by French mime artist Marcel Marceau.

SESSION 17 QUIZ 2

History

1 What was the nature of the government formed by Churchill during World War II?

2 In 1781 Charles Cornwallis surrendered to George Washington, bringing what to an end?

3 In which year was Hong Kong returned to China?

4 Who led the New Model Army?

5 Who was emperor of Japan during World War II?

6 What was the name of the dictator of Albania who died in 1985?

7 Who was the first American president to be impeached?

8 What nationality was Kim Il Sung?

9 Why was Julian the Apostate so called?

10 The word 'seax', meaning short sword, gave rise to the name of which people who invaded England?

11 Who were the Lollards?

12 Who was Atahualpa?

13 Which was the first Axis capital to be taken during World War II?

14 In which county does Bosworth Field lie?

15 In what year did Columbus 'sail the ocean blue'?

ANSWERS

1. A coalition government. 2. The American War of Independence. 3. 1997. 4. Thomas Fairfax. 5. Hirohito. 6. Enver Hoxha. 7. Andrew Johnson. 8. Korean. 9. Because he renounced Christianity when his family was massacred. 10. The Saxons. 11. Followers of John Wyclif the English reformer. 12. The last of the Inca rulers, killed by Pizarro. 13. Rome, although by that stage Italy had changed sides. 14. Leicestershire. 15. 1492.

SESSION 17 | QUIZ 3

Sports

1   Cardiff beat which team in the 1927 FA Cup Final?

2   Whose hand did Jesse Owens not shake?

3   Which two teams are known as the Auld Firm?

4   In karate the judges do not carry a whistle. True or false?

5   In which town is the football team, Heart of Midlothian based?

6   How far does a greyhound run in the Derby?

7   Who once beat Red Rum at a snail's pace?

8   What does it mean to wear the yellow jersey in the Tour de France?

9   What is a British Lion?

10   How many games did Scotland lose at the 1974 World Cup Finals? Was it (a) none, (b) one or (c) two?

11   At what sport did Donovan Reid and Mike McFarlane compete?

12   What has 336 dimples?

13   What are the names of Sheffield's two football teams?

14   Why was Paolo di Canio suspended in 1998?

15   Name the two famous Davis brothers of snooker fame.

ANSWERS

1. Arsenal. 2. Hitler. 3. Glasgow Rangers and Celtic. 4. False. 5. Edinburgh. 6. 500 metres. 7. 'L'escargot', which is French for 'snail'. 8. The leader. 9. A rugby union player touring for the British Isles. 10. (a) none. 11. Athletics. They were both sprinters. 12. A golf ball. 13. United and Wednesday. 14. Pushing the referee over during a game. 15. Fred and Joe.

SESSION 17 · QUIZ 4

General knowledge

1   Which channel made its first broadcast on 21 April 1964?

2   What is a CV?

3   What are the colours of the Swiss flag?

4   What is the least populated country in the world?

5   Why do most children suffer from clinophobia?

6   The Charleston dance takes its name from the South Carolina city. True or false?

7   Who succeeded Elijah as prophet?

8   Who were Icarus and Daedalus?

9   Who went for a televised drive in LA county in June 1994?

10   Who invented the jet engine?

11   What is suttee?

12   Anthrax is a disease of which animals?

13   'He who sups with the devil' should have a long what?

14   Who wrote *Madame Bovary*'?

15   The measurement acre was fixed by which English king?

ANSWERS

1. BBC 2. 2. A curriculum vitae, a summary of a person's education and employment. 3. A white cross on a red background. 4. The Vatican. 5. It is fear of going to bed. 6. True. It originated there in 1923. 7. Elisha. 8. Father and son who flew using wings made from feathers and wax. 9. O. J. Simpson. 10. Frank Whittle. 11. When a widow is burnt on her husband's funeral pyre. 12. Cattle and sheep. 13. Spoon. 14. Gustave Flaubert. 15. Edward I in 1305.

140

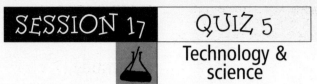
1 What is the common name of the hypothesis made popular by James Lovelock in 1968?

2 What is the common name for sodium chloride?

3 What is the name of the main sugar in milk?

4 What is the chief ore of lead?

5 If you suffered from cynophobia, what would you be afraid of?

6 In science, what is the prefix 'mega' used to mean?

7 What was the name of the first spacecraft to orbit Jupiter?

8 In which branch of science did Edwin Hubble specialize?

9 What is the most dense product obtained from the distillation of petroleum?

10 What is the chemical symbol for calcium?

11 What is an isothere?

12 Where would you find Phong shading?

13 What was the name of the comet first sighted in 1995?

14 What is the name for the hypothetical perfect radiator and absorber of energy?

15 An alternative abbreviation for GMT is UT, what do the initials UT stand for?

ANSWERS

1. Gaia hypothesis. 2. Salt. 3. Lactose. 4. Galena. 5. Dogs. 6. 10^6 (one million). 7. 'Galileo'. 8. Astronomy. 9. Bitumen. 10. Ca. 11. A line on a map connecting places with the same temperature in summer. 12. Shading used in computer animation. 13. Hale-Bopp. 14. Black body. 15. Universal Time.

SESSION 17   QUIZ 6

Geography

1 Which country is enclosed by Senegal?

2 What is the state capital of Queensland, Australia?

3 What is 'Brown Willy': (a) a lake in the Rockies, (b) the highest point on Bodmin Moor or (c) a river in Australia?

4 In which American state is the Mojave desert?

5 In which country could you travel on the 'bullet' train?

6 What is the capital of Peru?

7 If you were studying Hadley cells and Ferrel cells would you be looking at: (a) ocean currents, (b) air currents or (c) electrical currents?

8 Fastnet Rock is south of the Scilly Isles. True or false?

9 What is the marshy area called between Montpellier and Marseille?

10 What was the Latin name for St Albans?

11 Which is the highest mountain in Africa?

12 Which Swiss town lies between Lake Thun and Lake Brienz?

13 On which island is Carisbrooke Castle?

14 The state of Qatar is a peninsula on the Persian Gulf. Which country is on its southern border?

15 Which Canadian province is between Ontario and Saskatchewan?

ANSWERS

1. The Gambia. 2. Brisbane. 3. (b) the highest point on Bodmin Moor. 4. California. 5. Japan. 6. Lima. 7. (b) air currents. 8. False, it is just south of Ireland. 9. The Camargue. 10. Verulamium. 11. Mount Kilimanjaro. 12. Interlaken. 13. Isle of Wight. 14. Saudi Arabia. 15. Manitoba.

SESSION 17 · QUIZ 7

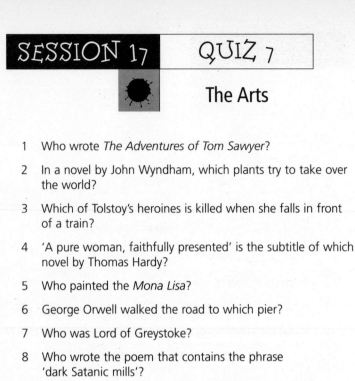

The Arts

1 Who wrote *The Adventures of Tom Sawyer*?

2 In a novel by John Wyndham, which plants try to take over the world?

3 Which of Tolstoy's heroines is killed when she falls in front of a train?

4 'A pure woman, faithfully presented' is the subtitle of which novel by Thomas Hardy?

5 Who painted the *Mona Lisa*?

6 George Orwell walked the road to which pier?

7 Who was Lord of Greystoke?

8 Who wrote the poem that contains the phrase 'dark Satanic mills'?

9 What nationality was the painter Renoir?

10 Which architect designed the Glasgow School of Art?

11 Who wrote the play *A Streetcar Named Desire*?

12 Which 15th-century knight wrote down the Arthurian legends in *Le Morte D'Arthur*?

13 Which of these was not one of the Three Musketeers: (a) Porthos, (b) Athos, (c) Davros or (d) Aramis?

14 Who wrote *The Wind in the Willows*?

15 What name is given to the annual national gathering of Welsh bards?

ANSWERS

1. Mark Twain. 2. Triffids. 3. Anna Karenina, from the book of the same name. 4. *Tess of the D'Urbervilles*. 5. Leonardo da Vinci. 6. Wigan. 7. Tarzan. 8. William Blake. 9. French. 10. Charles Rennie Mackintosh. 11. Tennessee Williams. 12. Thomas Malory. 13. (c) Davros. 14. Kenneth Grahame. 15. Eisteddfod.

SESSION 17   QUIZ 8

Pot Luck

1   Which city's zoo contains the Rocher, an artificial mountain for wild sheep?

2   From which country does the Borzoi dog originate?

3   Which lighthouse was swept away in 1703 with its inventor Henry Winstanley inside?

4   What single word is the distress signal used by ships in grave and imminent danger?

5   What are 'Chablis', 'Burgundy' and 'Madeira'?

6   A mangosteen is: (a) a fish, (b) a fruit or (c) a type of steel?

7   Which Scottish engineer gave his name to a widely used road surface which was developed after his death?

8   Which country's car registration mark is SF?

9   Which chemical weapon was known in the ancient World as Greek fire?

10   The word 'extirpate' means: (a) to destroy, (b) to accomplish or (c) to depart?

11   Which unit of measurement was defined by the Romans as one thousand paces?

12   Vinson, Tyree, Shinn and Gardner are the very high peaks of which continent?

13   What was signified by a red lattice on the side of a house?

14   The human brain is physically unable to feel pain. True or false?

15   What is the Scottish word for New Year celebrations?

ANSWERS

SESSION 18 QUIZ 1

TV, music & entertainment

1   US pianist and composer, Herbie Hancock, is a pioneer of which jazz style?

2   Who starred in *I Love Lucy*?

3   Who sang 'Ol' Man River' in the 1936 film *Show Boat*?

4   Who is the lead singer with Jamiroquai?

5   What was the profession of Fitz in the TV drama series *Cracker*?

6   Who or what was 'Harvey' in the film of the same name?

7   Who recorded the 1968 album 'Electric Ladyland'?

8   Which former Page 3 girl has her own TV chat show?

9   Which film actor was mayor of Carmel, California from 1986 to 1988?

10   With which band is Michael Stipe the lead singer?

11   Who plays Mandy Dingle in *Emmerdale*?

12   In *101 Dalmatians*, why does Cruella de Vil want the puppies?

13   Singer Natalie Imbruglia used to be in *Neighbours*. True or false?

14   Who is Mulder and Scully's immediate superior in *The X Files*?

15   What is unusual about the gangster musical *Bugsy Malone*?

ANSWERS

1. Fusion. 2. Lucille Ball. 3. Paul Robeson. 4. Jay K. 5. Criminal psychologist.
6. An imaginary six-foot rabbit. 7. Jimi Hendrix. 8. Melinda Messenger. 9. Clint Eastwood.
10. R.E.M. 11. Lisa Riley. 12. To have a fur coat made from their skins. 13. True.
14. 'Skinner'. 15. All the parts are played by children.

SESSION 18 QUIZ 2

History

1   What was W. E. Gladstone's middle name?

2   Who was Henry VIII's first wife?

3   1337 saw the beginning of which drawn-out war?

4   Who was tutor to Alexander the Great?

5   Where was the peace treaty of 1919 signed?

6   Which people founded Carthage in 814 BC?

7   Who won the Battle of Blenheim in 1714?

8   In 1698 a tax in Russia was introduced on which gentleman's item?

9   With what name do you associate a 'Younger' and an 'Elder'?

10   What was the name of the last British governor of Hong Kong?

11   Did Queen Victoria reign: (a) 54, (b) 63 or (c) 68 years?

12   According to Tennyson, how many soldiers took part in the charge of the Light Brigade?

13   In which war did the Battle of Bull Run take place?

14   Who first published a book on British Aristocracy in 1802?

15   What did John Wilkes Booth do at the theatre?

ANSWERS

1. Ewart. 2. Catherine of Aragon. 3. The Hundred Years War. 4. Aristotle. 5. Versailles. 6. The Phoenicians. 7. Marlborough. 8. Beards. 9. Pitt. 10. Chris Patten. 11. (b) 63 years. 12. 600. 13. The American Civil War. 14. Debrett. 15. He killed Abraham Lincoln.

SESSION 18   QUIZ 3

Sports

1　Which brothers have both played on the wing for England at rugby union?

2　By what name is Mary Twomey better known?

3　The opening sequence to the film *Chariots of Fire* was filmed at which famous golf club?

4　Where do Leicester City play?

5　When were the Wimbledon Lawn Tennis Championships first held: (a) 1859, (b) 1860 or (c) 1877?

6　The biathlon is made up of which two sports?

7　Which British boxer won an Olympic Middleweight gold at the 1968 Olympics?

8　Where might you find gutta percha?

9　If men have to do ten of them; how many do women do?

10　What is a bisque in golf?

11　What gave Kevin Keegan a great smell?

12　Where is the Maracana stadium?

13　Who played opposite Willie Carson on 'A Question of Sport'?

14　Who was Fred Stole's partner in men's doubles?

15　Where were the 1994 Winter Olympics?

ANSWERS

1. Tony and Rory Underwood. 2. Mary Rand who won the Olympic long jump in 1964.
3. St Andrews. 4. Filbert Street. 5. (c) 1877. 6. Cross-country skiing and rifle shooting.
7. Chris Finnegan. 8. In a golf ball. 9. Seven. The men do ten events in the the decathlon
while women perform the heptathlon. 10. A handicap stroke. 11. Brut aftershave.
12. Rio de Janeiro. 13. Bill Beaumont. 14. Bob Hewitt. 15. Lillehammer, Norway.

SESSION 18 · QUIZ 4

General knowledge

1 The snack bar 'Snickers' was formerly called what?

2 The current calendar is the Gregorian. What was the former one called?

3 What were the trade routes between Europe and Asia once called?

4 Astronauts get shorter in space. True or false?

5 Which commonplace kitchen appliance did Percy Spencer invent in the 1940s?

6 Where does a car with the letter 'V' hail from?

7 What is a banshee?

8 Which American state is known as the 'Cotton State'?

9 How many items are there in a 'baker's dozen'?

10 Is the 'jipijapa': (a) a palm-like plant, (b) a dance or (c) a throw in judo?

11 What function does a muezzin perform five times each day?

12 What is a Portuguese man-of-war?

13 Who was the author of *Three Men in a Boat*?

14 What does 'non sequitur' mean?

15 In which country is the carrot believed to have originated?

ANSWERS

1. 'Marathon'. 2. Julian. 3. 'The Silk Road'. 4. False, they get taller. 5. Microwave. 6. Vatican City. 7. A wailing spirit usually announcing death. 8. Alabama. 9. 13. 10. (a) a palm-like plant. 11. He calls the faithful to pray in Islam. 12. A jellyfish. 13. Jerome K. Jerome. 14. It does not follow. 15. Afghanistan.

SESSION 18   QUIZ 5

Technology & science

1   Where in the body is the 'maxilla'?

2   What is the square root of 225?

3   What is monosodium glutamate usually used for?

4   What is the SI unit of electric capacitance?

5   Who was the 17th-century philosopher who laid the foundations of modern scientific research?

6   What is SAD?

7   If you suffered from photophobia, what would you fear most?

8   What type of animal comprises the phylum Annelida?

9   Who discovered the first safe smallpox vaccine?

10   What is the chemical symbol for arsenic?

11   What is the technical name for the collarbone?

12   Name the physicist who established a fundamental constant relating energy of electromagnetic radiation to frequency of radiation.

13   What is the term for a young deer?

14   Lack of which vitamin causes rickets in children?

15   Plumbago is another name for which mineral?

ANSWERS

1. It is the bone of the upper jaw. 2. 15. 3. To intensify the flavour of food. 4. Farad. 5. Francis Bacon (1561-1626). 6. Seasonal Affective Disorder, a form of depression brought on by lack of daylight in the winter months. 7. Light. 8. Ringed worms (earthworm, lugworm, leech). 9. Edward Jenner. 10. As. 11. Clavicle. 12. Max Planck. 13. Fawn. 14. Vitamin D. 15. Graphite.

SESSION 18   QUIZ 6

Geography

1   Which island in the Persian Gulf lies between Saudi Arabia and Qatar?

2   In Australia, the Indian Pacific Railway goes from Perth in the west to which city on the east coast?

3   In which American state is Yellowstone National Park?

4   What is the capital of Romania?

5   In 1964, which island united with Tanganyika to form Tanzania?

6   What is the name of the peninsula between the River Mersey and the River Dee?

7   Which is the most northerly of the Channel Islands?

8   Mont Blanc is on the border of France and which other country?

9   Which city is served by Orly airport?

10   Which country, consisting of islands off the coast of Venezuela, is the world's largest source of natural asphalt?

11   Of which Canadian province is Edmonton the capital?

12   In which country is the port of Durban?

13   Which is the highest mountain in Nepal?

14   In which English county is the Long Mynd?

15   The Stanley Falls are at Kisangani on which river?

ANSWERS

1. Bahrain. 2. Sydney. 3. Montana. 4. Bucharest. 5. Zanzibar. 6. The Wirral. 7. Alderney. 8. Italy. 9. Paris. 10. Trinidad and Tobago. 11. Alberta. 12. South Africa. 13. Mount Everest. 14. Shropshire. 15. River Zaïre (River Congo).

SESSION 18 — QUIZ 7

The Arts

1 Who disappeared, leaving only a smile?

2 Which French artist painted many scenes of young ballet dancers?

3 Who wrote the Barchester chronicles?

4 Which sea captain was obsessed with the capture of Moby Dick?

5 Who originally illustrated the *Winnie the Pooh* stories?

6 Browning sighed, 'Oh, to be in England, Now that...' which month is there?

7 In *Treasure Island*, who does Billy Bones get the Black Spot from?

8 What is the name of the lion in *The Lion, The Witch and the Wardrobe*?

9 What type of pot did Keats address as 'Thou still unravish'd bride of quietness'?

10 Who wrote *A Portrait of the Artist as a Young Man*?

11 Which prize is awarded annually to a young British artist?

12 Which county is the setting for Winston Graham's *Poldark* novels?

13 Who wrote *One Day in the Life of Ivan Denisovich*?

14 In which country was the modern design school the Bauhaus established?

15 Which English sculptor's works are often characterized by natural forms pierced with holes?

ANSWERS

1. The cheshire cat. 2. Edgar Degas. 3. Anthony Trollope. 4. Captain Ahab.
5. E. H. Shepard. 6. April. 7. Blind Pew. 8. Aslan. 9. A Grecian Urn. 10. James Joyce.
11. Turner Prize. 12. Cornwall. 13. Alexander Solzhenitsyn. 14. Germany. 15. Henry Moore.

SESSION 18 QUIZ 8

Pot Luck

1   What name is given to a cat or other animal that is a witch's magical companion?

2   Used for ornaments and drinking vessels, what are gourds?

3   What is campanology?

4   Which is the odd one out: (a) dolphin, (b) whale or (c) shark?

5   From which county do Salopians hail?

6   Which hand is your 'sinister' hand?

7   Indolent means: (a) playful, (b) stupid or (c) lazy?

8   Which two words which sound similar mean a male parent/ a longer distance?

9   What does a green V-shaped tick mean on food products?

10   What happens to people who are 'defenestrated'?

11   Who is more senior, a major or a general?

12   Which Royal mistress was an orange seller?

13   What is the *vox populis*?

14   What is the wine 'saki' made from?

15   What type of angel was Gabriel?

ANSWERS

1. Familiar. 2. Dried fruit. 3. Bell-ringing. 4. (c) shark, it is a fish; the others are mammals. 5. Shropshire. 6. Left. 7. (c) lazy. 8. Father/farther. 9. Suitable for vegetarians. 10. They are thrown out of a window. 11. General. 12. Nell Gwyn. 13. The voice of the people. 14. Rice. 15. An archangel.

SESSION 19   QUIZ 1

TV, music & entertainment

1. Which 'Friend' was *Lost in Space* in 1998?

2. Is the lead singer with the band Hole: (a) Courteney Cox, (b) Courtney Love or (c) Courtney Pine?

3. What kind of creatures are the cartoon characters Ren and Stimpy?

4. Who played Superman's father in the 1978 film *Superman*?

5. What was the first band to play in the Live Aid concert at Wembley?

6. Which member of the *EastEnders* cast was once Dr Who's assistant?

7. In which film did Al Jolson say, 'You ain't heard nothin' yet!'?

8. Which US entertainer described himself as 'a one-eyed Jewish Negro'?

9. Who is novelist Jackie Collins's famous sister?

10. What was the name of the character played by Marilyn Monroe in *Some Like It Hot*?

11. Peter Shaffer's play *Amadeus* was about the life (and death) of which classical composer?

12. Who is the star of US comedy series *Seinfeld*?

13. By what name is Zorro more properly known?

14. Where was Freddie Mercury of Queen born?

15. Is Peter Alliss a TV commentator on: (a) golf, (b) cricket or (c) motor racing?

ANSWERS

1. Matt LeBlanc. 2. (b) Courtney Love. 3. Ren is a chihuahua and Stimpy is a cat. 4. Marlon Brando. 5. Status Quo. 6. Louise Jameson, who plays Rosa di Marco in *EastEnders*. 7. *The Jazz Singer*. 8. Sammy Davis Jr. 9. Joan Collins. 10. Sugar. 11. Wolfgang Amadeus Mozart. 12. Jerry Seinfeld. 13. Don Diego de Vega. 14. Zanzibar. 15. (a) golf.

SESSION 19 QUIZ 2

History

1 Before their marriage, what relation were Victoria and Albert?

2 Who is known as the father of America?

3 Who said, 'Man is born free but is everywhere in chains'?

4 Which country was the home of the Incas?

5 The Thirty Years War began as a fight between which two groups?

6 Who wrote a book of Martyrs?

7 Which Roman road went from Exeter to Lincoln?

8 What nationality were the Huguenots?

9 What was the last part of France to belong to England?

10 Which laws were introduced into England in 1815 and 1828?

11 What crashed in 1926?

12 Which religious order did St Francis of Assissi found in 1210?

13 Who was killed by Macbeth in 1040?

14 What did Offa, king of Mercia build?

15 In 630 AD Mohammed took which city?

ANSWERS

1. First cousins. 2. George Washington. 3. Jean Jacques Rousseau. 4. Peru. 5. Protestants and Catholics. 6. John Foxe. 7. Fosse Way. 8. French. They were victims of religious persecution. 9. Calais, retaken by the French in 1558. 10. The Corn Laws. 11. Wall Street. 12. The Franciscans. 13. Duncan. 14. A dyke between England and Wales. 15. Mecca.

154

SESSION 19 · QUIZ 3

Sports

1   Which basketball team appear to the strains of 'Sweet Georgia Brown'?

2   What sport do the Cleveland Indians play?

3   Which footballer was known as 'sniffer'?

4   Where is the Irish Grand National run?

5   Why should Larry Gaetjens' name fill English football with shame?

6   Which team were the runners-up in the 1974 and 1978 World Cups?

7   Where were the first Olympics after World War II held?

8   Gillian Gilkes played which sport?

9   In what year did the football league introduce three points for a win?

10   What is the surname of tennis sisters, Venus and Serena?

11   Which New Zealand rugby player looks set to appear in a James Bond movie as a villain?

12   Liem Swie King plays badminton for which Asian country?

13   Who is the 110–metre hurdle world record holder?

14   How many times did Liverpool win the league in the 1980s?

15   What takes place at RAF Cosford?

ANSWERS

1. Harlem Globe Trotters. 2. Baseball. 3. Allan Clarke. 4. Fairyhouse. 5. He scored the goal in the USA's victory over England in 1950. 6. Holland. 7. London. 8. Badminton. 9. 1981. 10. Williams. 11. Jonah Lomu. 12. Indonesia. 13. Colin Jackson. 14. Six. 15. Indoor athletics.

SESSION 19 QUIZ 4

General knowledge

1 What do the initials SRN stand for?

2 By what name is the disease *varicella* more commonly known?

3 Who or what is the 'Empress of Blandings'?

4 Who makes 'exceedingly good cakes'?

5 What do Americans call courgettes?

6 In Australian slang, a 'plonko' is an alcoholic. True or false?

7 Where did Carter, Sadat and Begin forge an historic agreement?

8 According to Norse tradition, who go to Valhalla?

9 Which city has a 'room with a view'?

10 How does one calculate the area of a rectangle?

11 Which animal has the longest gestation period?

12 Who invented dynamite?

13 Which country has the highest population of Hindus?

14 Who spent *A Year in Provence*?

15 Who painted *The Adoration of the Magi*?

ANSWERS

1. State Registered Nurse. 2. Chicken pox. 3. A pig in the P. G. Wodehouse novels.
4. 'Mr Kipling'. 5. Zucchini. The English have borrowed from the French, the Americans from
the Italians. 6. True. 7. Camp David. 8. Warriors slain in battle. 9. Florence It is the title of a
book and subsequently a film. 10. By multiplying the length by the width. 11. The elephant
with approximately 660 days. 12. Alfred Nobel. 13. India. 14. Peter Mayle.
15. Andrea Mantegna.

SESSION 19

QUIZ 5

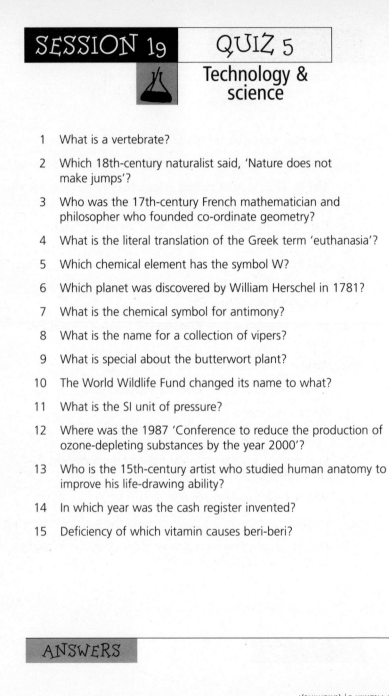

Technology & science

1   What is a vertebrate?

2   Which 18th-century naturalist said, 'Nature does not make jumps'?

3   Who was the 17th-century French mathematician and philosopher who founded co-ordinate geometry?

4   What is the literal translation of the Greek term 'euthanasia'?

5   Which chemical element has the symbol W?

6   Which planet was discovered by William Herschel in 1781?

7   What is the chemical symbol for antimony?

8   What is the name for a collection of vipers?

9   What is special about the butterwort plant?

10 The World Wildlife Fund changed its name to what?

11 What is the SI unit of pressure?

12 Where was the 1987 'Conference to reduce the production of ozone-depleting substances by the year 2000'?

13 Who is the 15th-century artist who studied human anatomy to improve his life-drawing ability?

14 In which year was the cash register invented?

15 Deficiency of which vitamin causes beri-beri?

ANSWERS

1. An animal with a backbone. 2. Carolus Linnaeus, founder of the classification system of living things. 3. René Descartes (1596-1650). 4. Easy death. 5. Tungsten. 6. Uranus. 7. Sb. 8. Nest. 9. It is carnivorous and feeds on insects. 10. World Wide Fund for Nature. 11. Pascal. 12. Montreal. 13. Leonardo da Vinci. 14. 1879 (James Ritty). 15. Vitamin B, (thiamine).

SESSION 19   QUIZ 6

Geography

1   In which county would you find Chesil Bank?

2   From Paris, which city is nearer, Edinburgh or Rome?

3   The Great Saint Bernard Pass crosses the Alps from Switzerland to which other country?

4   Caracas is the capital of which South American country?

5   Which mountain range lies along the boundary of France and Spain?

6   In which forest would you find the villages of Coleford, Cinderford and St Briavels?

7   In which European capital would you see the Schönbrunn Palace?

8   Atlanta is the capital of which American state?

9   Which sea lies between Vietnam and Malaysia?

10   What is the capital of Sicily?

11   Which is the largest lake in Africa?

12   In which country are the Great Karroo Mountains and the Drakensburg Escarpment?

13   Which is the largest city in New Zealand?

14   In which country do the Suya, Wayana and Kayapo Indians live?

15   In Lagos, Nigeria the lowest recorded temperature in degrees Celsius is: (a) 16, (b) 9 or (c) 4?

ANSWERS

1. Dorset. 2. Edinburgh. 3. Italy. 4. Venezuela. 5. Pyrenees. 6. Forest of Dean. 7. Vienna. 8. Georgia. 9. The South China Sea. 10. Palermo. 11. Lake Victoria (Victoria Nyanza). 12. South Africa. 13. Auckland. 14. Brazil. 15. (a) 16.

SESSION 19 QUIZ 7

The Arts

1   Who wrote trilogies about the Mallen family and Tilly Trotter?

2   Which American artist is famous for his portrait of his mother, which is now in the Louvre?

3   The Kelmscott Press was founded by which writer, artist, wallpaper designer and central figure of the arts and crafts movement?

4   Who killed Cock Robin with his bow and arrow?

5   In which Italian museum are Botticelli's *Primavera* and *The Birth of Venus*?

6   Who carved the 'Contrapuntal Forms'?

7   Who wrote the novel *Kane and Abel*?

8   In music, what does 'pianissimo' mean?

9   Which Dutch town is famous for its pottery, particularly its blue and white tiles?

10 What is the name of the woven cloth onto which artists apply their paint?

11 Who told his friend Mole that he liked nothing better than 'simply messing about in boats'?

12 Which powerful Florentine family were great patrons of the arts during the 15th century?

13 Which instrument was invented by Adolphe Sax?

14 Which colour is associated with the fashion designer Schiaparelli?

15 Which British film featured W. H. Auden's poem 'Funeral Blues'?

ANSWERS

1. Catherine Cookson. 2. James Whistler. 3. William Morris. 4. The Sparrow. 5. Uffizi, Florence. 6. Barbara Hepworth. 7. Jeffrey Archer. 8. Very softly. 9. Delft. 10. Canvas. 11. Rat, in *The Wind in the Willows*. 12. Medici. 13. Saxophone. 14. Shocking Pink. 15. *Four Weddings and a Funeral*.

SESSION 19   QUIZ 8

Pot Luck

1   Which highwayman rode Black Bess?

2   What makes jelly jelly-like?

3   What type of clothing are 'plus-fours'?

4   A gregarious person is: (a) friendly, (b) sulky or (c) big-headed?

5   A trichologist specializes in: (a) nails, (b) hair or (c) skin?

6   Where on your body might you suffer from fallen arches?

7   What colour is jade?

8   What is the Greek wine retsina made from?

9   What was special about Clive Sinclair's 'Zike' bicycle?

10   What type of herb is pennyroyal?

11   Which British prime minister said, 'Never complain and never explain'?

12   What is the 'Ally Pally'?

13   In which month is the Feast of the Annunciation, or Lady Day?

14   Who was the Greek god of woods, shepherds and flocks?

15   Which star sign is also called The Ram?

ANSWERS

1. Dick Turpin. 2. Gelatine. 3. Knee-length trousers. 4. (a) friendly. 5. (b) hair. 6. Feet. 7. Green. 8. Pine resin. 9. It had an electric motor. 10. Mint. 11. Disraeli. 12. Alexandra Palace. 13. March (the 25th). 14. Pan. 15. Aries.

SESSION 20   QUIZ 1

TV, music & entertainment

1   What is the name of The Simpsons dog?

2   What style of rock music was pioneered by Seattle bands like Nirvana and Pearl Jam?

3   Who said kissing Marilyn Monroe was like kissing Hitler?

4   Who played Batman in the 1960s TV series?

5   Who has been Elton John's songwriting partner for most of his career?

6   In which film was Tom Cruise confined to a wheelchair?

7   Who was the original question master in *University Challenge*?

8   Who was the guest vocalist on Space's 'The Ballad of Tom Jones'?

9   Which major star appeared uncredited in the film *Broadcast News*?

10   Who played Charlene in *Neighbours* in the 1980s?

11   How did Dennis Wilson of the Beach Boys die?

12   Who is Warren Beatty's famous sister?

13   Which character in *M*A*S*H* always wore a dress?

14   Which band recorded the 1997 album 'OK Computer'?

15   What kind of adventure did Bill and Ted have in 1988?

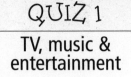

ANSWERS

1. Santa's Little Helper. 2. Grunge. 3. Tony Curtis. 4. Adam West. 5. Bernie Taupin.
6. *Born on the Fourth of July*. 7. Bamber Gascoigne. 8. Cerys Matthews. 9. Jack Nicholson.
10. Kylie Minogue. 11. He drowned. 12. Shirley McLaine. 13. Corporal Klinger.
14. Radiohead. 15. Excellent.

SESSION 20   QUIZ 2

History

1 In which year did the Battle of Verdun take place?

2 How long did the Spanish Civil War last in the 1930s?

3 Which was the first country to give women the vote?

4 What great event took place in 1851?

5 Who killed Dietrich Bonhoeffer, the German theologian?

6 Where was the capital of the Byzantine Empire?

7 Against what injustice did William Wilberforce devote his political life?

8 Which dynasty ruled Russia for over 300 years?

9 Who led a slave revolt in the Roman Empire in 73 BC?

10 Who won the battle at the heights of Abraham?

11 Did the Korean War begin in: (a) 1949, (b) 1950 or (c) 1951?

12 Which two countries participated in the 'Cod War'?

13 The Irish Free State was established in 1920. True or false?

14 Who nationalized the Suez Canal, provoking a crisis?

15 With whom did Ulrike Meinhof combine to form a terrorist group?

ANSWERS

1. 1916. 2. Three years. 3. New Zealand in 1893. 4. The Great Exhibition. 5. The Nazis. 6. Constantinople. 7. The Slave Trade. 8. The Romanov dynasty. 9. Spartacus. 10. General Wolfe of Quebec. 11. (b) 1950. 12. England and Iceland. 13. False. 14. Nasser of Egypt. 15. Andreas Baader. It was 1921.

SESSION 20   QUIZ 3

Sports

1   At which football ground do Wasps play?

2   Which football club, nicknamed the 'Superhoops', plays there?

3   What was Basil d'Oliveira's nickname?

4   Which football international was known as 'the giraffe'?

5   What nationality is Ben Crenshaw?

6   What ball is made of celluloid?

7   In what game is there a backward point, third man and long on?

8   How long does an American Football game last?

9   Which commentator said, 'The World Cup – a truly international event'?

10 What nationality was Emil Zatopek?

11 Which races did he win at the 1952 Olympics?

12 Terry Venables has played for England at every level. True or false?

13 Which way do athletes run around the track?

14 Which Italian club did Gazza play for?

15 Which Australian tennis player was born Margaret Smith?

ANSWERS

1. Loftus Road. 2. Queens Park Rangers. 3. Dolly. 4. Jack Charlton. 5. American.
6. A table tennis ball. 7. Cricket. 8. 60 minutes of playing time. 9. John Motson.
10. Czech. 11. 5,000, 10,000 and marathon. 12. True. 13. Anti-clockwise. 14. Lazio.
15. Margaret Court.

SESSION 20 QUIZ 4

General knowledge

1   Which ancient book tells how Rome was founded?

2   Whose massive shoe collection gained her even greater notoriety?

3   What rank is below Major in the British Army?

4   Which Central American country is popular for registering ships?

5   Did Blériot fly across the Channel in: (a) 1908, (b) 1910 or (c) 1912?

6   What is the exclusive licence to manufacture, exploit and produce known as?

7   Which potato product does Gary Lineker advertise?

8   'Liberty or Death' is the national motto of which country?

9   Who wrote *The Common Sense Book of Baby and Child Care*?

10   What do ergophobics suffer from?

11   What is the last letter in the Greek alphabet?

12   Which book of the Bible begins, 'Vanity, vanity ...'?

13   The mountain ash is also known as what?

14   In June 1994 George Michael lost a court case against which record company?

15   How old was Tony Blair when he was elected leader of the Labour Party? Was he: (a) 39, (b) 40 or (c) 41?

ANSWERS

1. *The Aeneid by Virgil*. 2. Imelda Marcos of the Philippines. 3. Captain. 4. Panama. 5. (a) 1908. 6. Patent. 7. Walkers Crisps. 8. Greece. 9. Benjamin Spock. 10. fear of going to work. 11. Omega. 12. Ecclesiastes. 13. Rowan. 14. Sony. 15. (c) 41.

SESSION 20

QUIZ 5

Technology & science

1   What is the name of the acid that is found in some ants?

2   If a metal is ductile, what special property does it possess?

3   FoE are the initials of the charity organization that aims to protect the planet from environmental degradation; what is its full name?

4   In 1772 Daniel Rutherford isolated a colourless inert gas; what was it?

5   What is a catalytic converter?

6   For what medical treatment is lithium prescribed?

7   Which has been the warmest year on record so far?

8   What does 9.805 metres per second per second represent?

9   In 1997, where was the United Nations Conference on global warming held?

10   Who was the 20th-century philosopher and mathematician who was a major exponent of logical positivism?

11   What is the name of the process by which one cell divides to produce two genetically identical cells, each known as a daughter cell?

12   In medicine, what does IV stand for?

13   If you can have a pride of lions, what collective noun is used for swans?

14   In what year was the contraceptive pill invented?

15   Which main deficiency symptom does lack of Vitamin A cause?

ANSWERS

1. Formic acid. 2. It can be drawn into wire. 3. Friends of the Earth. 4. Nitrogen. 5. A device fitted to vehicle exhausts to reduce toxic emissions. 6. Manic-depressive illnesses. 7. 1989. 8. Acceleration due to gravity. 9. Kyoto, Japan. 10. Bertrand Russell (1872-1970). 11. Mitosis. 12. Intravenous. 13. Bevy or wedge. 14. 1954 (Gregory Pincus). 15. Night blindness.

SESSION 20 QUIZ 6

Geography

1 In which country are the Apennines?

2 The Massif Central is the highest point between the Alps and the Pyrenees. True or false?

3 Which Tropic runs through Namibia, Botswana and Mozambique?

4 Paramaribo is the capital of which South American country?

5 Into which sea does the River Volga flow: (a) Aral, (b) Black or (c) Caspian?

6 In which National Park is Kinder Scout?

7 In which country is the Midi Canal?

8 On which island is Mount Teide?

9 On the borders of Peru and Bolivia is the world's highest navigable lake; what is it called?

10 Which country was called Northern Rhodesia before its independence in 1964?

11 Baton Rouge is the capital of which American state?

12 Which former British island in the Caribbean was invaded by America in 1983?

13 What is the highest mountain in Kenya?

14 Which Australian city has the higher rainfall, Perth or Sydney?

15 What is the name of the grasslands of Argentina?

ANSWERS

1. Italy. 2. True. 3. Tropic of Capricorn. 4. Surinam. 5. (c) Caspian. 6. Peak District. 7. France. 8. Tenerife. 9. Lake Titicaca. 10. Zambia. 11. Louisiana. 12. Grenada. 13. Mount Kenya. 14. Sydney. 15. Pampas.

SESSION 20 · QUIZ 7

The Arts

1 Which tragic lady from a poem by Tennyson was painted by John Waterhouse?

2 Who wrote *Trainspotting*?

3 For what was Dame Margot Fonteyn famous?

4 Who wrote the orchestral piece *Peter and the Wolf*?

5 Where do the phrases 'the salt of the earth' and 'hide one's light under a bushel' come from?

6 Sherlock Holmes said 'Elementary, my dear Watson'.
True or false?

7 What animals are the main characters in *Watership Down*?

8 How old was Mozart when he wrote his first composition?

9 Who wrote the *Seven Pillars of Wisdom*?

10 In *Oliver Twist*, what is the name of the bully who kills Nancy?

11 Which Nobel Prize winner wrote *A Farewell to Arms* and *For Whom the Bell Tolls*?

12 Which prize for American literature is awarded each year?

13 Which Scottish-born American philanthropist founded many of the public libraries in Britain and America?

14 'Shall I compare thee ...' To what?

15 Who lives in Hundred Acre Wood?

ANSWERS

1. *The Lady of Shalott*. 2. Irvine Welsh. 3. Ballet dancing. 4. Sergei Prokofiev.
5. Jesus' words in The Sermon on the Mount. 6. False, he never said it. 7. Rabbits.
8. Five years old. 9. T. E. Lawrence (of Arabia). 10. Bill Sykes. 11. Ernest Hemingway.
12. Pulitzer Prize. 13. Andrew Carnegie. 14. A summer's day (sonnet by Shakespeare).
15. Owl (from *Winnie the Pooh*).

SESSION 20 QUIZ 8

Pot Luck

1 Who is the patron saint of music, her feast day being 22 November?

2 What is measured by a sphygmomanometer?

3 What colour is the gemstone lapis lazuli?

4 In which seaside town is John Nash's elaborate Royal Pavilion?

5 Which British explorer died on South Georgia Island on his fourth Antarctic expedition?

6 The extract from which tree is used in an eye soothing lotion?

7 Where is the native country of the Dalai Lama?

8 In which region of France is Camembert, the village famous for its cheese?

9 According to a traditional rhyme, seeing a pair of which birds indicates happiness?

10 Which country had the first woman MP?

11 With what meat is the orange sauce 'bigarade' normally served?

12 What number is feared by people with triskaidekaphobia?

13 Which of these was not named after a person: (a) Cardigan, (b) Wellington or (c) Balaclava?

14 How is the blue-flowered plant *Myosotis* commonly known?

15 Who was the famous son of Philip II of Macedonia?

ANSWERS

1. St Cecilia. 2. Blood pressure. 3. Blue. 4. Brighton. 5. Ernest Shackleton. 6. Witch hazel. 7. Tibet. 8. Normandy. 9. Magpies. 10. Ceylon. 11. Duck. 12. 13. 13. (c) Balaclava. 14. 'Forget-me-not'. 15. Alexander the Great.

SESSION 21   QUIZ 1

TV, music & entertainment

1 Which member of the *EastEnders* cast was a regular in the *Carry On films*?

2 In *Indiana Jones and the Last Crusade*, what are Jones and his father searching for?

3 Who was the composer of the opera *Madame Butterfly*?

4 Which member of the cast of *Friends* appeared in Bruce Springsteen's video for 'Dancing in the Dark'?

5 In which country was film actor Andy Garcia born?

6 With which Prince song did Tom Jones have a hit?

7 Which singer/actress attacked Russell Harty with her handbag on his chat show?

8 Who played Irish republican revolutionary Michael Collins in the film of the same name?

9 Oasis recorded a cover version of which Slade song?

10 Who is the presenter of *The South Bank Show*?

11 Which film star was described as looking like 'a taxicab with both doors open' because of his big ears?

12 Which young woman featured in the titles of two of Buddy Holly's hits?

13 Was *The Colbys* a spin-off of: (a) *Dynasty*, (b) *Dallas* or (c) *Falcon Crest*?

14 Which film actor provided the voice of Woody in Walt Disney's *Toy Story*?

15 Who was known as 'the Empress of the Blues'?

ANSWERS

1. Barbara Windsor, who plays Peggy Mitchell. 2. The Holy Grail. 3. Giacomo Puccini. 4. Courteney Cox. 5. Cuba. 6. 'Kiss'. 7. Grace Jones. 8. Liam Neeson. 9. 'Cum on Feel the Noize'. 10. Melvyn Bragg. 11. Clark Gable. 12. Peggy Sue (in 'Peggy Sue' and 'Peggy Sue Got Married'). 13. (a) *Dynasty*. 14. Tom Hanks. 15. Bessie Smith.

SESSION 21 QUIZ 2

History

1 Which English king was beheaded at the age of 48?

2 Who was the father of Elizabeth I?

3 Against what did the American Carrie Amelia Nation fight?

4 What brightened London for the first time in 1814?

5 What names were given to the two sides fighting the American Civil War?

6 What was the name of the British nurse shot by the Germans in 1915?

7 Who is known as the father of modern Turkey?

8 When did Julius Caesar die?

9 What was the name of the Parliamentary army in the English Civil War?

10 What came into use for the first time in 1840 in England?

11 What happened at St Peter's Fields, Manchester in 1819?

12 Which country did the adventurous Polynesians reach in 768 AD?

13 What was completed in 1086?

14 What did Burke and Hare steal?

15 Who fought the Battle of Jutland?

ANSWERS

SESSION 21 QUIZ 3

Sports

1 Which footballer was disgraced for taking banned substances at the 1978 World Cup?

2 Why is the Calcutta Cup so named?

3 What did Lella Lombardi have the distinction of becoming?

4 If the score is 15-40 in tennis from which side of the court will the next serve take place?

5 Rugby Union has never been an Olympic sport. True or false?

6 Which was the first year of the Winter Olympics? Was it:
(a) 1920, (b) 1924 or (c) 1928?

7 Which newspaper brought Zola Budd to England?

8 In which year did Gazza injure himself in the FA Cup Final?

9 Who sponsors Rugby Union's premier league?

10 At what sport has Mike Tredgett represented England?

11 Which football team plays at Boghead Park?

12 What number wood is a driver?

13 Who was the England manager before Bobby Robson?

14 What did Henry Marsh fall over in the Helsinki Athletics Championships?

15 For what sport is Jim Watt known?

ANSWERS

1. Willie Johnston of Scotland. 2. It is made from melted-down Indian rupees. 3. She was the first woman to drive in a Formula 1 Grand Prix. 4. The right hand side. 5. False. It has been in the Olympics four times. 6. (b) 1924 at Chamonix. 7. *The Daily Mail*. 8. 1991. 9. Allied Dunbar. 10. Badminton. 11. Dumbarton. 12. One. 13. Ron Greenwood. 14. The last hurdle in the 3,000-metre steeplechase. 15. Boxing.

SESSION 21 · QUIZ 4

General knowledge

1 What is the name of the independent state that is an enclave in the city of Rome?

2 *The King of Barataria* is the sub-title to which operetta by Gilbert and Sullivan?

3 What, according to Dan Cook, 'Ain't over until the fat lady sings'?

4 What is the chemical symbol for gold?

5 What feast is celebrated on 2 February?

6 How many time zones are there in the US?

7 What were detected in space for the first time in 1938?

8 The ancient city of Babylon lies in which modern country?

9 Is the Suez Canal: (a) 55, (b) 101 or (c) 255 miles long?

10 Which philosophical system says that there is no knowledge outside of science?

11 What is the capital of Albania?

12 What does WYSIWYG stand for?

13 Who wrote the 'Mary Poppins' books?

14 What flavour is mocha?

15 Which member of the Royal Family is heavily involved with the work of Save The Children?

ANSWERS

1. Vatican City. 2. *The Gondoliers*. 3. The Opera. 4. Au. 5. Candlemas. 6. Four. 7. Radio waves. 8. Iraq. 9. (b) 101 miles. 10. Positivism. 11. Tirana. 12. What you see is what you get. 13. P. L. Travers. 14. A mixture of coffee and chocolate. 15. Princess Anne.

SESSION 21 | QUIZ 5

Technology & science

1 What is the one kind of rock that can float on water?

2 What are the primary colours of white light?

3 In which year was the far side of the Moon first shown?

4 Which two planets in the solar system are furthest from the Sun?

5 What is the planet in the solar system nearest to the Sun?

6 What is the dye that turns red in the presence of acid and blue in the presence of alkali?

7 What is the chemical name for 'laughing gas'?

8 Which element is the last member of the alkaline earth metals?

9 How fast does the heart beat?

10 A unit of length was formerly called a 'micron'; what is it now called?

11 Titan and Tethys are both what?

12 When was the first artificial satellite launched?

13 What is a googol?

14 For what is 'Y' the chemical symbol?

15 What is the temperature scale with freezing point of water as 0 degrees and boiling point as 100 degrees?

ANSWERS

1. Pumice stone. 2. Red, green and blue. 3. 1959 (Luna 3). 4. Pluto and Neptune. 5. Mercury. 6. Litmus. 7. Nitrous oxide. 8. Radium. 9. 70-80 beats per minute (average adult). 10. A micrometre. 11. Satellites of the planet Saturn. 12. 1957. 13. A very large number (one followed by a hundred zeros). 14. Yttrium. 15. Celsius.

SESSION 21 — QUIZ 6

Geography

1   The Caspian Sea is the largest lake in the world. True or false?

2   The Mezzogiorno is the south of which country?

3   Jakarta is the capital of: (a) the Philippines, (b) Indonesia or (c) Malaysia?

4   Where would you find the 'Forbidden City'?

5   On which river are Worcester and Gloucester?

6   Which American state, sandwiched between Maine and Vermont, has Concord as its capital?

7   Ojos del Salado is the world's highest active volcano; in which mountain range is it?

8   Lombardy is a region of: (a) Italy, (b) Switzerland or (c) France?

9   What is the debris of rocks and gravel left by a glacier called?

10   What was the name of St Petersburg during the Communist rule in Russia?

11   Which Scandinavian country generates most of its electricity by hydroelectric power?

12   Which landlocked country, between Vietnam and Thailand, was designated the poorest country in Asia in 1989?

13   How many roads pass through tunnels through the Alps: (a) 4, (b) 5 or (c) 6?

14   What is the port of Edinburgh?

15   In which country is the city of Casablanca?

ANSWERS

1. True. 2. Italy. 3. (b) Indonesia. 4. Beijing (Peking). 5. River Severn. 6. New Hampshire. 7. Andes. 8. (a) Italy. 9. Moraine. 10. Leningrad. 11. Norway. 12. Laos. 13. (c) 6. 14. Leith. 15. Morocco.

SESSION 21   QUIZ 7

The Arts

1 What was the name of the paranoid android in *A Hitchhiker's Guide to the Galaxy*?

2 Who wrote *Death on the Nile*?

3 Which poet wrote, 'The best laid schemes o' mice an' men gang aft a-gley'?

4 Which monarch wrote *Leaves from a Journal of Our Life in the Highlands 1848-61*?

5 Which Yorkshire town was the birthplace of the composer Delius?

6 What term describes a ballet dancer spinning around on one leg?

7 Which architect designed St Paul's Cathedral?

8 Who was the quick-witted heroine of *Vanity Fair*?

9 With whom did W. S. Gilbert co-write his operas?

10 With whom was the long-nosed Cyrano de Bergerac in love?

11 What name was given to Victorian women who showed an interest in literature and intellectual pursuits?

12 In which University is the Bodleian Library?

13 Which German composer wrote the opera series *Ring of the Nibelung*?

14 Who wrote the *Just William* stories?

15 Which doctor could talk to the animals?

ANSWERS

1. Marvin. 2. Agatha Christie. 3. Robert Burns. 4. Queen Victoria. 5. Bradford. 6. Pirouette. 7. Sir Christopher Wren. 8. Becky Sharpe. 9. Arthur Sullivan. 10. Roxanne. 11. Bluestocking. 12. Oxford. 13. Wagner. 14. Richmal Crompton. 15. Dr Dolittle.

SESSION 21 — QUIZ 8

Pot Luck

1 What is the name of the Great Circle around the Earth at 0 degrees latitude?

2 What was a 'cat o' nine tails'?

3 What is glossolalia?

4 Who was the one-eyed giant of Greek mythology?

5 Which saint's feast day is 23 April?

6 What is a 'bratwurst'?

7 How many chambers are there in a cow's stomach?

8 At the age of 69 who was the oldest man to be elected president of the USA?

9 How many million nerve cells are contained in the human body: (a) 13,000, (b) 3,000 or (c) 100,000?

10 In which century was the first set of dentures used?

11 Samantha Fox went to a convent school. True or false?

12 What two words sounding the same mean a jumping insect/ to run away?

13 What part of Los Angeles is nicknamed 'Tinseltown'?

14 What would you do with a tisane: (a) eat it, (b) drink it or (c) sleep on it?

15 What type of person possibly first wore corduroy?

ANSWERS

1. Equator. 2. A knotted rope for flogging. 3. Speaking in tongues. 4. Cyclops. 5. St George. 6. Sausage. 7. Four. 8. Ronald Reagan. 9. (a) 13,000 million. 10. 16th. 11. True. 12. Flea/flee. 13. Hollywood. 14. (b) drink it; it is an infusion of leaves. 15. A King, 'Cord of the roi' ('king').

SESSION 22 | QUIZ 1

TV, music & entertainment

1   Which film star said, 'It's not the men in my life, it's the life in my men that counts'?

2   In the cartoon series *King of the Hill*, what is the name of the father in the Hill family?

3   Which opera by Richard Wagner is about Scandinavian warrior maidens?

4   Which Hitchcock film climaxes in a struggle to the death on the Mount Rushmore National Monument?

5   In *Coronation Street*, what is Curly Watts proper first name?

6   Which US singer/songwriter had his first US No. 1 with 'Fingertips (Part 2)' at the age of 13?

7   Who played the young Amish widow in the film *Witness*?

8   Is Batman's alter ego: (a) Clark Kent, (b) Bruce Wayne or (c) Peter Parker?

9   Which US city is the centre of the country music industry?

10 Who is the actress daughter of Debbie Reynolds and Eddie Fisher?

11 Who were 'The Two Ronnies'?

12 Who killed John Lennon?

13 Who played Lorelei Lee in *Gentlemen Prefer Blondes*?

14 Who were the two main presenters of cult TV music show *The Tube*?

15 Who was *Home Alone* in 1980?

ANSWERS

1. Mae West. 2. Hank. 3. *The Valkyries*. 4. *North by Northwest*. 5. Norman.
6. Stevie Wonder. 7. Kelly McGillis. 8. (b) Bruce Wayne. 9. Nashville, Tennessee.
10. Carrie Fisher. 11. Ronnie Barker and Ronnie Corbett. 12. Mark Chapman.
13. Marilyn Monroe. 14. Jools Holland and Paula Yates. 15. Macaulay Culkin.

SESSION 22 QUIZ 2

History

1 Who first sailed around the Cape to India?

2 Did India and Pakistan separate in: (a) 1947, (b) 1948 or (c) 1949?

3 Henry I was the son of which king?

4 What was the name of the influential family of bankers in Florence in the 15th, 16th and 17th centuries?

5 What name was given to that part of France not occupied by the Germans during World War II?

6 Hitler came to power by democratic means. True or false?

7 What did suffragette Emily Davison do in 1913?

8 What unappetizing meeting did Luther attend in 1521?

9 Who was king of Assyria from 705 BC onwards?

10 By what name was Richard Neville, Earl of Warwick better known?

11 How many prime ministers were there during the reign of Victoria?

12 Who began 'witch hunts' against communists in America during the 1950s?

13 What was founded in 1930 much to the delight of young walkers?

14 Which politician first used the words 'Iron Curtain'?

15 What do the initials EFTA stand for?

ANSWERS

1. Vasco de Gama. 2. (a) 1947. 3. William the Conqueror. 4. The Medici family. 5. Vichy. 6. True. 7. She threw herself under the king's horse at the Derby. 8. The Diet of Worms. 9. Sennacherib. 10. The Kingmaker. 11. 20. 12. Joseph McCarthy. 13. YHA - The Youth Hostel Association. 14. Winston Churchill. 15. Europe Free Trade Association.

SESSION 22 | QUIZ 3

Sports

1 Who was manager at Chelsea before Ruud Gullit?

2 Diane Leather broke through which athletics barrier?

3 Which English team plays in the Scottish League?

4 Phil Bennett started it, but who finished the classic Barbarians try against the All Blacks?

5 Who were the first winners of the football league in 1888/89?

6 Who won the Commonwealth Games 100-metre race for men in 1998?

7 What is golf's Mr Rafferty's first name?

8 By what other name is the golf course, Royal St George known as?

9 What is Jack Charlton's favourite pastime?

10 What happened in baseball in 1919?

11 Which golfer was born in Maryland USA?

12 How many players are there in a netball team?

13 How wide is the goal in football?

14 What is a rounders ball made of?

15 Which rugby player won a Junior Wimbledon Tennis tournament in 1967?

ANSWERS

1. Glenn Hoddle. 2. Five minutes for the women's mile. 3. Berwick. 4. Gareth Edwards. 5. Preston North End. 6. Ato Boldon. 7. Ronan. 8. Sandwich. 9. Fishing. 10. Chicago White Sox threw the World Series to Cincinnati Reds. 11. Paul Azinger. 12. Seven. 13. 24 feet. 14. Leather. 15. J. P. R. Williams.

SESSION 22   QUIZ 4

General knowledge

1   Peter Tatchell is a prominent campaigner for what?

2   If you are omniscient, what is your specialist field?

3   Who were the *Maquis*?

4   What do the initials TIR stand for?

5   Are there: (a) less than 1,000, (b) less than 2,500 or (c) more than 4,000 languages in the world?

6   What financial institution is based at Threadneedle Street?

7   How is speed at sea measured?

8   Rhinitis affects what part of the body?

9   Chimpanzees have 48 chromosomes. True or false?

10   What do acrophobes hate?

11   According to the saying, what do 'hard cases' make?

12   In cookery, what would you be doing if you were braising meat?

13   In which year did the Great Train Robbery take place?

14   What were the Christian names of G. K. Chesterton?

15   Who was Hero's lover in Greek mythology?

ANSWERS

1. Gay rights. 2. Everything. 3. A French resistance group during World War II. 4. Transports Internationaux Routiers, French for 'International Road Transport'. 5. (c) more than 4,000. 6. The Bank of England. 7. In knots. 8. The nose. 9. True. 10. Heights. 11. Bad law. 12. You would be browning it in oil and then cooking it slowly in a liquid. 13. 1963. 14. Gilbert Keith. 15. Leander.

SESSION 22 QUIZ 5

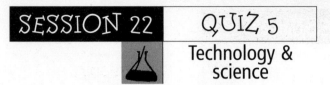

Technology & science

1 What is the brightest artificial light?

2 What name is given to the group of elements which include fluorine, chlorine, bromine and iodine?

3 Who discovered ozone?

4 The auricle or pinna are names of the external part of what?

5 What is a quasar?

6 For what achievement was Otto Hahn awarded the Nobel Prize for Chemistry in 1944?

7 Name the process of separating mixtures of liquids through a semi-permeable membrane.

8 What is crocidolite and why is it dangerous?

9 What is visible to people of Earth once every 76 years?

10 What name is commonly given to the line of longitude lying at 0 degrees?

11 What is 'blue vitriol'?

12 At the base of what is the pituitary gland located?

13 Who discovered dialysis?

14 In which year did the US spacecraft *Mars Pathfinder* land on Mars?

15 MDMA is another name for which illegal drug?

ANSWERS

1. Laser light. 2. The halogens. 3. Christian Friedrich Schönbein. 4. The ear. 5. A quasi-stellar object (usually a source of radio waves). 6. Splitting of the uranium atom. 7. Dialysis. 8. A form of asbestos that causes asbestosis. 9. Halley's comet. 10. The Greenwich Meridian. 11. Copper sulphate. 12. The brain. 13. Thomas Graham. 14. 1997. 15. Ecstasy.

SESSION 22   QUIZ 6

Geography

1 In which two countries do the Kjolen Mountains lie?

2 Is Timbuktu in: (a) Morocco, (b) Algeria or (c) Mali?

3 In which county is Stonehenge?

4 The French cities of Nantes, Tours and Orleans are on which river?

5 What is the capital of Uruguay?

6 In which American state is Cape Cod?

7 Is the flag of the Vatican City: (a) red and white, (b) blue and white or (c) yellow and white?

8 Which volcanic island gained independence from Denmark in 1918?

9 On 21 June, the summer solstice, the Sun is directly overhead at the Equator. True or false?

10 Which is the largest city in Switzerland?

11 In which country is Mount Pinatubo, the volcano which erupted in 1991?

12 Sand deserts are also known as: (a) erg, (b) hammada or (c) reg?

13 Which country has the largest oil reserves?

14 Which is the most densely populated country in Europe: (a) Luxembourg, (b) the Netherlands or (c) the United Kingdom?

15 On the Beaufort wind scale, hurricane force is force 12. True or false?

ANSWERS

1. Norway and Sweden. 2. (c) Mali. 3. Wiltshire. 4. Loire. 5. Montevideo. 6. Massachusetts. 7. (c) yellow and white. 8. Iceland. 9. False, it is directly overhead at the Tropic of Capricorn. 10. Zurich. 11. The Philippines. 12. (a) erg. 13. Saudi Arabia. 14. (b) the Netherlands. 15. True.

182

SESSION 22 — QUIZ 7

The Arts

1 How many Leagues did Jules Verne take us under the sea?

2 At which shop does Little Nell live?

3 The *Edda* are books of Scandinavian poems and myths from which country?

4 Who wrote *Confessions of an Opium Eater*?

5 In which country did Lord Byron die?

6 Whose works included the oratorios 'The Creation' and 'The Seasons'?

7 Onto what surface is 'fresco' painting applied?

8 Which Dutch artist painted two views of Delft?

9 With which group of writers and thinkers are Jean-Paul Sartre and Simone de Beauvoir associated?

10 Who wrote *To the Lighthouse* and *Mrs Dalloway*?

11 In Jules Verne's *Around the World in 80 Days*, what was the name of Phileas Fogg's valet?

12 Whose voice 'was ever soft, gentle and low, an excellent thing in woman'?

13 Which country was the birthplace of the poet William Butler Yeats?

14 What did Yankee Doodle call his pony?

15 Which pair of twins fought over a rattle?

ANSWERS

1. 20,000. 2. The Old Curiosity Shop. 3. Iceland. 4. Thomas de Quincey. 5. Greece. 6. Joseph Haydn. 7. Plaster. 8. Jan Vermeer. 9. Existentialists. 10. Virginia Woolf. 11. Passepartout. 12. King Lear's daughter Cordelia. 13. Ireland. 14. Macaroni. 15. Tweedledum and Tweedledee.

SESSION 22 — QUIZ 8

Pot Luck

1 Which toy derives its name from a Dutch phrase *leg godt*, meaning 'play well'?

2 Who is Judy Garland's famous daughter?

3 From which British towns do Cantabrigians hail?

4 Is a lachrymose person: (a) happy, (b) sad or (c) bored?

5 What herb was once believed to protect against drunkenness?

6 What is the full name of the food additive called MSG?

7 What are 'galoshes'?

8 Why was the disease scrofula also called the 'King's Evil'?

9 Which animals' young are called leverets?

10 When is a posthumous medal awarded?

11 In the hierarchy of angels which is superior, a cherub or a seraph?

12 Which of these does not eat meat: (a) carnivore, (b) herbivore or (c) omnivore?

13 Which vegetable is called an 'eggplant' in America?

14 'Moxa' is: (a) nasal mucus, (b) a downy substance from the dried leaves of a plant or (c) a cooperative association of shopkeepers?

15 Whose catchphrase was 'We are not amused'?

ANSWERS

1. Lego. 2. Liza Minelli. 3. Cambridge. 4. (b) sad. 5. Parsley. 6. Monosodium glutamate. 7. Waterproof overshoes. 8. It was thought that the king's touch would cure it. 9. Hares. 10. After death. 11. Seraph. 12. (b) herbivore. 13. Aubergine. 14. (b) a downy substance from the dried leaves of a plant. 15. Queen Victoria.

SESSION 23   QUIZ 1

📺 TV, music & entertainment

1 In which film did Melanie Griffith say, 'I have a head for business and a body for sin'?

2 Who is Vic Reeves's comedy partner?

3 Which bandleader died in 1944 when his plane disappeared on a flight from England to France?

4 What is Omar Sharif's nationality?

5 Name the five Tracy brothers in *Thunderbirds*.

6 Which Beatles' song did Frank Sinatra describe as 'the greatest love song of the past fifty years'?

7 Who directed the films *Reservoir Dogs* and *Pulp Fiction*?

8 What is TV chat-show host Mrs Merton's real name?

9 Which singer is known as 'the Godfather of Soul'?

10 Which real-life husband and wife played Matilda's parents in the film of Roald Dahl's book *Matilda*?

11 What was Popeye the Sailorman's favourite food?

12 Which rock singer's real name is Vincent Furnier?

13 What is the name of the spaceship in the film *Alien*?

14 Which role was played by Cesar Romero on TV and by Jack Nicholson in the cinema?

15 With which band is Chrissie Hynde the lead singer?

ANSWERS

1. *Working Girl*. 2. Bob Mortimer. 3. Glenn Miller. 4. Egyptian. 5. Scott, Virgil, Gordon, Alan and John. 6. *Something*. 7. Quentin Tarantino. 8. Caroline Aherne. 9. James Brown. 10. Danny De Vito and Rhea Perlman. 11. Spinach. 12. Alice Cooper. 13. *Nostromo*. 14. The Joker in *Batman*. 15. The Pretenders.

SESSION 23   QUIZ 2

History

1   By what name did the Scots know James I of England?

2   What was discovered in 1912, but proven to be a fake in 1953?

3   On which side did Robert Lee fight during the American Civil War?

4   What is the name of Jawaharial Nehru's daughter?

5   By what name is the period of bad economic health in the 1930's known?

6   Who was 'Bloody Mary'?

7   What did the Roman Empire finally conquer in 146 BC?

8   The term 'Fascism' originates from 'fasces', symbols of power in ancient Rome. True or False?

9   In which country did the Amritsar Massacre take place in 1919?

10   Where did the British Navy destroy the Franco-Spanish fleet in 1797?

11   What was Martin Luther King awarded in 1964?

12   In 1648 the 'Society of Friends' was formed. What are they known as today?

13   Where did the Aztecs live?

14   What did Martin Luther do with a Papal Bull of condemnation?

15   What movement sought revolutionary ends by constitutional means in the 1830s and 1840s in Britain?

ANSWERS

1. James VI. 2. Piltdown Man. 3. Confederate. 4. Indira Gandhi. 5. The Great Depression. 6. Mary Tudor. 7. Greece. 8. True. 9. India. British troops fired upon unarmed supporters of Indian self-government. 10. Cape St Vincent. 11. The Nobel Peace prize. 12. The Quakers. 13. Mexico. 14. He burnt it. 15. Chartism.

SESSION 23 | QUIZ 3

Sports

1 Pheidippides the Greek was the first person to run what race?

2 With which sport do you associate Joanne Conway?

3 How many times did Graham Hill win the Formula 1 Racing Championship?

4 If you win the Calcutta Cup what nationality could you be?

5 What famous run is at St Moritz?

6 The goalkeeper Lev Yashin played for which country?

7 What is the last event in the heptathlon?

8 In the 1936 Olympics which country won the most golds?

9 What is a 'mashie' in golf?

10 AC Milan is one. What is Milan's other football team called?

11 By what name is George Hermas Ruth better known?

12 Which cricketer's autobiography is called 'All Round View'?

13 In Australian Rules football, how many players are there on each side?

14 If you take part in the America's Cup, what will you be doing?

15 What is 4 miles 856 yards long?

ANSWERS

1. The marathon. 2. Skating. 3. Twice. 4. English or Scottish. 5. The Cresta Run. 6. Russia. 7. 800 metres. 8. Germany with 33. 9. A number five iron. 10. Inter. 11. Babe Ruth. 12. Imran Khan. 13. 18. 14. Yachting. 15. The Grand National.

SESSION 23   QUIZ 4

General knowledge

1   What is a 'kraken'?

2   What faculty does Kim's game test?

3   How many degrees are there in a radian?

4   What is the first day of Lent known as?

5   George Bernard Shaw won the Nobel Prize for Literature in 1953. True or false?

6   Which country has the most Buddhists?

7   In what city did the newspaper *The Guardian* begin?

8   Where would you *Run for your Wife*?

9   What is the most expensive property in the game of 'Monopoly'?

10   Where is the Sistine Chapel?

11   Which is the higher rank in the RAF: a Flying Officer or a Flight Lieutenant?

12   From which country does Aeroflot operate?

13   What cool object did Jacob Perkins invent?

14   What escaped from Bhopal in India on 3 December 1984?

15   What is Foyles of London known for?

ANSWERS

1. A mythical sea monster off the coast of Norway. 2. The memory. 3. 57.3.
4. Ash Wednesday. 5. True. 6. Japan. 7. Manchester. 8. At the theatre. It is a play.
9. Mayfair. 10. The Vatican. 11. Flight Lieutenant. 12. Russia. 13. The refrigerator.
14. Poisonous gas. 15. Selling books.

SESSION 23 · QUIZ 5

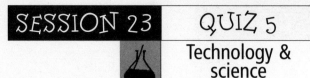

Technology & science

1 What are the colours of the rainbow?

2 What does AIDS stand for?

3 In degrees, what do the angles of a triangle add up to?

4 What is cassiterite?

5 Why is there no noise on the Moon?

6 What name is used for the class of chemical compounds used in fridges that are harmful to the ozone layer?

7 What is the common name for *Atropa belladonna*?

8 What is the name of the effect that describes the deflection of winds and currents as a result of the Earth's rotation?

9 The list of the naturally occuring elements arranged according to their atomic numbers is known as what?

10 What kind of astral body is Eros?

11 What is oriental topaz?

12 From which flower does the insecticide pyrethrum come?

13 Which cereal diseases can cause food poisoning and gangrene of the fingers if consumed?

14 What are viroids?

15 Which tropical disease does an insect of the *Anopheles* genus transmit?

ANSWERS

1. Red, orange, yellow, green, blue, indigo, violet. 2. Acquired Immune Deficiency Syndrome. 3. 180 degrees. 4. The main ore of tin. 5. There is no atmosphere to transmit sound waves. 6. CFCs (chlorofluorocarbons). 7. Deadly nightshade. 8. Coriolis effect. 9. Periodic table. 10. An asteroid. 11. A yellow-brown variety of sapphire. 12. Chrysanthemum. 13. Ergot. 14. Discovered in 1971, they are 'bugs' smaller than viruses. 15. Malaria (mosquito genus).

SESSION 23 QUIZ 6

Geography

1 Riyadh is the hottest capital city in the world. Which country is it in?

2 The population of Taiwan is about ten times greater than the population of Mongolia. True or false?

3 In which country is Mons, the scene of heavy fighting in World War I?

4 Which is the largest island in Japan: (a) Hokkaido, (b) Honshu or (c) Kyushu?

5 The French city of Toulouse is on the River Seine. True or false?

6 Two states surround Chesapeake Bay in America; one is Virginia, what is the other?

7 What is the capital of Iceland?

8 Which of these is furthest south: (a) Gloucester, (b) Oxford or (c) Ipswich?

9 Which country is the site of the most remains of the Aztec civilization?

10 In which ocean would you find the Barents Sea, Kara Sea and Laptev Sea?

11 Newport is the capital of which island?

12 In 1986, what killed 96 people in Gopalganj, Bangladesh: (a) floods, (b) typhoon, or (c) hailstones?

13 Which Middle Eastern country has the largest natural gas reserves?

14 In which country is the Yukon Territory?

15 Which African country is surrounded by Tanzania, Mozambique and Zambia?

ANSWERS

1. Saudi Arabia. 2. True. 3. Belgium. 4. (b) Honshu. 5. False, it is on the River Garonne. 6. Maryland. 7. Reykjavik. 8. (b) Oxford. 9. Mexico. 10. Arctic. 11. Isle of Wight. 12. (c) hailstones. 13. Iran. 14. Canada. 15. Malawi.

SESSION 23 QUIZ 7

The Arts

1 Who wrote the World War I trilogy *Regeneration*?

2 In which Gilbert and Sullivan opera does 'Pooh-bah' appear?

3 Which Jules Verne character made a bet that he could travel round the world in eighty days?

4 Who wrote *2001: a Space Odyssey*?

5 Where is Poet's Corner?

6 Who created the Famous Five?

7 Stravinsky's *The Firebird* is: (a) a ballet, (b) an opera or (c) a play?

8 What was the title of Dickens' final unfinished novel?

9 Which plump bespectacled school boy attended Greyfriars School?

10 During which wars is *War and Peace* set?

11 Which king did Shakespeare portray as a murderous hunchback?

12 What was the name of Robinson Crusoe's only human companion?

13 What is the name of Wendy's family in *Peter Pan*?

14 Who is the author of *Wilt* and *Porterhouse Blue*?

15 Which gothic novel was written by Bram Stoker?

ANSWERS

1. Pat Barker. 2. *The Mikado*. 3. Phileas Fogg. 4. Arthur C. Clarke. 5. Westminster Abbey.
6. Enid Blyton. 7. (a) a ballet. 8. *The Mystery of Edwin Drood*. 9. Billy Bunter.
10. Napoleonic. 11. Richard III. 12. (Man) Friday. 13. Darling. 14. Tom Sharpe. 15. Dracula.

SESSION 23   QUIZ 8

Pot Luck

1 The word 'gravitas' means: (a) seriousness, (b) meat juices or (c) a steep slope?

2 President Franklin Roosevelt was the son of President Theodore Roosevelt. True or false?

3 How much perspiration does the average pair of feet give off daily?

4 What would you find in a 'campanile'?

5 What title is given to the chief law officer of the Crown?

6 What does it mean to be *au courant* of events?

7 An ampersand is: (a) a unit of electricity, (b) a gemstone or (c) a symbol for 'and'?

8 The green aromatic stalks of which plant are used to decorate cakes?

9 In the medical practice of trepanning a hole is drilled into what?

10 Which red-bricked palace was the capital of the Moorish kings in Granada?

11 What colour hair would you have if you were an albino?

12 What birds are described collectively as 'a clamour' or 'a parliament'?

13 Which slow-moving mammal hangs upside down in trees?

14 What percentage of a mushroom is above the ground?

15 In Australia is *drongo* a compliment or an insult?

ANSWERS

1. (a) seriousness. 2. False, they were distant cousins. 3. Half a pint. 4. Bells; it is a bell tower. 5. Attorney General. 6. Up to date or informed about them. 7. (c) symbol for 'and'; &. 8. Angelica. 9. The skull. 10. The Alhambra. 11. White. 12. Rooks. 13. Sloth. 14. 10 per cent. 15. An insult; it means 'fool'.

SESSION 24   QUIZ 1

TV, music & entertainment

1. In which film did Tom Hanks say, 'Houston, we have a problem'?

2. In the 1960s TV series *The Avengers*, who were Steed's three female assistants?

3. Who was the lead singer with both the Jam and the Style Council?

4. By what name were Frank Sinatra, Dean Martin, Sammy Davis Jnr, Peter Lawford and Joey Bishop collectively known in the 50s and 60s?

5. In *Dallas*, how was Bobby Ewing's apparent return from the dead after being out of the show for a whole season explained away?

6. Who composed 'The Blue Danube Waltz'?

7. In the film *The Greatest Story Ever Told*, which famous actor's only line is 'Truly this man was the son of God'?

8. Which actor starred in the TV series *Drop the Dead Donkey* and *Ballykissangel*?

9. Which members of the Bee Gees are twins?

10. In *Blue Hawaii*, Angela Lansbury played Elvis Presley's mother. Was she: (a) 10 years, (b) 15 years or (c) 20 years older than him?

11. What was the name of the character played by Tony Robinson in the *Blackadder* comedy series?

12. What event prompted Eric Clapton to write the song 'Tears in Heaven'?

13. Which famous actor/film-maker regularly plays the saxophone at Michael's Pub in Manhattan on Monday evenings?

14. What do the initials EMI stand for?

15. Ella Fitzgerald was known for her skill in scat singing. What is scat?

ANSWERS

1. *Apollo 13*. 2. Cathy Gale, Emma Peel and Tara King. 3. Paul Weller. 4. 'The Rat Pack'. 5. His wife, 'Pam', had dreamt the whole of the previous season's events while 'Bobby' had been in the shower. 6. Johann Strauss the Younger. 7. John Wayne. 8. Stephen Tompkinson. 9. Maurice and Robin Gibb. 10. (a) 10 years older. 11. Baldrick. 12. The death of his four-year-old son, Conor. 13. Woody Allen. 14. Electrical and Musical Industries. 15. A type of jazz singing using improvised meaningless vocal sounds instead of words.

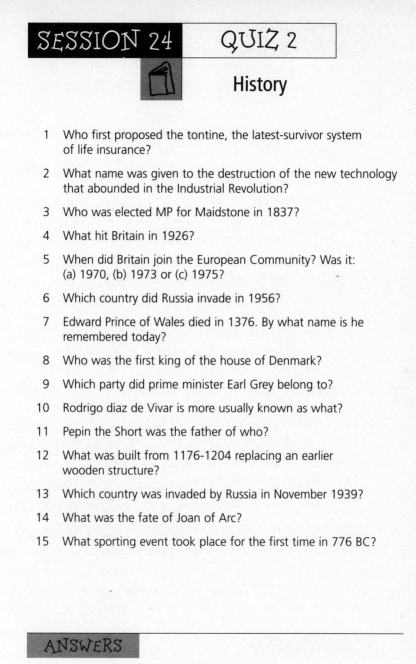

SESSION 24   QUIZ 2

History

1   Who first proposed the tontine, the latest-survivor system of life insurance?

2   What name was given to the destruction of the new technology that abounded in the Industrial Revolution?

3   Who was elected MP for Maidstone in 1837?

4   What hit Britain in 1926?

5   When did Britain join the European Community? Was it: (a) 1970, (b) 1973 or (c) 1975?

6   Which country did Russia invade in 1956?

7   Edward Prince of Wales died in 1376. By what name is he remembered today?

8   Who was the first king of the house of Denmark?

9   Which party did prime minister Earl Grey belong to?

10   Rodrigo diaz de Vivar is more usually known as what?

11   Pepin the Short was the father of who?

12   What was built from 1176-1204 replacing an earlier wooden structure?

13   Which country was invaded by Russia in November 1939?

14   What was the fate of Joan of Arc?

15   What sporting event took place for the first time in 776 BC?

ANSWERS

1. Lorenzo Tonti. 2. Luddism. 3. Disraeli. 4. The General Strike. 5. (b) 1973. 6. Hungary. 7. The Black Prince. 8. Canute. 9. Whig. 10. El Cid. 11. Charlemagne. 12. London Bridge. 13. Finland. 14. She was burnt at the stake. 15. The Olympic Games.

SESSION 24   QUIZ 3

Sports

1 Who was criticized for appearing to be too casual as he received his gold medal at the 1984 Olympics?

2 What sport takes place at the 'Brickyard' in America?

3 With what sport do you associate Barry Sheene?

4 Which England footballer was sent off for throwing away the ball in a World Cup Match?

5 On what day does a racehorse celebrate its birthday?

6 Where is the thousand guineas run?

7 Which British athlete's biography is called *Running Tall*?

8 Which game was invented by Colonel Sir Neville Chamberlain in India?

9 What nationality was Abebe Bikila?

10 Who came third in the 1978 World Cup?

11 Which were Olga Korbut's Olympics?

12 Against which South American country did Johnny Haynes plays his last match for England?

13 Which German club did Kevin Keegan play for?

14 In which sport do contestants have to walk, trot and canter?

15 Who was the captain when South Africa won the Rugby World Cup?

ANSWERS

1. Daley Thompson. 2. Indy Motor Racing. 3. Motorcycle racing. 4. Ray Wilkins.
5. 1 January. 6. Newmarket. 7. Sally Gunnell. 8. Snooker. 9. Ethiopian. 10. Brazil.
11. 1972. 12. Brazil. 13. Hamburg. 14. Dressage. 15. François Pienaar.

SESSION 24 — QUIZ 4

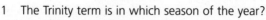

General knowledge

1 The Trinity term is in which season of the year?

2 What is the tricolore?

3 What is the most populous city on the west side of the Atlantic Ocean?

4 What is the correct name for a fear of spiders?

5 Dancing in a single file is called the what?

6 In the Bible, Jonah was swallowed by a fish because he refused to go to which city?

7 Which small bird makes one quake with fear?

8 What is the occupation of 'Carlos the Jackal'?

9 Which gamble paid off for the first time on 10 November 1994?

10 What is the shape of Tinky Winky's aerial?

11 Who said, 'Open Sesame'?

12 According to Sophocles, what is a woman's best garment?

13 Which is the warmest planet in our solar system?

14 What did the British change in 1752?

15 Which zodiac sign runs from 22 June to 22 July?

ANSWERS

1. The summer. 2. The French flag. 3. Mexico City with over 20 million inhabitants. 4. Arachnophobia. 5. The Conga. 6. Nineveh. 7. The quail. 8. A terrorist. 9. The National Lottery. 10. An inverted triangle. 11. Ali Baba. 12. Silence. 13. Venus. 14. The calendar. 15. Cancer.

SESSION 24 — QUIZ 5

Technology & science

1 What name is given to the process by which the world's atmosphere is becoming continually warmer?

2 Who discovered the neutron?

3 Who was the first to use the term 'ovary'?

4 What is a Fibonacci series?

5 What is galvanized metal coated with?

6 What are the parts of a typical comet?

7 The first man-made object ever to reach the Moon was Russian. What was it called?

8 What does the prefix 'quindeca' stand for?

9 Which two letters of the alphabet are not used in the periodic table?

10 What is the Haber process?

11 In computing, what is a 'GUI'?

12 In which year was the Hubble Space Telescope put into orbit by the space shuttle?

13 What, in computing, is PROM?

14 What are Fraunhofer lines?

15 Name two of the six noble gases.

ANSWERS

1. Greenhouse effect (global warming). 2. James Chadwick (1932). 3. Regnier de Graaf, after whom the Graafian follicles were named. 4. A number series in which each successive number is the sum of the previous two: 1, 1, 2, 3, 5, 8 etc. 5. Zinc. 6. A nucleus, a coma and a tail. 7. *Luna 2*. 8. 15. 9. J and Q. 10. Industrial production of ammonia (from hydrogen and nitrogen). 11. A graphical user interface. 12. 1990. 13. Programmable read only memory. 14. Dark lines in the solar spectrum. 15. Helium, neon, argon, krypton, xenon and radon.

SESSION 24   QUIZ 6

Geography

1   What is the capital of Finland?

2   Which of these towns is furthest from London: (a) Penzance, (b) Newcastle or (c) Holyhead?

3   Lusaka is the capital of which country?

4   In which country are the Appalachian Mountains?

5   In which large European country do rivers and canals carry as much freight as the roads?

6   In which London park is London Zoo?

7   The continents of Africa and America are slowly moving together. True or false?

8   Which country has a flag that is plain emerald green?

9   What percentage of the Earth is covered by oceans or seas: (a) 60%, (b) 70% or (c) 80%?

10   In which desert are the mountain massifs of Hoggar and Tibesti?

11   Which country is both the greatest importer and the greatest exporter of goods?

12   Which European country gets three-quarters of its electricity from nuclear power: (a) Denmark, (b) Germany or (c) France?

13   In which country are the Pindos mountains?

14   Which island group in the Atlantic Ocean has its capital at Ponta Delgada and belongs to Portugal?

15   Which country was formerly called British Honduras?

ANSWERS

1. Helsinki. 2. (a) Penzance. 3. Zambia. 4. America. 5. Germany. 6. Regents Park. 7. False, they are moving apart at about 40 mm per year. 8. Libya. 9. (b) 70%. 10. Sahara. 11. USA. 12. (c) France. 13. Greece. 14. Azores. 15. Belize.

SESSION 24 · QUIZ 7

The Arts

1 Who wrote *The Secret Garden* and *A Little Princess*?

2 Which female British poet published *Some of Me Poetry*, shortly after appearing on *Opportunity Knocks*?

3 Which Yorkshire-born playwright wrote a series of monologues called *Talking Heads*?

4 What type of book is written by Robert Heinlein and Arthur C. Clarke?

5 Which family were at the centre of the saga written by John Galsworthy?

6 Which eccentric Old Bailey barrister appears in many stories by John Mortimer?

7 In religious paintings which saint is often depicted as a wild man covered in hair?

8 For what type of decorative art is William de Morgan best known?

9 The historian Gibbon chronicled the decline and fall of which Empire?

10 In a play who are the *Dramatis Personae*?

11 How many ships were said to have been launched by the face of Helen of Troy?

12 Which American novelist wrote the 1950s classic *On the Road*?

13 Of which of his characters did Mark Twain say, 'There were things he stretched, but mainly he told the truth'?

14 What animal is portrayed in Landseer's *Monarch of the Glen*?

15 In which city are the Doulton, Minton, Spode and Wedgwood potteries?

ANSWERS

1. Frances Hodgson Burnett. 2. Pam Ayres. 3. Alan Bennett. 4. Science Fiction. 5. Forsythe. 6. Horace Rumpole. 7. John the Baptist. 8. Tiles. 9. Roman. 10. The characters. 11. 1,000. 12. Jack Kerouac. 13. Huckleberry Finn. 14. A stag. 15. Stoke-on-Trent.

SESSION 24   QUIZ 8

Pot Luck

1   What word means two or more words that sound the same but have different meanings?

2   The verb 'eschew' means: (a) to display, (b) to avoid or (c) to sneeze?

3   Who was Capability Brown?

4   What is a 'capercaillie'?

5   How many humps does a dromedary camel have?

6   What biscuits are named after an Italian military leader?

7   Which legendary city of gold was believed to lie near the Amazon?

8   Which monster, half-man, half-bull, lived in a labyrinth on Crete?

9   How did Buffalo Bill get his name?

10   'You can't make a silk purse out of' – what?

11   In monetary slang, how much is a 'monkey'?

12   What animal is a cross between a mare and an ass?

13   From which county do 'Eccles cakes' originate?

14   What does a 'somnambulist' do?

15   Which common herb is sometimes called 'milfoil', meaning many-leaved?

ANSWERS

1. Homonym. 2. (b) to avoid. 3. An 18th-century landscape gardener. 4. A bird, type of grouse. 5. One. 6. 'Garibaldi'. 7. El Dorado. 8. Minotaur. 9. He killed a record number of buffalo in a day. 10. A sow's ear. 11. £500. 12. A mule. 13. Lancashire. 14. Sleepwalks. 15. Yarrow.

SESSION 25 — QUIZ 1

TV, music & entertainment

1   Who or what was 'Aloysius' in *Brideshead Revisited*?

2   Whose first screen-test report read, 'Can't act. Can't sing. Slightly bald. Can dance a little'?

3   Who wrote the song 'Perfect Day', which was used for the BBC 'Children in Need' Appeal in 1997?

4   Which member of the *Coronation Street* cast recorded the song 'Wind Beneath My Wings'?

5   Which Hollywood star became paralysed after a riding accident in 1995?

6   Who played lead guitar on the Beatles' 'While My Guitar Gently Weeps'?

7   Who provided the voice of Bugs Bunny?

8   Which actor appeared in both *Trainspotting* and *The Full Monty*?

9   At the Brit Awards in 1998, Danbert Nobacon of Chumbawamba tipped a bucket of water over a prominent Labour politician. Was it: (a) Peter Mandelson, (b) Gordon Brown or (c) John Prescott?

10   Name the three Cartwright brothers in TV's *Bonanza*.

11   Which artist was portrayed by Kirk Douglas in the film *Lust for Life*?

12   Who composed the oratorio *The Messiah*?

13   Which film actor played taxi dispatcher Louie De Palma in the TV sitcom *Taxi*?

14   In which film did Robert Duvall say, 'I love the smell of napalm in the morning'?

15   Did jazzman Gene Krupa play: (a) drums, (b) clarinet or (c) piano?

ANSWERS

1. The teddy bear that 'Sebastian' carried about with him. 2. Fred Astaire. 3. Lou Reed.
4. William Tarmey, who plays Jack Duckworth. 5. Christopher Reeve. 6. Eric Clapton.
7. Mel Blanc. 8. Robert Carlyle. 9. (c) John Prescott. 10. 'Adam', 'Hoss' and 'Little Joe'.
11. Vincent van Gogh. 12. George Frederick Handel. 13. Danny De Vito.
14. *Apocalypse Now*. 15. (a) drums.

SESSION 25   QUIZ 2

History

1 Which country did the Black and Tans go to?

2 Jane Seymour was which wife of Henry VIII?

3 Was the National Health Service Act passed in (a) 1945, (b) 1946 or (c) 1947?

4 Who invented the horse-drawn drill?

5 With which country is Robert Clive normally associated?

6 Who was the oldest man to become a US president?

7 What was Charles Davis Lucas the first military man to receive?

8 What did Argentina export to Europe for the first time in 1877?

9 Who wrote the book *The City of God*?

10 How did Kitchener die?

11 What nationality was Henry the Navigator?

12 Which founding members of the Church of England were burnt at the stake in Oxford?

13 By what name is Hitler's last major offensive in the Ardennes commonly known?

14 What book by William Langland was published about 1362?

15 What report in 1942 promised health care from 'the cradle to the grave'?

ANSWERS

1. Ireland. 2. Third. 3. (b) 1946. 4. Jethro Tull. 5. India. He was Clive of India. 6. Ronald Reagan, aged 69. 7. Victoria Cross. 8. Frozen meat. 9. Augustine of Hippo. 10. He drowned whilst aboard the HMS *Hampshire*. 11. Portuguese. 12. Cranmer, Latimer and Ridley. 13. The Battle of the Bulge. 14. *The Vision of William concerning Piers the Plowman*. 15. The Beveridge Report.

SESSION 25 — QUIZ 3

Sports

1   Ken Bates is chairman of which football club?

2   Which English footballer with a nautical name moved from Plymouth to Ipswich?

3   What sport do the Worthing Bears play?

4   For which rugby team does Lawrence Dallaglio play?

5   Who sponsor the English Premier League?

6   Who was the voice of rugby league in the 50s and 60s?

7   Where was John Barnes born?

8   Which team beat the Pittsburgh Steelers to win the AFC Championship in 1998?

9   Which county finished bottom of the county league in 1998?

10   How many games did England lose under Terry Venables?

11   Which golfer was born in 1959 in Seattle, USA?

12   How long does a game of Gaelic football usually last?

13   Are there (a) five, (b) six or (c) seven players in a handball team?

14   How many paddles does a Canadian canoe have?

15   Which club did Bob Wilson play for?

ANSWERS

1. Chelsea. 2. Paul Mariner. 3. Basketball. 4. Wasps. 5. Carling. 6. Eddie Waring. 7. Jamaica. 8. Denver Broncos. 9. Essex. 10. One. 11. Fred Couples. 12. 70 minutes. 13. (c) seven. 14. One. 15. Arsenal.

SESSION 25   QUIZ 4

General knowledge

1. What is the smallest particle of matter that can exist on its own?

2. Cantilever, arch and suspension are types of what?

3. What has five sides, each measuring 291 feet long?

4. Who said, 'God is dead'?

5. Which is the 'Blue Grass State' in America?

6. In 'Scrabble' what does the letter 'Z' score?

7. What is a quinquereme?

8. Who led the 'Long March'?

9. Who records all that is said at a trial?

10. By what name is the 'bending of light' better known?

11. What morbid business must be done within five days in England and within eight days in Scotland?

12. What do the initials BOTB stand for?

13. Which salad vegetable comes in romaine, leaf and iceberg varieties?

14. Who is known as the 'father of medicine'?

15. Where in the body is the mitral valve?

ANSWERS

1. The atom. 2. Bridge. 3. The Pentagon, USA. 4. Friedrich Nietzsche. 5. Kentucky. 6. 10 points. 7. A five-oared Roman galley. 8. Mao Tse-tung. It was the retreat of the communists into north west China. 9. A stenographer. 10. Refraction. 11. Notification of death. 12. British Overseas Trade Board. 13. Lettuce. 14. Hippocrates. 15. The heart.

204

SESSION 25   QUIZ 5

Technology & science

1   What did Thomas Edison invent in 1879?

2   What are the tiny air sacs in the lungs called?

3   A siemens is a unit of what?

4   What does RNA stand for?

5   What is the name of the spacecraft launched in 1997 to explore Saturn and Titan, which it is due to reach in 2004?

6   How often does Neptune orbit the Sun (approximately)?

7   What does *aqua regia*, which can dissolve gold, contain?

8   What does the Internet domain '.com' in an email address specify?

9   Who invented the aqualung?

10   What is a henry?

11   What is the lightest metal?

12   What is a bubble chamber?

13   What is vitreous humour?

14   What is the term for the behaviour guidelines evolved by users of the Internet?

15   What was the first sub-atomic particle to be discovered?

ANSWERS

1. The incandescent light bulb. 2. Alveoli. 3. Electrical conductance. 4. Ribonucleic acid. 5. Cassini. 6. Every 165 years. 7. A mixture of nitric and hydrochloric acids. 8. A commercial organization. 9. Jacques Cousteau. 10. A unit of electric inductance. 11. Lithium. 12. A device for studying sub-atomic particles. 13. A jelly-like substance in the eyeball. 14. Netiquette (Internet etiquette). 15. The electron.

SESSION 25 — QUIZ 6

Geography

1 Which two countries are divided by the Gulf of Bothnia?

2 Inside which country is the Republic of San Marino?

3 What is the capital of Morocco?

4 What country is surrounded by Argentina, Bolivia and Brazil?

5 In 1963 a volcano formed a new island called Surtsey. To which country does it belong?

6 Which is the highest mountain in Greece?

7 In which English county are the Polden Hills?

8 Which of these countries produces over a fifth of the world's uranium: (a) Australia, (b) Russia or (c) Canada?

9 Which is the largest island in the Caribbean?

10 What is the name for the expanse of shingle jutting out to sea on the edge of Romney Marsh?

11 What is the name of Austria's second largest town, on the banks of the River Mur?

12 Which mainland American state enjoys the warmest winters?

13 Which of these countries has the highest population: (a) Egypt, (b) Morocco or (c) Algeria?

14 Where is the world's largest protected sea area?

15 Which river runs through Rome?

ANSWERS

1. Sweden and Finland. 2. Italy. 3. Rabat. 4. Paraguay. 5. Iceland. 6. Mount Olympus. 7. Somerset. 8. (c) Canada. 9. Cuba. 10. Dungeness. 11. Graz. 12. Florida. 13. (a) Egypt. 4. The Great Barrier Reef Marine Park. 15. Tiber.

SESSION 25   QUIZ 7

The Arts

1 Which famous statue by Michelangelo is in The Academy in Florence?

2 Which advertising executive has a huge collection of modern British art?

3 What did Giotto draw to prove his artistic skill to the Pope?

4 To whom did Bumble the beadle refuse a second helping?

5 Which British composer wrote *Peter Grimes*?

6 Which boy's school days are recounted by Thomas Hughes?

7 Anne Bracegirdle was: (a) a character in *Bleak House*, (b) an actress or (c) a suffragette?

8 Lady Pecunia is the rich heiress in which comedy by Jonson?

9 What is vanity publishing?

10 What type of books did Jean Plaidy write?

11 Holly Golightly is the heroine of which novel by Truman Capote?

12 In which Shakespeare play are the Montagues the enemies of the Capulets?

13 A burlesque is: (a) a tragedy, (b) a comedy or (c) a riddle?

14 The title of which book by Ray Bradbury is the temperature at which paper spontaneously combusts?

15 Who wrote the James Bond novels?

ANSWERS

SESSION 25 — QUIZ 8

Pot Luck

1 Which newspaper was founded as The Daily Universal Register in 1785?

2 What are the two main ingredients of cock-a-leekie soup?

3 What would you do with a pair of brothel-creepers?

4 What is produced by sericulture?

5 What are made by cartography?

6 By what name is the river Thames known at Oxford?

7 What is 'chintz'?

8 Which British magazine is the equivalent of the Spanish Hola!?

9 What is depicted in the Overlord embroidery at Portsmouth?

10 Which comic featured Desperate Dan?

11 What does a numismatist collect?

12 What do the initials GCHQ stand for?

13 Of which city's name is Bedlam a corruption?

14 When was the so-called 'belle époque'?

15 Which chain of chemists also once acted as a circulating library?

ANSWERS

1. *The Times*. 2. Chicken and leeks. 3. Wear them, they are rubber-soled shoes. 4. Silk. 5. Maps. 6. Isis. 7. Printed cotton fabric, often floral. 8. *Hello!* 9. The events of D-day. 10. *The Dandy*. 11. Coins. 12. Government Communications Headquarters. 13. Bethlehem. 14. The period just before World War I. 15. Boots.

SESSION 26 QUIZ 1

📺 TV, music & entertainment

1 Actor Nicolas Cage is film director Francis Ford Coppola's nephew. True or false?

2 Which 'James Bond' theme song is sampled in Robbie Williams's hit, 'Millennium'?

3 Which former Mr Universe played The Incredible Hulk in the TV series of the same name?

4 Who played Harry Lime in the film *The Third Man*?

5 Which singer/songwriter was originally called Robert Zimmerman?

6 Wallace, of 'Wallace and Gromit' fame, is partial to what kind of cheese: (a) Cheddar, (b) Wensleydale or (c) Cheshire?

7 Which Shakespearean hero has been played in films by, among others, Laurence Harvey, Leonard Whiting, and Leonardo DiCaprio?

8 Which band had a hit in 1991 with 'Should I Stay or Should I Go?', which was first released in 1982?

9 What was the name of Dick Dastardly's dog in *Wacky Races*?

10 A replica of which 17th-century theatre was built on the theatre's original site in London, and opened in 1996?

11 The Boyzone hit, 'Words', was originally a hit for which band?

12 In *EastEnders*, how many husbands has Pat had?

13 Who played Jim Morrison in the feature film *The Doors*?

14 Which country-and-western singer wrote and recorded 'Crazy' and 'I Fall to Pieces'?

15 Who wrote the TV drama series Boys from the Black Stuff?

ANSWERS

1. True. 2. 'You Only Live Twice'. 3. Lou Ferrigno. 4. Orson Welles. 5. Bob Dylan. 6. (b) Wensleydale. 7. 'Romeo'. 8. The Clash. 9. 'Muttley'. 10. The Globe Theatre. 11. The Bee Gees. 12. Four – Pete Beale, Brian Wicks, Frank Butcher, and Roy Evans. 13. Val Kilmer. 14. Patsy Cline. 15. Alan Bleasdale.

SESSION 26   QUIZ 2

History

1 What does Richard III have the dubious honour of being?

2 Where was Italian banker Roberto Calvi found hanging?

3 Of whom did Graham Greene say that he was 'the nearest we are ever likely to get to a human Mickey Mouse'?

4 Which king was known as 'Beauclerc'?

5 Who were opponents in the Peloponnesian Wars?

6 Which historian chronicled the 'Jewish War'?

7 What was the country of origin of the Vandals?

8 Which prison was Voltaire sent to?

9 Who was the inventor of the 'spinning Jenny'?

10 Who demanded 'No taxation without representation'?

11 Which king of France reigned for 72 years?

12 Whose premiership straddled the reigns of George IV and William IV?

13 How many men did Garibaldi have when he acted to unite Italy?

14 Who was the commander of the British troops during the Crimean War?

15 How many American states ceded from the Union prior to the Civil War?

ANSWERS

1. He was the last British monarch to be killed in battle. 2. Under Blackfriars Bridge, London. 3. Fred Astaire. 4. Henry I. 5. Athens and Sparta. 6. Josephus. 7. Germany. 8. The Bastille. 9. James Hargreaves. 10. The American colonists. This was one of their complaints that led to the fight for independence. 11. Louis XIV. 12. The Duke of Wellington. 13. 1,000. 14. Lord Raglan. 15. 11.

SESSION 26   QUIZ 3

Sports

1   What is the length of a cricket pitch?

2   Which athlete was called the Ebony Express?

3   Who was beaten by Roberto Duran in Montreal?

4   How did Graham Hill die?

5   Who was Gentleman Jim?

6   Rodney Marsh of Australia was primarily a: (a) bowler, (b) batsman or (c) wicket keeper?

7   Horse racing is supposed to be the sport of which section of society?

8   Where do Middlesex play cricket?

9   What is the name of the playing area in baseball?

10   What sport are John Lowe and Bobby George renowned for playing?

11   Which competition did a politician win in 1971?

12   What fence could you sit on at Aintree?

13   What is the name of the ball in hurling?

14   Which two clubs contested the 1981 FA Cup Final?

15   What mind-bending sport does Bobby Fischer play?

ANSWERS

1. 22 yards. 2. Jessie Owens. 3. Sugar Ray Leonard. 4. In a plane crash. 5. The boxer J ames J. Corbett. 6. (c) wicket keeper. 7. Kings. 8. Lords. 9. The diamond. 10. Darts. 11. Admiral's Cup (the yachting competition was won by Edward Heath). 12. The Chair. 13. A slitter. 14. Spurs and Manchester City. 15. Chess.

SESSION 26   QUIZ 4

General knowledge

1 Is the lunula found in: (a) the hair, (b) the nose or (c) the nail?

2 What, according to Shakespeare, is the soul of wit?

3 What would you do with a chowder?

4 The religious group the Amish are vegetarians. True or false?

5 The Chetniks were Croatians. True or false?

6 Who described the jewellery his company made as 'crap'?

7 What was the name of the Waco cult leader whose centre was burnt down by the FBI?

8 Where are Scylla and Charybdis thought to have lain in wait for passing ships?

9 In what game can 'en passant' occur?

10 Who wrote *The History of Mr Polly*?

11 Which country has the highest chicken population in the world?

12 What is the commonest name in the London telephone directory?

13 Who was the first leader of the Soviet Union, from 1918-24?

14 What is the seventh commandment?

15 To which sport does the 'butterfly' stroke belong?

ANSWERS

1. (c) the nail. It is the white crescent-shaped area at the base. 2. Brevity. 3. Drink it. It is a thick soup. 4. False. 5. False. They were a Serb guerilla group that fought in both World Wars. 6. Gerald Ratner. 7. David Koresh. 8. The Straits of Messina. 9. Chess. 10. H. G. Wells. 11. China. 12. Smith. 13. Vladimir Ilyich Lenin. 14. Do not commit adultery. 15. Swimming.

SESSION 26 QUIZ 5
Technology & science

1   Which part of the brain is also known as the 'little brain'?

2   What dietary deficiency may cause goitre?

3   What is the chemical symbol for silver?

4   Which vitamin is required in blood clotting?

5   What was the name of the Belgian bacteriologist who discovered the complement system of blood serum and developed a vaccine for whooping cough?

6   What is the name of the orange food colour with e-number E102?

7   Where in the human body would you find the thalamus gland?

8   Which two scientists shared the Nobel Prize with Alexander Fleming for their work on penicillin?

9   What do histologists study?

10 Who is the computer programming language Ada named after?

11 What is the technical term for the outer layer of a mushroom cap?

12 What is the brightest star in the sky?

13 What is the test used to find out if an organic substance is a reducing agent?

14 What is the full name for the drug LSD?

15 In biology, what is a colony?

ANSWERS

1. Cerebellum. 2. Iodine. 3. Ag. 4. Vitamin K. 5. Jules Bordet. 6. Tartrazine. 7. Front of the brain. 8. Howard Florey and Ernst Chain. 9. Animal and plant tissue. 10. Mathematician Ada (Augusta) Byron, Countess of Lovelace and daughter of Lord Byron. 11. Pellicle. 12. Sirius. 13. Fehling's test. 14. Lysergic acid diethylamide. 15. A group of similar animals or plants that live together for mutual benefit.

213

SESSION 26 QUIZ 6

Geography

1. The wide drains in Sedgemoor, Somerset are called: (a) chines, (b) rhines or (c) tines?

2. Which of these countries produces most sugar: (a) Cuba, (b) China or (c) India?

3. What is the port, on the River Schelde, which is the second largest city in Belgium?

4. In which country is the Godafoss waterfall: (a) Norway, (b) Denmark or (c) Iceland?

5. Which American state, with Topeka as the state capital, is sandwiched between Nebraska and Oklahoma?

6. Which is the largest country which is completely in Europe: (a) the Ukraine, (b) Poland or (c) France?

7. Valparaiso is the chief port of which South American country?

8. In which English county is Chatsworth House, owned by the Duke and Duchess of Devonshire?

9. The enclave of Cabinda on the west coast of Africa belongs to: (a) Sierra Leone, (b) Gabon or (c) Angola?

10. How many volcanoes are there under the sea: (a) less than 10, (b) between 10 and 100 or (c) over 100?

11. The world's largest hydroelectric power station, on the banks of the Parana River, is jointly owned by Paraguay and which other country?

12. Which of these island groups is furthest south: (a) Azores, (b) Canary Isles or (c) Madeira?

13. Gamla Stan is the historic centre of which Scandinavian city?

14. The flag of Gabon has a middle stripe of yellow; does this represent: (a) the Sun, (b) gold or (c) the Equator?

15. From which city would you see the highest fountain in the world, in Lac Leman?

ANSWERS

1. (b) rhines. 2. (c) India. 3. Antwerp. 4. (c) Iceland. 5. Kansas. 6. (a) the Ukraine. 7. Chile. 8. Derbyshire. 9. (c) Angola. 10. (c) over 100. 11. Brazil. 12. (b) Canary Isles. 13. Stockholm. 14. (a) the Sun. 15. Geneva.

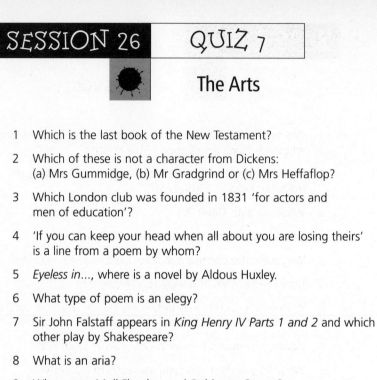

SESSION 26   QUIZ 7

The Arts

1 Which is the last book of the New Testament?

2 Which of these is not a character from Dickens:
   (a) Mrs Gummidge, (b) Mr Gradgrind or (c) Mrs Heffaflop?

3 Which London club was founded in 1831 'for actors and
   men of education'?

4 'If you can keep your head when all about you are losing theirs'
   is a line from a poem by whom?

5 *Eyeless in....*, where is a novel by Aldous Huxley.

6 What type of poem is an elegy?

7 Sir John Falstaff appears in *King Henry IV Parts 1 and 2* and which
   other play by Shakespeare?

8 What is an aria?

9 Who wrote *Moll Flanders* and *Robinson Crusoe*?

10 In which London street is the Theatre Royal?

11 What type of books were written by Elizabeth David?

12 What is doggerel?

13 Who wrote *Up the Junction* and *Poor Cow*?

14 Which 'Madame' was created by Flaubert: (a) 'Madame Butterfly',
   (b) 'Madame Buttercup' or (c) 'Madame Bovary'?

15 Who wrote *Brighton Rock*?

ANSWERS

1. *Revelation.* 2. (c) Mrs Heffaflop. 3. The Garrick. 4. Rudyard Kipling, *If.* 5. *Gaza.*
6. One of mourning. 7. *The Merry Wives of Windsor.* 8. A solo song, usually in an opera.
9. Daniel Defoe. 10. Drury Lane. 11. Cookery books. 12. Comic, trivial or poorly written verse.
13. Nell Dunn. 14. (c) Madame Bovary. 15. Graham Greene.

SESSION 26 QUIZ 8

Pot Luck

1 The aircraft Concorde actually gets several centimetres longer when it is flying at full speed. True or false?

2 Which of these vegetables is not a brassica: (a) cabbage, (b) broad bean or (c) broccoli?

3 What are Bath Olivers?

4 Which compulsory licence was abolished in 1988?

5 Why were the German *Baedeker* raids of 1942 so called?

6 How does a woman qualify as a dowager?

7 With which country was Britain involved in the 'cod wars' of the 1970s?

8 Hobby, Merlin and Kestrel are all types of what bird?

9 What do you do if you send someone to Coventry?

10 Which iridescent gemstone is often considered to bring bad luck to its wearer?

11 What term describes words like 'and' and 'or' which join words, phrases or clauses together?

12 Beggars used to pray to be delivered from Hull, Hell and which other place?

13 What post has been held by Donald Coggan, Robert Runcie and George Carey?

14 *In The House That Jack Built* who was 'all shaven and shorn'?

15 Whose catchphrase was 'I've started so I'll finish'?

ANSWERS

1. True, friction causes the metal to heat up and expand. 2. (b) broad bean. 3. Biscuits. 4. Dog licence. 5. It was believed that they were targeting towns with three stars in the *Baedeker* Guide to Britain. 6. If she has inherited a title or property from her late husband. 7. Iceland. 8. Hawk. 9. Ignore them, not speak to them. 10. Opal. 11. Conjunctions. 12. Halifax, because cloth stealers were beheaded there. 13. Archbishop of Canterbury. 14. The priest. 15. Magnus Magnusson.

216

QUIZ 1
TV, music & entertainment

1. Who wrote the operettas *The Desert Song* and *The Student Prince*?

2. Who plays Jimmy Corkhill in Brookside?

3. Who played Zorba the Greek in the film of the same name?

4. What is the connection between TV's *Murder She Wrote* and Disney's *Beauty and the Beast*?

5. Who had a hit in 1998 with 'It's Like That'?

6. Australian actress Diane Cilento was once married to which Hollywood star?

7. In *Absolutely Fabulous*, what is Eddi's and Patsy's favourite tipple?

8. Who was the father-in law of Phil Lynott of Thin Lizzy?

9. What was the name of the character played by Paul Newman in both *The Hustler* and *The Colour of Money*?

10. Which actor starred in both L.A. Law and N.Y.P.D. Blue?

11. What is Smokey Robinson's real name?

12. Who was the first Black actor to win the Academy Award for Best Actor?

13. Each episode of which US sitcom was preceded by the words 'Confused? You will be'?

14. In 1977, the Stranglers had a hit with a double A side. 'Peaches' was on one side. What was on the other?

15. Which US actress was murdered by Charles Manson and his followers?

ANSWERS

1. Sigmund Romberg. 2. Dean Sullivan. 3. Anthony Quinn. 4. Angela Lansbury, who played Jessica Fletcher in *Murder She Wrote* and provided the voice of Mrs Potts in *Beauty and the Beast*. 5. Run DMC. 6. Sean Connery. 7. 'Bolly' (Bollinger champagne). 8. Leslie Crowther. 9. Fast Eddie Felson. 10. Jimmy Smits. 11. William Robinson. 12. Sidney Poitier. 13. *Soap*. 14. 'Go Buddy, Go'. 15. Sharon Tate.

SESSION 27 QUIZ 2

History

1 What was the year of 'Revolution in Europe'?

2 What new invention did Singer introduce in 1851?

3 What ship was sunk 7 May 1915?

4 For what dreadful deed is Herod the Great remembered?

5 Whose reforming ways led to the invasion of Czechoslovakia by the Soviets in 1968?

6 Which president took over from the assassinated Lincoln?

7 Richard III was the last of which royal house?

8 In which war was the battle of Saratoga fought?

9 Who was commander of Fighter Command during the Battle of Britain?

10 Which religious group did J. N. Darby found?

11 Which military man has given his name to apples, trees and boots?

12 If you had marched to London in 1936 where would you have left from?

13 Who were the Gnostics?

14 Who became the first king of a united Italy in 1861?

15 Who was the Irish nationalist known as the 'Liberator'?

ANSWERS

1. 1848. During this year there were a number of revolutionary upheavals throughout Europe. 2. The sewing machine. 3. The *Lusitania*. 4. The Massacre of the Innocents as recorded in the Bible. 5. Alexander Dubcek. 6. Andrew Johnson. 7. The Plantagenets. 8. The American War of Independence. 9. Sir Hugh Dowding. 10. The Plymouth Brethren. 11. The Duke of Wellington. 12. Jarrow, protesting about economic conditions in the north-east of England. 13. A group of early Christian heretics who emphasized a mystical knowledge. 14. Victor Emmanuel II. 15. Daniel O'Connell.

SESSION 27 QUIZ 3

Sports

1 Who is Edson Arantes do Nascimento?

2 What is the last event in the decathlon?

3 What nationality is footballer Dino Zoff?

4 Who has scored the most runs in first-class cricket?

5 In football who are the Saints?

6 At what sport did Austrian Karl Schnabl compete?

7 What are dart tips usually made from?

8 Tony Jacklin won the US Open in 1971. True or false?

9 Tie breaks were introduced to Wimbledon in: (a) 1965, (b) 1971 or (c) 1976?

10 Were there: (a) 86, (b) 184 or (c) 211 competitors at the first Olympic games?

11 Where were Torvill and Dean when they won gold in 1984?

12 How many gold medals did America win at the 1980 Olympics?

13 Despite a great tradition in the event, Britain has never won the 4 x 400 metres at the Olympics. True or false?

14 In golfing terms, what is an albatross?

15 Who gave his name to Lords cricket ground?

ANSWERS

1. Pelé. 2. 1,500 metres. 3. Italian. 4. Jack Hobbs. 5. Southampton. 6. Ski-jumping. 7. Tungsten. 8. False. He won in 1969. 9. (b) 1971. 10. (c) 211. 11. Sarajevo. 12. None, they had boycotted it in protest over the invasion of Afghanistan. 13. False. They won in 1936. 14. Completing a hole in three under par. 15. Thomas Lord.

SESSION 27 QUIZ 4

General knowledge

1 What is the largest Christian denomination?

2 In what part of London did Jack the Ripper operate?

3 What began life as 'The Daily Universal Register' on 1 March 1788?

4 Who played James Bond in *Thunderball*?

5 By what name is Alighieri better known?

6 What was Frank Lloyd Wright's occupation?

7 What rank is immediately above captain in the Royal Navy?

8 Which is Europe's busiest airport?

9 What is Mattel's biggest selling toy for girls?

10 What is the commonest type of work-related injury in the UK?

11 Who is Britain's richest pop star?

12 To which area of medicine does paediatrics refer?

13 Which London road used to be famous for newspapers?

14 Which animals are believed to be musophobic?

15 What is a 'blue moon'?

ANSWERS

1. Roman Catholic. 2. Whitechapel. 3. *The Times*. 4. Sean Connery. 5. Dante, which is in fact, his Christian name. 6. An architect. 7. Commodore. 8. Heathrow. 9. Barbie. 10. Back injuries. 11. Paul McCartney, with assets of over £400 million. 12. Treatment of children's diseases. 13. Fleet Street. 14. Elephants. It is a fear of mice. 15. A rare event.

220

SESSION 27 · QUIZ 5

Technology & science

1 Which was the first rare earth element to be discovered?

2 The alloy constantan is made up of which two metallic elements?

3 In computer terms, what does the abbreviation DVD represent?

4 What is the technical term for the tear glands?

5 For what is Albert Bruce Sabin famous?

6 By what name is the largest of the dark plains on the Moon known?

7 Which scientist wrote *The Sceptical Chymist*, published in 1661?

8 What is phyllite?

9 What was the name of the communications satellite launched in 1965?

10 What is the cube root of 64?

11 Name the author of the popular account of cosmology called *A Brief History of Time*, published in 1988?

12 Where did the term 'robot' originate?

13 Maglev is a form of high speed surface transport. What does maglev stand for?

14 At what temperature do the Celsius and Fahrenheit scales converge?

15 Which planet in the solar system takes over 247 years to orbit the Sun?

ANSWERS

1. Lanthanum. 2. Nickel and copper. 3. Digital video/versatile disc. 4. Lacrimal glands. 5. The Sabine vaccine against polio(myelitis). 6. Ocean of Storms. 7. Robert Boyle. 8. Rock that is rich in mica. 9. *Early Bird*. 10. Four. 11. Stephen Hawking. 12. It was invented by the Czech playwright Karel Čapek in his 1921 play *R U R (Rossum's Universal Robots)*. 13. Magnetic levitation. 14. Minus forty degrees. 15. Pluto.

SESSION 27 QUIZ 6

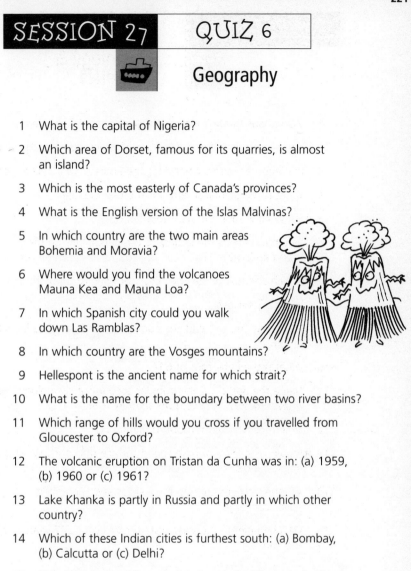

Geography

1 What is the capital of Nigeria?

2 Which area of Dorset, famous for its quarries, is almost an island?

3 Which is the most easterly of Canada's provinces?

4 What is the English version of the Islas Malvinas?

5 In which country are the two main areas Bohemia and Moravia?

6 Where would you find the volcanoes Mauna Kea and Mauna Loa?

7 In which Spanish city could you walk down Las Ramblas?

8 In which country are the Vosges mountains?

9 Hellespont is the ancient name for which strait?

10 What is the name for the boundary between two river basins?

11 Which range of hills would you cross if you travelled from Gloucester to Oxford?

12 The volcanic eruption on Tristan da Cunha was in: (a) 1959, (b) 1960 or (c) 1961?

13 Lake Khanka is partly in Russia and partly in which other country?

14 Which of these Indian cities is furthest south: (a) Bombay, (b) Calcutta or (c) Delhi?

15 The three longest rivers in Britain are the Thames, the Severn and which other?

ANSWERS

1. Abuja. 2. Portland. 3. Newfoundland. 4. Falkland Islands. 5. Czech Republic. 6. Hawaii. 7. Barcelona. 8. France. 9. Dardanelles. 10. Watershed. 11. Cotswolds. 12. (c) 1961. 13. China. 14. (a) Bombay. 15. The River Trent.

SESSION 27 QUIZ 7

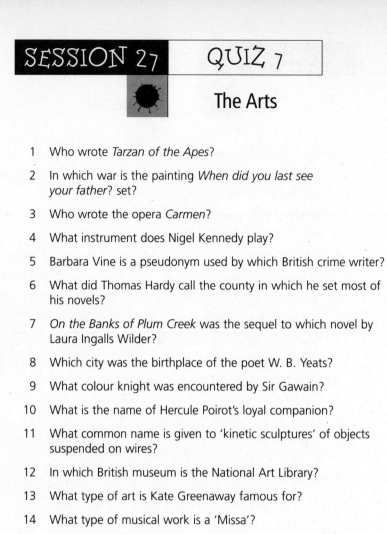

The Arts

1 Who wrote *Tarzan of the Apes*?

2 In which war is the painting *When did you last see your father?* set?

3 Who wrote the opera *Carmen*?

4 What instrument does Nigel Kennedy play?

5 Barbara Vine is a pseudonym used by which British crime writer?

6 What did Thomas Hardy call the county in which he set most of his novels?

7 *On the Banks of Plum Creek* was the sequel to which novel by Laura Ingalls Wilder?

8 Which city was the birthplace of the poet W. B. Yeats?

9 What colour knight was encountered by Sir Gawain?

10 What is the name of Hercule Poirot's loyal companion?

11 What common name is given to 'kinetic sculptures' of objects suspended on wires?

12 In which British museum is the National Art Library?

13 What type of art is Kate Greenaway famous for?

14 What type of musical work is a 'Missa'?

15 Who composed the *Moonlight Sonata*?

ANSWERS

1. Edgar Rice Burroughs. 2. English Civil War. 3. Bizet. 4. Violin. 5. Ruth Rendell. 6. Wessex. 7. *Little House on the Prairie*. 8. Dublin. 9. Green. 10. Captain Hastings. 11. Mobiles. 12. Victoria and Albert Museum, London. 13. Children's book illustrations. 14. A mass. 15. Beethoven.

SESSION 27   QUIZ 8

Pot Luck

1   What is a Cox's orange pippin?

2   Who was condemned as 'a turbulent priest': (a) Thomas Aquinas, (b) Thomas de Quincey or (c) Thomas à Becket?

3   Which large retail enterprise was begun by a door to door salesman called Michael Marks?

4   The duffle coat is named after the Lancashire town of Duffle. True or false?

5   If 'A was an apple pie' and 'B baked it, what did C do?

6   In which century did the last native speaker of Cornish die?

7   How are Quasi-Autonomous Non-Governmental Organizations more commonly known?

8   What name is given to a supposed mischievous imp said to interfere with machinery?

9   What does a lepidopterist collect?

10 'Carte blanche' is: (a) a kind of blancmange, (b) freedom to do as one chooses or (c) a white screen?

11 What is a jamboree?

12 What is added to rum and pineapple juice to make a pin á colada?

13 In a financial context what is your PIN?

14 The fossilized skull of Piltdown Man was a hoax. True or false?

15 In World War II, who were nicknamed 'Jilleroos'?

ANSWERS

1. An apple. 2. (c) Thomas à Becket. 3. Marks and Spencer. 4. False, it is named after the Belgian town of Duffle. 5. Cut it (and D dealt it). 6. The 18th, in 1777. 7. Quangos. 8. A gremlin. 9. Butterflies and moths. 10. (b) freedom to do as one chooses. 11. A celebration. 12. Coconut milk. 13. Personal Identification Number, for use at cashpoints. 14. True, it was a modern skull with an ape's jaw attached. 15. Australian land girls.

224

QUIZ 1

TV, music & entertainment

1 Which role was played by Julie Newmar on TV and by Michelle Pfeiffer in film?

2 Which member of an Irish pop group played Jimmy Rabbit's little sister in the film *The Commitments*?

3 Which EastEnder went on to become a country policeman in *Heartbeat*?

4 In *Butch Cassidy and the Sundance Kid*, did Paul Newman play Butch or Sundance?

5 Which former member of the Stone Roses served a prison sentence in 1998 as a result of an air-rage incident?

6 Who played Bob and Terry in *The Likely Lads*?

7 In which film did Alec Guinness play eight members of the same family?

8 Who is film actress Liv Tyler's rock-star father?

9 Who wrote *Rumpole of the Bailey*?

10 What was the name of the devil-child in *The Omen*?

11 Which German composer continued to compose after he lost his hearing?

12 What was the roll call at the beginning of each episode of the children's TV programme, *Trumpton*?

13 What was Linda Blair's most famous film role?

14 What does the 'B. B.' stand for in B. B. King?

15 Was the family in *The Beverly Hillbillies* called: (a) the Clantons, (b) the Clintons or (c) the Clampetts?

ANSWERS

1. Catwoman. 2. Andrea Corr of the Corrs. 3. Nick Berry. 4. Butch. 5. Ian Brown. 6. Rodney Bewes played Bob and James Bolam played Terry. 7. *Kind Hearts and Coronets*. 8. Steve Tyler of Aerosmith. 9. John Mortimer. 10. Damien. 11. Ludwig van Beethoven. 12. 'Pugh, Pugh, Barney McGrew, Cuthbert, Dibble, Grubb.' 13. Regan, the possessed child in *The Exorcist*. 14. Blues Boy. 15. 'The Clampetts'.

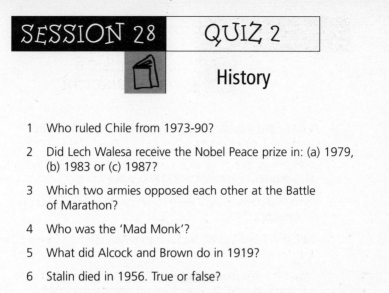

SESSION 28 QUIZ 2

History

1 Who ruled Chile from 1973-90?

2 Did Lech Walesa receive the Nobel Peace prize in: (a) 1979, (b) 1983 or (c) 1987?

3 Which two armies opposed each other at the Battle of Marathon?

4 Who was the 'Mad Monk'?

5 What did Alcock and Brown do in 1919?

6 Stalin died in 1956. True or false?

7 Who did Shevardnadze succeed as Foreign Minister in 1985?

8 How long did the American Civil War last?

9 Who was crowned Emperor of the French, by the Pope, in 1804?

10 Which Spaniard conquered Peru?

11 In 1578, Drake reached which part of Canada?

12 Which scientist claimed that he was 'Thinking God's thoughts after Him'?

13 Who rebuilt London after the Great Fire?

14 In what year did the Crimean War end?

15 What astronomical feature is recorded in the Bayeux Tapestry?

ANSWERS

1. Augusto Pinochet. 2. (b) 1983. 3. The Greeks and the Persians. 4. Grigoriy Rasputin. 5. Fly non-stop across the Atlantic. 6. False. He died in 1953. 7. Gromyko. 8. Four years. 9. Napoleon. 10. Francisco Pizarro. 11. Vancouver. 12. Isaac Newton. 13. Sir Christopher Wren. 14. 1856. 15. Halley's Comet.

SESSION 28   QUIZ 3

Sports

1   With which sport is John Francome associated?

2   Where are the twin towers?

3   Who scored the second goal for Germany in the World Cup Final of 1966?

4   In golf what is the 'honour'?

5   Who is the British 800-metre record holder?

6   In what do Ally McCoist and John Parrott compete against each other?

7   What nationality was the athlete Michel Jazy?

8   At what sport did Neil Eckersley and Kerrith Brown win medals in the Los Angeles Olympics?

9   Which player has played in three winning World Cup teams?

10   Eddie Edwards was the first British entrant ever at ski-jumping. True or false?

11   Which Cuban won gold in the 400 metres and the 800 metres at the 1976 Olympics?

12   In which sport do you have chukkas?

13   What sort of race is run over ash or shale?

14   What is the football league title called in Italy?

15   Who has been the longest-serving English national football team manager?

ANSWERS

1. Horse racing. 2. Wembley. 3. Wolfgang Weber. 4. The privilege of playing first from the tee. 5. Seb Coe. 6. In the BBC programme 'A Question of Sport'. 7. French. 8. Judo. 9. Pelé. 10. True. 11. Alberto Juantorena. 12. Polo. 13. Speedway. 14. The Scudetto. 15. Walter Winterbottom.

SESSION 28   QUIZ 4

General knowledge

1 Who suffers in uxoricide?

2 What unit of length was used in the Bible?

3 According to Greek legend, where did the gods live?

4 Which monument in Whitehall honours the dead of both world wars?

5 What sets in at death?

6 How did Judas betray Jesus?

7 Who was the last politician to rule East Germany?

8 What is the name of the Russian space station?

9 Was Fidel Castro born in: (a) 1920, (b) 1927 or (c) 1930?

10 What is a Barmecide feast?

11 Titania and Oberon are moons of which planet?

12 Which is the largest animal in the world?

13 What is the tenth wedding anniversary?

14 What are Eastern, Central, Mountain and Pacific?

15 What does crustaceous mean?

ANSWERS

1. A man's wife. It is when he kills her. 2. The cubit, which is based upon the forearm. 3. Olympus. 4. The Cenotaph. 5. Rigor mortis. 6. With a kiss. 7. Erich Honecker. 8. Mir. 9. (b) 1927. 10. Something that appears to be sumptuous to the beholder, but in reality is not. 11. Uranus. 12. The blue whale. 13. Tin. 14. Time zones in America. 15. Having a shell or rind.

228

SESSION 28 — QUIZ 5

Technology & science

1. What is the common name for the astronomical phenomenon known as the *aurora borealis*?

2. Two units of measurement have the abbreviation 'nm'. What is one of them?

3. Where is the deltoid muscle?

4. What is the difference between an isobar and an isotherm?

5. In what year did man first land on the Moon?

6. In computing, what is FORTRAN a contraction of?

7. Which colourless, poisonous gas with a smell like geraniums was used in chemical warfare during World War II?

8. What is one tenth of a bel?

9. What is the chemical formula for caustic soda?

10. Isaac Newton published several scientific works. Which is considered his greatest?

11. What is a fumarole?

12. What is the lowest temperature theoretically possible?

13. What is a Ringelmann chart used for?

14. What is the name of translation (programming language).

15. What is the name of the process by which soft fats and oils are hardeneded to produce margarine?

ANSWERS

1. The Northern Lights. 2. Nanometre, nautical mile. 3. In the back, over the shoulder. 4. An isobar connects places of the same atmospheric pressure; an isotherm connects places of the same temperature. 5. 1969. 6. Formula translation. 7. Lewisite. 8. A decibel. 9. NaOH. 10. *Principia Mathematica* (1687). 11. A vent in a volcano through which vapour and gases are released. 12. 0 K (Kelvin) equal to minus 273 degrees Celsius. 13. A device for measuring the density of smoke. 14. JAVA (launched in 1995). 15. Hydrogenation.

SESSION 28   QUIZ 6

Geography

1   On which island would you find The Needles?

2   What is the name for the protected area of countryside around a city?

3   An anticyclone is an area with above average pressure. True or false?

4   How far is the source of the River Amazon from the sea: (a) 3,500 km, (b) 5,300 km or (c) 6,500 km?

5   In which country are the lakes Ercek, Cildir and Haza?

6   Luanda is the capital of which African country?

7   In which hills would you find the source of the rivers Swale, Ure and Nidd?

8   The territory of Guadeloupe is a department of which country?

9   The amount of ozone is greatest over the equator. True or false?

10   In which English seaside town could you sit on the Torre Abbey sands?

11   In which country is the site of the Chernobyl nuclear reactor?

12   Which republic, a member of the Commonwealth, lies at the southern tip of the Malay peninsula?

13   In which country is Table Mountain?

14   Which river flows through Winchester?

15   Which of these countries produces most of the world's silver: (a) Russia, (b) Australia or (c) Mexico?

ANSWERS

1. Isle of Wight. 2. Green belt. 3. True. 4. (c) 6,500 km. 5. Turkey. 6. Angola. 7. Pennines. 8. France. 9. False. 10. Torquay. 11. The Ukraine. 12. Singapore. 13. South Africa. 14. River Itchen. 15. (c) Mexico.

SESSION 28   QUIZ 7

The Arts

1 What fraction of a whole note is a minim?

2 According to Geoffrey of Monmouth which island race were founded by Brutus the Trojan?

3 Which fat jovial priest was a member of Robin Hood's band of outlaws?

4 Whose mandolin was the subject of a best-selling novel by Louis de Bernières?

5 What is the nickname of Hugh Drummond, the ex-army officer created by Sapper?

6 Who wrote *The Cruel Sea*?

7 In which country are the tales of the 'Mabinogion' set?

8 Which war poet's autobiography was called *Siegfried's Journey*?

9 What is blank verse?

10 Where might you hear 'plainchant'?

11 Who wrote the crime novels *The Sculptress* and *The Echo*?

12 Who was sent to fetch the Golden Fleece?

13 What animals are the heroes of the *Duncton Wood* stories?

14 Who was the first English printer?

15 Fay Weldon has written a novel about *The Lives and Loves of...* what?

ANSWERS

14. William Caxton. 15. ...*a She-Devil*.
10. In church. 11. Minette Walters. 12. Jason and the Argonauts 13. Moles.
6. Nicholas Monsarrat. 7. Wales. 8. Siegfried Sassoon. 9. Poetry without rhymes.
1. A half. 2. The British. 3. Friar Tuck. 4. Captain Corelli's. 5. 'Bulldog Drummond'.

230

SESSION 28 QUIZ 8

Pot Luck

1　What is a bird's 'gizzard'?

2　How many bottles of wine are contained in a Nebuchadnezzar?

3　Who said, 'I think therefore I am'?

4　Is the word for a large gun spelt 'cannon' or 'canon'?

5　How many years of marriage are celebrated by a ruby wedding?

6　What is the maximum speed reached by a flea when jumping. Is it: (a) 0.724 kph, (b) 7.24 kph or (c) 72.4 kph?

7　What is made with seven parts saltpetre, to five parts charcoal and five parts sulphur?

8　Föhn, sirocco and chinook are all types of what weather phenomenon?

9　'Chakra' is: (a) a centre of power in the human body, (b) a type of paint or (c) an Indian vegetable?

10　What was banned under Prohibition in the United States?

11　What was *The Flying Dutchman*?

12　What two words that sound similar mean 'the place at which two pieces of fabric are joined together' and 'to appear to be'?

13　'Flit on cheering angel' is an anagram of which nurse's name?

14　What are you doing if you are talking through your hat?

15　On what day are hot-cross buns traditionally eaten?

ANSWERS

1. Its second stomach. 2. 20. 3. René Descartes. 4. Cannon. 5. Forty. 6. (b) 7.24 kph. 7. Gunpowder. 8. Wind. 9. (a) a centre of power in the human body. 10. The sale of alcohol. 11. A legendary ship. 12. Seam/seem. 13. Florence Nightingale. 14. Talking nonsense. 15. Good Friday.

232

QUIZ 1

TV, music & entertainment

1   Which Canadian singer/songwriter recorded the 1995 album, 'Jagged Little Pill'?

2   What was the name of the twins in Hergé's *Adventures of Tintin*?

3   What was the last line in *Casablanca*?

4   With which Liverpool band is Tommy Scott the lead singer?

5   In *Coronation Street*, how did Alan Bradley die?

6   Actress Kelly Preston is married to which Hollywood star?

7   Who were Bob Marley's backing band?

8   What was the name of the extremely tall butler in *The Addams Family*?

9   Which actor provided the voice of Darth Vader in the *Star Wars* films?

10 In which country was composer Frédéric Chopin born?

11 Which comic actor/writer plays brother and sister Paul and Pauline Calf?

12 What is the name of the band in which Keanu Reeves plays bass guitar?

13 Jim Morrison of the Doors went to film school at UCLA along with which famous film director?

14 What is the name of the fictional island where *Father Ted* is set?

15 Which film role was played by, among others, Johnny Weissmuller, Buster Crabbe and Christopher Lambert?

ANSWERS

1. Alanis Morissette. 2. The Thompson Twins. 3. Louis, 'I think this is the beginning of a beautiful friendship.' 4. Space. 5. He was knocked down by a tram in Blackpool. 6. John Travolta. 7. The Wailers. 8. Lurch. 9. James Earl Jones. 10. Poland. 11. Steve Coogan. 12. Dogstar. 13. Francis Ford Coppola. 14. Craggy Island. 15. Tarzan.

SESSION 29   QUIZ 2

History

1   Who was crowned Emperor of the West, by Pope Leo III, in AD 800?

2   What was the fate of the atheist MP Charles Bradlaugh?

3   In 1299, the Palazzo Vecchio was begun in which city?

4   On which island did the Knights of St John settle?

5   What road connecting Rome and Capua was begun in 312 BC?

6   Who did Nero infamously murder in AD 59 near Baia, Naples?

7   Where was the 'King and Country' debate of 1933 conducted?

8   What style implemented between the late 16th and early 18th centuries was known for its extensive ornamentation?

9   Which member of the Romanov dynasty is reputed to have survived the Russian Revolution?

10   David Ben-Gurion was the first prime minister of which state?

11   Who did Nelson want to kiss as he lay dying?

12   Where was Martin Luther King assassinated?

13   How many of William the Conqueror's sons became kings?

14   Who became prime minister in 1951?

15   Which financial institution was established in 1694?

ANSWERS

1. Charlemagne. 2. He couldn't take his seat in Parliament for six years. 3. Florence. 4. Malta. 5. The Appian Way. 6. His mother, Agrippina. 7. The Oxford Union. 8. Baroque. 9. Anastasia. 10. Israel. 11. It was supposedly Hardy. 12. Memphis, Tennessee. 13. Two, William and Henry. 14. Winston Churchill. The previous administration was elected before the war against Japan had concluded. 15. The Bank of England.

234

Sports

1   Who did Joe Frazier tussle with in Manila?

2   Which normally travels the furthest: the (a) shot, (b) javelin (c) discus?

3   What is the surname of the Indian brothers Vijay and Anand?

4   What feature now seen before every Olympics, was introduced by the Germans in 1936?

5   Who was England's captain in the infamous 'hand of God' football match?

6   What are the three components of the three-day event?

7   Who are the Wallabies?

8   Rob Andrew directs rugby at which club?

9   What did 'Cape Verdi' win in 1998?

10   Who beat Wigan Warriors at Wembley in the 1998 Rugby League Challenge Cup Final?

11   In the 1960s Palmer and Nicklaus were two of the 'Big Three'. Who was the third player?

12   What is the least number of darts that can be used to score 501?

13   The American football star Jim Brown was in which film about a group of mercenaries?

14   Which swimmer became a jungle swinger?

15   On which golf course could you find a postage stamp?

ANSWERS

1. Muhammad Ali. 2. (b) javelin. 3. Amritraj. 4. The torch carrying the Olympic Flame. 5. Peter Shilton. 6. Dressage, endurance and show jumping. 7. Australian Rugby Union team. 8. Newcastle. 9. The thousand guineas. 10. Sheffield Eagles. 11. Gary Player. 12. Nine. 13. *The Dirty Dozen.* 14. Johnny Weissmuller. 15. Troon. It is the name of the 8th hole.

235

SESSION 29 — QUIZ 4

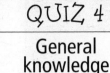

General knowledge

1 Who ordered all boys under the age of two to be killed?

2 'Big Bang' and 'Oscillating' are both theories concerning what important event?

3 What name is given to a Chinese boat which can also mean rubbish?

4 Who always get their man?

5 What was the outcome of the 13th Amendment in America?

6 What can be seen at the entrance to the Louvre?

7 What is the body's smallest gland?

8 What is sophistry?

9 For the Romans she was Venus; who was she for the Greeks?

10 How is the number zero represented in Morse Code?

11 In which country will you find the regions of Assam, Manipur and Orissa?

12 Who were 'the Flowerpot Men'?

13 By what name is John Birks Gillespie better known?

14 What nationality was Aristotle Onassis at his death?

15 Who appeared naked in *The Blue Room*?

ANSWERS

1. King Herod, in the bible. 2. The origin of the universe. 3. A junk. 4. The Canadian Mounties. 5. The abolition of slavery. 6. A glass pyramid. 7. The pituitary gland. 8. A fallacious argument. 9. Aphrodite. 10. Five dashes. 11. India. 12. Bill and Ben. 13. Dizzy. 14. Argentinian, though he had been born Greek. 15. Nicole Kidman.

SESSION 29

QUIZ 5

Technology & science

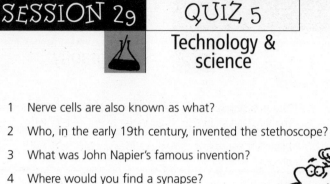

1   Nerve cells are also known as what?

2   Who, in the early 19th century, invented the stethoscope?

3   What was John Napier's famous invention?

4   Where would you find a synapse?

5   What is the origin of the word tulip?

6   The letters 'http' usually precede the address of a web site. What are these letters an abbreviation for?

7   What was the name of the first space shuttle, and when was it launched?

8   Why is Wallace Carothers famous?

9   What is pinchbeck?

10 What is the popular name for vitamin B_6?

11 What is the Mercalli scale used for?

12 Which constellation near the north celestial pole is recognizable by the conspicuous 'W' pattern of its brightest stars?

13 What is the name of the hard tough substance that occurs in the hard shells of crabs, insects and spiders?

14 How hot does it get on the Moon?

15 What is the name of the heaviest noble gas known which is formed from the natural radioactive decay of radium?

ANSWERS

1. Neurons or neurones. 2. René Laënnec in 1816. 3. Logarithms. 4. In the body, where two nerves meet. 5. It comes from the Turkish *tülbend*, turban. 6. Hypertext transfer (or transport) protocol. 7. *Columbia*. 8. He invented nylon. 9. An alloy of copper and zinc used as imitation gold. 10. Pyridoxine. 11. Measuring the intensity of earthquakes. 12. Cassiopeia. 13. Chitin. 14. More than one hundred degrees Celsius. 15. Radon.

SESSION 29   QUIZ 6

Geography

1 The peak of Skiddaw rises to the east of the most northerly of the large lakes in Cumbria. What is the lake called?

2 In which European capital could you visit the Tivoli amusement park?

3 What is the name of the desert in northern Chile?

4 What is the capital of Somalia?

5 Which river runs through Glasgow?

6 Which is the odd one out of these French seaside resorts: (a) Antibes, (b) Biarritz or (c) Cannes?

7 What American city would you be in if you took a ferry ride from Fisherman's Wharf to Alcatraz Island?

8 What does the abbreviation 'P' represent on an Ordnance Survey map?

9 Which large river joins the Ganges to form a delta in Bangladesh?

10 On a weather map a warm front is shown by a line with red triangles along it. True or false?

11 In which country are the Dolomites?

12 On which continent would you find the Great Rift Valley?

13 Which of these is not a 'greenhouse' gas: (a) nitrogen, (b) carbon dioxide or (c) methane?

14 At the autumnal equinox the Sun is directly overhead at the equator. True or false?

15 On which river is the Kariba Dam: (a) Zambezi, (b) Zaire or (c) Limpopo?

ANSWERS

1. Bassenthwaite Lake. 2. Copenhagen. 3. Atacama desert. 4. Mogadishu. 5. River Clyde. 6. (b) Biarritz – it is on the west coast, the others are on the south coast. 7. San Francisco. 8. Post Office. 9. Brahmaputra. 10. False, it is a line with red semicircles. 11. Italy. 12. Africa. 13. (a) nitrogen. 14. True. 15. (a) Zambezi.

SESSION 29   QUIZ 7

The Arts

1. Which former jockey has written many novels about horse-racing?

2. Which Yorkshire village was the home of the Brontë sisters?

3. In which county is John Constable's *Flatford Mill*?

4. What colour did Henri Matisse paint his series of four nudes in 1952?

5. Which composer wrote *The Four Seasons*?

6. Van Gogh painted: (a) *The Potato Eaters*, (b) *The Lotus Eaters* or (c) *The People Eaters*?

7. What preceded Picasso's 'Rose Period'?

8. Which of these is not an artistic movement: (a) expressionism, (b) fauvism or (c) passism?

9. Who wrote the *William Tell Overture*?

10. Which animals did Sir Alfred Munnings specialize in painting?

11. What is the full title of the cultural centre in London called the ICA?

12. Man Ray was: (a) a photographer, (b) a cartoonist or (c) a fashion designer?

13. Linseed oil, which is used in oil painting, is extracted from which plant?

14. What type of art exhibition is called a retrospective?

15. In which British town is the Lowry Art Gallery?

ANSWERS

1. Dick Francis. 2. Haworth. 3. Suffolk. 4. Blue. 5. Vivaldi. 6. (a) *The Potato Eaters*. 7. His 'Blue Period'. 8. (c) passism. 9. Rossini. 10. Horses. 11. The Institute of Contemporary Arts. 12. (a) a photographer. 13. Flax. 14. One that looks back at an artist's career. 15. Salford.

SESSION 29 — QUIZ 8

Pot Luck

1 Which country is known as the Land of the Midnight Sun?

2 Where would you see the *Pleiades*?

3 Winston Churchill said, 'I have nothing to offer but blood, sweat and tears'. True or false?

4 What kind of person is said to be *non compos mentis*?

5 What is said to happen 'When the cat's away...'?

6 What group of people are collectively called a company, cast or troupe?

7 In Greek legend the Titans were: (a) giants, (b) dwarves or (c) horses?

8 Which is the world's smallest bird?

9 In which month is the Queen's official birthday?

10 From which city do the A7 and A9 roads radiate?

11 Which charity is popularly known as the RNLI?

12 What is an MP's 'maiden speech'?

13 Leeds Castle is in Yorkshire. True or false?

14 In what year was the summit of Everest first reached?

15 What two-word expression means a phrase with two meanings, one of which is usually indecent?

ANSWERS

1. Norway. 2. In the night sky, they are stars. 3. False, he said, 'blood, toil, tears and sweat'. 4. A mad person, 'not of sound mind'. 5. 'The mice will play'. 6. Actors. 7. (a) giants. 8. The bee hummingbird. 9. June. 10. Edinburgh. 11. The Royal National Lifeboat Institution. 12. Their first speech in the House of Commons. 13. False, it is in Kent. 14. 1953. 15. *Double entendre.*

SESSION 30

QUIZ 1

TV, music & entertainment

1. Whose radio broadcast of *The War of the Worlds* in 1938 was so realistic that thousands of Americans believed aliens really were attacking?

2. What was the name of Dr Who's time machine?

3. Who wrote the Everly Brothers' hit 'Claudette'?

4. What was the name of Liza Minnelli's character in *Cabaret*?

5. In *Brookside*, who or what was 'the Moby'?

6. Which major soul singer appeared as a waitress in the film *The Blues Brothers*?

7. Which fictional detective was played in films by, among others, Humphrey Bogart, Dick Powell and Robert Mitchum?

8. In *Postman Pat*, is Pat's black-and-white cat called: (a) Jess, (b) Tess or (c) Joss?

9. What was Johnny Rotten of the Sex Pistols' real name?

10. Lloyd, Beau and Jeff Bridges are brothers. True or false?

11. 'Does my bum look big in this?' is the catchphrase of which member of the cast of *The Fast Show*?

12. After Keith Moon's death, who took his place as drummer with the Who?

13. Who was the creator of *The Rocky Horror Show*?

14. In *The Muppets*, who were the two old men who hurled abuse at the stage from their box?

15. In which country was jazz pianist Oscar Peterson born?

ANSWERS

1. Orson Welles. 2. The Tardis. 3. Roy Orbison. 4. Sally Bowles. 5. Ron Dixon's mobile shop. 6. Aretha Franklin. 7. Philip Marlowe. 8. Jess. 9. John Lydon. 10. False. Lloyd is the father of Beau and Jeff. 11. Arabella Weir. 12. Kenny Jones. 13. Richard O'Brien. 14. Statler and Waldorf. 15. Canada.

SESSION 30 · QUIZ 2

History

1 What was press-ganging?

2 Which king was believed to have been killed by an arrow while hunting in the New Forest?

3 Where was the Russian Tsars' winter palace built?

4 What organization was set up to 'promote literacy and Christian knowledge'?

5 Was the Boston Tea party in: (a) 1773, (b) 1777 or (c) 1780?

6 What was besieged in 1857 during the Indian Mutiny?

7 In 1879 Somerville opened its doors to whom?

8 What did Pedro Cabral discover in 1500?

9 Which king ruled in England from 871 AD onwards?

10 Carol II was king of which European country this century?

11 St Basil the Great, St Gregory of Nazianzus and St Gregory of Nyssa were collectively known as what?

12 Cetewayo was the last king of which people?

13 Which American landed in Paris, thus ending the first successful transatlantic flight?

14 Where did Richard the Lionheart die?

15 Where did General Gordon die?

ANSWERS

1. Forced recruitment to the navy. 2. William II, known as Rufus. 3. St Petersburg. 4. SPCK, The Society for the Promotion of Christian Knowledge. 5. (a) 1773. 6. Lucknow. 7. Women. 8. Brazil. 9. Alfred the Great. 10. Romania. 11. The Cappadocian Fathers. 12. The Zulus. 13. Charles Lindbergh. 14. While laying siege to the castle at Chalus in France. 15. Khartoum.

SESSION 30 QUIZ 3

Sports

1 Where is Pebble Beach golf club?

2 In what sport do you have a goal attack, goal defence and centre?

3 What did the cricketer Larwood do?

4 What was Franz Beckenbauer's nickname?

5 Len Ganley is a referee in which sport?

6 What was the name of Hitler's favourite boxer?

7 How many gold medals did the USSR win at the 1984 Olympics?

8 What sport did the 'Dream Team' play?

9 In what year did the 'Dream Team' make its first Olympic appearance?

10 When might one have heard Ravel's *Bolero* at the Olympics?

11 Which county won the 1998 Nat West cricket trophy?

12 Who won the silver medal behind Sebastian Coe at the Los Angeles Olympics?

13 If you shoot the lights out in golf, should you be pleased?

14 With what sport do you associate Brooklands?

15 *Against the Odds* was the autobiography of which football figure?

ANSWERS

1. Monterey Peninsula, California. 2. Netball. 3. He bowled 'bodyline'. 4. The Kaiser. 5. Snooker. 6. Max Schmeling. 7. None. They boycotted the Olympics. 8. Basketball. 9. 1992. 10. Watching Torvill and Dean in 1984 at Sarajevo. 11. Lancashire. 12. Steve Cram. 13. Yes. It is a brilliantly low score. 14. Motor racing. 15. Bobby Robson.

SESSION 30 | QUIZ 4

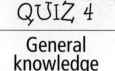

General knowledge

1   Who is Chief Justice William Rehnquist?

2   What is stored in ingots?

3   What is a theodolite?

4   Which country's name means 'Low Lands'?

5   What organization is based at 2 Marlow Road, Maidenhead?

6   What is the DCM?

7   Are there: (a) 2.54, (b) 2.98 or (c) 3.54 centimetres in an inch?

8   Where might you want to go to if you have cystitis?

9   What does a gerontologist study?

10 If a person has both X and Y chromosomes they are male. True or false?

11 Complete the following: 'Tell the truth and shame the...'.

12 What does 'per annum' mean?

13 What did the Michelangelo virus affect?

14 What opened in Paris on 12 April 1992?

15 Between which two towns was the 'Good Samaritan' travelling?

ANSWERS

1. He is the judge who presided over the impeachment of Bill Clinton. 2. Metals, especially gold. 3. A surveying instrument for measuring vertical and horizontal angles. 4. The Netherlands. 5. The Commonwealth War Graves Commission. 6. Distinguished Conduct Medal. 7. (a) 2.54. 8. The toilet. It is a bladder disorder. 9. The ageing process. 10. True. 11. Devil. 12. Annually. 13. Computers. 14. EuroDisney. 15. Jerusalem and Jericho.

244

SESSION 30

QUIZ 5

Technology & science

1 Which condition, usually affecting children, is characterized by a harsh cough and difficulty in breathing?

2 What is the name given to the former large single mass that all continents are derived from?

3 In which part of the body is the brachial artery?

4 What was the first entirely computer-animated full length feature film?

5 Who was the first British astronaut?

6 Which scientific unit is the Greek letter omega a symbol for?

7 What was the philosopher's stone?

8 What chemical substance can come in a form known as 'Plaster of Paris'?

9 What is the principal use of the element germanium?

10 Who discovered the uncertainty principle?

11 What is 'plate tectonics'?

12 In statistics, what is the mode of a set of values?

13 What is ALGOL?

14 How cold does it get on the Moon?

15 What is the name of the set of thick and thin black lines that contains coded information and is used on a product?

ANSWERS

1. Croup. 2. Pangaea. 3. Arm. 4. *Toy Story* (1996). 5. Helen Sharman. 6. Ohm (used as a measure of electric resistance). 7. A hypothetical substance believed to turn base metals into gold. 8. Calcium sulphate. 9. In electronics as an electronic semi-conductor. 10. Werner Heisenberg. 11. The theory of the formation of the Earth's surface based on the interaction of rigid plates moving over the underlying mantle. 12. The value that occurs most frequently. 13. A computer programming language (*algorithmic oriented language*). 14. Below minus 180 degrees Celsius. 15. Bar code.

245

SESSION 30 QUIZ 6

Geography

1 Which French city lies at the confluence of the rivers Rhône and Saône?

2 On a weather map an area with less than average pressure is: (a) a cyclone, (b) an anticyclone or (c) a depression?

3 In which country is the Jutland peninsula?

4 In which English county is the Goonhilly Earth-tracking Station?

5 Is the town of Doncaster in: (a) North Yorkshire, (b) South Yorkshire or (c) West Yorkshire?

6 Which city lies at the northern end of the Suez Canal? Is it: (a) Port Said, (b) Cairo or (c) Alexandria?

7 To which country does the island of Sardinia belong?

8 What is the capital of Senegal?

9 A 'chinook' is a type of: (a) wind, (b) cloud or (c) snow?

10 In which Scottish city would you find bridges named after Victoria, Albert and George V?

11 St Peter Port is the capital of which of the Channel Islands?

12 What is the name of the treeless plain with permanently frozen subsoil in subarctic Russia?

13 Which of these countries produces most of the world's gold: (a) USA, (b) Australia or (c) South Africa?

14 The town of Pilsen, famous for its beer, is in Hungary. True or false?

15 In which country is the ancient citadel of Petra?

ANSWERS

1. Lyon. 2. (c) a depression. 3. Denmark. 4. Cornwall. 5. (b) South Yorkshire. 6. (a) Port Said. 7. Italy. 8. Dakar. 9. (a) wind. 10. Glasgow. 11. Guernsey. 12. Tundra. 13. (c) South Africa. 14. False, it is in the Czech Republic. 15. Jordan.

246

The Arts

1. *The Night Watch* in Amsterdam is the work of: (a) Rembrandt, (b) Vermeer or (c) Van Gogh?

2. By what English title is Mozart's *Die Zauberflöte* known?

3. The adventures of which Baron were told by Rudolf Raspe?

4. Which novel set in Revolutionary Russia brought Boris Pasternak international fame?

5. Pocahontas was a real person. True or false?

6. Who wrote the novel *The Horse Whisperer*?

7. The title *Erewhon* of a novel by Samuel Butler is an anagram of what word?

8. What is an epistolary novel?

9. Who wrote *A Clockwork Orange*?

10. What title was adopted by a man who escaped from many years imprisonment to recover his treasure and seek revenge?

11. Whose book of *Household Management* was first published in 1861?

12. For what type of stories is Andrew Lang best remembered?

13. Which animal's bristles are used to make the finest quality brushes for oil painting?

14. In which Italian city is the Borghese Gallery?

15. Which voice is higher, an alto or a soprano?

ANSWERS

1. (a) Rembrandt. 2. *The Magic Flute*. 3. Baron Munchausen. 4. *Dr Zhivago*. 5. True. 6. Nicholas Evans. 7. Nowhere. 8. One written in the form of letters. 9. Anthony Burgess. 10. *The Count of Monte Cristo*. 11. Mrs Beeton. 12. Fairy stories. 13. The white hog. 14. Rome. 15. Soprano.

SESSION 30 QUIZ 8

Pot Luck

1   Is gazpacho soup served hot or cold?

2   Is a female elephant called: (a) a doe, (b) a mare or (c) a cow?

3   In Cornish place names what is meant by the prefix 'Tre-'?

4   Which English county name is abbreviated to Hants?

5   Which religious group are also known as The Society of Friends?

6   What is a blunderbuss?

7   What colour is a bay horse?

8   What is added to vermouth to make a martini?

9   What is a megalith?

10   What two words which sound the same mean 'to exchange something for money' and 'a small room in a prison'?

11   A daguerreotype was an early form of: (a) typewriter, (b) photograph or (c) bicycle?

12   In which country did the ancient Etruscans live?

13   The character of Mr Brownlow appears in which novel by Charles Dickens?

14   Where would you eat an 'al fresco' meal?

15   Hypnos was the Greek god of: (a) wine, (b) fire or (c) sleep?

ANSWERS

1. Cold, usually iced. 2. (c) a cow. 3. A hamlet or village. 4. Hampshire. 5. The Quakers. 6. An old type of gun. 7. Reddish-brown. 8. Gin. 9. A large stone, like those of Stonehenge. 10. Sell/cell. 11. Photograph. 12. Italy. 13. *Oliver Twist*. 14. Outside. 15. (c) sleep.

SESSION 31 QUIZ 1

TV, music & entertainment

1 What was the name of the lioness featured in *Born Free*?

2 Which EastEnder played Tucker Jenkins in *Grange Hill*?

3 Shirley Jones and David Cassidy are mother and son in real life as they were in *The Partridge Family*. True or false?

4 Guy Pearce, who starred in *L.A. Confidential*, was an original cast member of *Neighbours*. True or false?

5 Who was the original presenter of the children's TV show *Newsround*?

6 Which country singer wrote and recorded 'Lovesick Blues', 'Your Cheatin' Heart', and 'Jambalaya'?

7 What was the name of the 1985 spoof rockumentary directed by Rob Reiner?

8 What was the name of the prime minister in *Yes, Prime Minister*?

9 Lou Reed was a founder member of which avant-garde rock group?

10 In which film did Mick Jagger make his acting debut?

11 TV discussion-show host Robert Kilroy-Silk used to be a Labour MP. True or false?

12 What was jazzman Duke Ellington's real name?

13 Who played 'Che Guevara' in the film *Evita*?

14 In which US state was the TV drama series *Northern Exposure* set?

15 Which Britpop band had a hit with *Parklife*?

ANSWERS

1. Elsa. 2. Todd Carty, who plays Mark Fowler. 3. False. She is his stepmother in real life. 4. True. 5. John Craven. 6. Hank Williams Snr. 7. *This Is Spinal Tap*. 8. Jim Hacker. 9. The Velvet Underground. 10. *Ned Kelly*. 11. True. 12. Edward Kennedy Ellington. 13. Antonio Banderas. 14. Alaska. 15. Blur.

SESSION 31   QUIZ 2

History

1. What was the name of the ship in which Sir Francis Drake sailed around the world?

2. Which of Henry VIII's wives was the last to be beheaded?

3. Which British prime minister had the shortest reign?

4. Who fled to Doorn in Holland at the end of World War I?

5. What was the name of the leader of Romania who was killed in the revolution of 1989?

6. Who was British prime minister during the Suez crisis?

7. Who led the British forces at the battle of Omdurman in 1898?

8. How many royal houses of England have there been since 1066?

9. Which war began in 1642 and ended in 1646?

10. Boudicca was the queen of which tribe?

11. The first pyramid was built in: (a) 3660 BC, (b) 2660 BC or (c) 1660 BC?

12. What is the other name for the house of Plantagenet?

13. Where did Jim Bowie and Davy Crockett die?

14. What was the objective behind the Truman Doctrine?

15. Which king was succeeded by Henry VI?

ANSWERS

1. The *Golden Hind*. 2. Catherine Howard. 3. The Duke of Wellington from 17 November - 10 December 1834. 4. Wilhelm II, the Kaiser. 5. Nicolae Ceausescu. 6. Anthony Eden. 7. General Kitchener. 8. 11. 9. The English Civil War. 10. The Iceni. 11. (b) 2660 BC. 12. The house of Anjou. 13. The Alamo, fighting the Mexicans. 14. The containment of communism. 15. Henry V.

SESSION 31 QUIZ 3

Sports

1 What television sports programme began in 1964?

2 What sporting event is held at Monaco every year?

3 What sport does Keith Deller play?

4 Jahangir Khan is one of the great players of which sport?

5 Against which country did Bryan Robson score his record breaking goal in the World Cup?

6 What is the Olympic motto?

7 Who did Max Schmeling knock out in 1936?

8 What nationality is Liam Brady?

9 What childhood illness did Wilma Rudolph overcome to become an Olympic champion?

10 Who got the blame for tripping Mary Decker in the 1984 Olympics?

11 Who did gymnast Luidmila Tourischeva marry?

12 In what year did Mario Kempes win the golden boot at the World Cup?

13 Brisbane hosted the 1986 Commonwealth Games. True or false?

14 What game do the Streatham Redskins play?

15 What nationality was the referee in the 1966 World Cup final?

ANSWERS

1. *World of Sport*. 2. A grand prix. 3. Darts. 4. Squash. 5. France. 6. Faster, Higher, Stronger. 7. Joe Louis. 8. Irish. 9. Polio. 10. Zola Budd. 11. Valeri Borzov. 12. 1978. 13. False. It hosted them in 1982. 14. Ice hockey. 15. Swiss.

SESSION 31 QUIZ 4

General knowledge

1 Who wrote *Diana: Her True Story*?

2 Which country has been plagued by the 'Shining Path' terrorist group?

3 Knossos lies in which Mediterranean island?

4 What is the name of the last book of the Bible?

5 Is canasta a derivative of: (a) whist, (b) poker or (c) rummy?

6 Who was the first Christian martyr?

7 The walrus is a carnivore. True or false?

8 Which country has the highest sheep population in the world?

9 Which is the most popular month for marriages in England and Wales?

10 How many squares are there in total on a chess board?

11 Which town did Michael Ryan devastate on 19 August 1987?

12 What do D. C. Thomson and Co. publish?

13 Which artist drew 'Number 32'?

14 In 1998 Bob Hoskins starred opposite what?

15 For what is Euclid loathed by generations of children?

ANSWERS

1. Andrew Morton. 2. Peru. 3. Crete. 4. Revelation. 5. (c) rummy. 6. Revelation. 7. True. 8. Australia. 9. August. 10. 64. 11. Hungerford, where he killed 16 people. 12. Comics such as the *Beano*. 13. Jackson Pollock. 14. A rabbit in the film *Who Framed Roger Rabbit?* 15. Writing down the laws of geometry.

SESSION 31

QUIZ 5

Technology & science

1. Where is bile stored in the human body?

2. What is the SI unit of illuminance?

3. What does the acronum ASCII (used in computing) represent?

4. What is turpentine made from?

5. What are isotopes?

6. For which invention is James Dewar noted?

7. Who was the first person to walk on the Moon?

8. Which creature gives its name to a protein found in human blood?

9. Which plant does neroli oil, used in perfumery, come from?

10. What causes gout?

11. What is a nephron?

12. The obstetricians Patrick Steptoe and Robert Edwards pioneered which technique?

13. Fool's gold is the non-technical name for what?

14. Which element did Joseph Priestley and Carl Scheele discover?

15. Which chemical element was first encountered by the Spanish in South America in the 16th century?

ANSWERS

1. The gall bladder. 2. The lux. 3. American Standard Code for Information Interchange. 4. The sap of the pine (or other coniferous) tree. 5. Atoms of an element with the same atomic number but different properties. 6. Vacuum flask, about 1872. 7. Neil Armstrong. 8. The rhesus monkey. 9. Seville orange. 10. Excess of uric acid in the blood. 11. A filtering unit in the kidney. 12. IVF, in vitro fertilization. 13. Iron pyrites (or pyrite). 14. Oxygen. 15. Platinum.

SESSION 31   QUIZ 6

Geography

1   What is the name of the river that forms part of the boundary between Norfolk and Suffolk? Is it the river: (a) Diss, (b) Bure or (c) Waveney?

2   What line of latitude is 23.5 degrees north?

3   On which island is the city of Syracuse, founded as a Greek colony in the 8th century BC?

4   In which county is Cheddar Gorge?

5   Which of these countries produces most of the world's iron: (a) Australia, (b) Brazil or (c) China?

6   Basle is a Swiss city, but its airport lies in which country?

7   Where was the first National Park in the world established in 1872?

8   Which of these Scandinavian countries has the greatest percentage of forest land: (a) Finland, (b) Norway or (c) Sweden?

9   During the last Ice Age, ice sheets completely covered Britain. True or false?

10   Where is the expanse of limestone cliffs known as the Burren?

11   Which of these rivers forms a delta: (a) the Seine, (b) the Danube or (c) the Elbe?

12   Which strait is the only outlet from the Black Sea into the Sea of Marmara?

13   Which European tourist area derives its name from the Arabic El-Gharb, which means 'west'?

14   What is the name for a rocky pinnacle, rising from the sea, where the roof of a natural arch has collapsed?

15   Which African country has Porto-Novo as its capital?

ANSWERS

1. (c) River Waveney. 2. Tropic of Cancer. 3. Sicily. 4. Somerset. 5. (c) China. 6. France. 7. Yellowstone National Park in America. 8. (a) Finland. 9. False. It only spread as far as the Bristol Channel. 10. Ireland. 11. (b) Danube. 12. The Bosphorus. 13. The Algarve. 14. Stack. 15. Benin.

SESSION 31   QUIZ 7

The Arts

1 A string quartet usually comprises two violins, a viola and which other instrument?

2 Who wrote *The Divine Comedy*?

3 What drug did Thomas De Quincey confess to being an eater of?

4 How is the 'danse macabre' also known?

5 Which novel by Umberto Eco is set in the library of a medieval monastery?

6 Which British portrait and landscape artist painted *The Blue Boy*?

7 Which is the first book of the New Testament?

8 Who was the wife of King Arthur?

9 After which Russian author is there a park named in Moscow?

10 Who wrote *North and South* and *Mary Barton*?

11 Which Irish poet was awarded the Nobel Prize for Literature in 1998?

12 Who wrote *The Planets Suite*?

13 Which novelist set up the weekly periodical *Household Words* in 1850?

14 Whose autobiography is called *Testament of Youth*?

15 Which writer is best known for her Regency romances including *Regency Buck* and *Faro's Daughter*?

ANSWERS

1. Cello. 2. Dante Alighieri. 3. Opium. 4. *Dance of Death*. 5. *The Name of the Rose*. 6. Thomas Gainsborough. 7. The Gospel According to St Matthew. 8. Guinevere. 9. Maxim Gorky. 10. Mrs Elizabeth Gaskell. 11. Seamus Heaney. 12. Gustav Holst. 13. Charles Dickens. 14. Vera Brittain. 15. Georgette Heyer.

SESSION 31   QUIZ 8

Pot Luck

1   What type of dog are Springer, King Charles and Cocker?

2   Where is Speaker's Corner?

3   In which northern city would you find the Whitworth Art Gallery?

4   What are seedless white raisins more usually called?

5   A driller on an oilrig is often called: (a) a redneck, (b) a roughneck or (c) a ringneck?

6   Attar is a perfume made from rose-petals. True or false?

7   If a dish is called 'au gratin' it is served with a crust of what?

8   What word beginning with 'g' means a picturesque cave, either real or artificial?

9   With what is a Dundee cake usually decorated?

10   In which African country is yellow the colour of mourning?

11   When is the *fin de siècle*?

12   What was the GLC?

13   What is a mickey finn?

14   Who was Lee Harvey Oswald?

15   At a university or college what is a Freshman?

ANSWERS

1. Spaniels. 2. Hyde Park in London. 3. Manchester. 4. Sultanas. 5. (b) a roughneck. 6. True. 7. Breadcrumbs and grated cheese. 8. Grotto. 9. Almonds. 10. Egypt. 11. End of the century. 12. Greater London Council. 13. A drugged drink. 14. The suspected assassin of John F. Kennedy. 15. A first-year student.

SESSION 32   QUIZ 1

TV, music & entertainment

1 Is Ainsley Harriott a TV expert on: (a) interior design, (b) cookery or (c) gardening?

2 What was the name of the character played by Gene Hackman in *The French Connection* and *French Connection II*?

3 Who duetted with David Bowie on the 1985 hit 'Dancin' in the Street'?

4 Who played 'Smiley' in the TV serial *Tinker, Tailor, Soldier, Spy*?

5 James Dean starred in only three major films. What were they?

6 From where did Duran Duran take their name?

7 What is the connection between Anthony Booth of *Till Death Us Do Part* and Prime Minister Tony Blair?

8 In the film *The Commitments*, Jimmy Rabbit kept having imaginary interviews with which broadcaster?

9 Pop duo Ant and Dec first met when both had acting parts in the children's TV drama *Byker Grove*. True or false?

10 In *Star Trek*, what planet did 'Mr Spock' come from?

11 In which film did the spirit of Humphrey Bogart continually appear, to give Woody Allen advice on how to deal with women?

12 Did Gilbert or Sullivan write the lyrics of their comic operas?

13 In *Neighbours*, what is Toadfish's proper name?

14 Which film doctor could talk to the animals?

15 Who recorded the album *The Dark Side of the Moon* in the 70s?

ANSWERS

1. (b) cookery. 2. Popeye Doyle. 3. Mick Jagger. 4. Alec Guinness. 5. *East of Eden, Rebel Without a Cause* and *Giant*. 6. From a character in the film *Barbarella*. 7. Tony Blair's wife Cherie is Anthony Booth's daughter. 8. Terry Wogan. 9. True. 10. Vulcan. 11. *Play It Again, Sam*. 12. Gilbert. 13. Jared Rebecchi. 14. *Dr Dolittle*. 15. Pink Floyd.

SESSION 32 QUIZ 2

History

1 Which war saw the battle of Bunker Hill?

2 What arrived in the New World for the first time in 1505?

3 Where did Lady Hamilton the mistress of Nelson, live?

4 Who sacked Rome in AD 455?

5 The Romans called it *Aquae Sulis*. By what name do we know it today?

6 What was Montgomery's army in North Africa called?

7 What did Wyclif translate into English in 1380?

8 Preacher Jonathan Edwards ushered in what revival in America?

9 Who was king of England from 1042–66?

10 What gift of the nation designed by Vanbrugh was completed in 1722?

11 What musical instrument set Nero aglow?

12 Lancet arch, flying buttress and ribbed vault are all features of which style of architecture that began in the 12th century?

13 Which American state was founded in 1862 as a refuge for Quakers?

14 What was the name of the Kurdish Sultan of Syria and Egypt from 1174?

15 Who arrived in the nick of time to help Wellington at Waterloo?

ANSWERS

1. The American War of Independence. 2. The first black slaves. 3. Naples. Her husband was an official there. 4. The Vandals. 5. Bath. 6. The Desert Rats. 7. The Bible. 8. The Great Awakening. 9. Edward the Confessor. 10. Blenheim Palace, home of John Churchill, Duke of Marlborough after his victory at the location of the same name. 11. The fiddle. He is reputed to have played it while Rome burned. 12. Gothic. 13. Pennsylvania. 14. Saladin. 15. The Prussian general Blücher.

SESSION 32 — QUIZ 3

Sports

1 What is the home of Crystal Palace?

2 What is the least number of darts needed to finish from 1001?

3 Which ex-tennis player now hosts *A Question of Sport*?

4 Rocky Graziano competed at which sport?

5 Who was the first person to take 300 wickets for England?

6 Who replaced Bobby Charlton in his last match against West Germany in the 1970 World Cup?

7 Alf Ramsey never played football for England. True or false?

8 Ski-jumping skis are wider than those used for downhill races. True or false?

9 Who won the Scottish League in 1983/84 and 1984/85?

10 Which runner famously trod on Brian Whittle's shoe, dislodging it?

11 In which year did Wimbledon join the Football League?

12 Alpine, biathlon are skiing events. What is the other type of skiing?

13 How many goals did Emlyn Hughes score for England? Was it: (a) 0, (b) 1 or (c) 2?

14 In what year did Stanley Matthews make his debut for England?

15 Martin Schmitt is well known as a jumper in which sport?

ANSWERS

1. Selhurst Park. 2. 17. 3. Sue Barker. 4. Boxing. 5. Fred Trueman. 6. Colin Bell. 7. False. 8. True. 9. Aberdeen. 10. Kriss Akabusi. 11. 1977. 12. Nordic. 13. (b) 1. 14. 1934. 15. Ski-jumping.

SESSION 32 | QUIZ 4

General knowledge

1   Who first 'discovered' the circulation of blood in the body?

2   Where is the European Parliament held?

3   What do Benny Andersson and Bjorn Ulvaeus do for a living?

4   What can be 'slope', 'drift' and 'open-cast'?

5   In a text book, what does 'ff' mean?

6   What has dimensions of 210 mm by 297 mm?

7   By what other name is a Boeing 747 known?

8   Sweetcorn originated in which mountain chain?

9   How many chromosomes are there in the human body?

10   Who gave Joseph his coat of many colours?

11   A lack of vitamin C gives rise to which disease?

12   What is the largest organ in the body?

13   If a car had the initials 'GR' on it what would be its country of origin?

14   Who said 'I have nothing to declare, but my genius'?

15   Whose book *Sex* was launched in 1992?

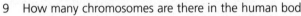

ANSWERS

1. William Harvey. 2. Strasbourg. 3. They write songs. They were the male members of ABBA. 4. Mines. 5. Folios following. 6. A4 paper. 7. Jumbo jet. 8. The Andes. 9. 46. 10. His father Jacob. 11. Scurvy. 12. The liver. 13. Greece. 14. Oscar Wilde. 15. Madonna.

SESSION 32   QUIZ 5

Technology & science

1 What was the well-known invention of Frank Whittle in 1930?

2 How many vertebrae are there in the human neck?

3 What is the name given to the IBM chess playing computer that defeated Garry Kasparov in 1996?

4 Who was the first woman in space?

5 What is a newton?

6 *Drosophila melanogaster* is the Latin name for which insect?

7 What is the difference between cocci and bacilli?

8 Which element makes up 78% of the Earth's atmosphere by volume?

9 What name is given to the unit of distance equal to a thousandth of a metre?

10 What is the heaviest organ in the human body?

11 Through which arteries does blood leave the human heart?

12 In astronomy, what is a red dwarf?

13 In computing, what does CPU represent?

14 Where in the body would you find the *corpus callosum*?

15 What name is given to the hydrated form of calcium sulphate that sets hard when it is mixed with water?

ANSWERS

1. Jet engine. 2. Seven. 3. *Deep Blue*. 4. Valentina Tereshkova from USSR in 1963. 5. A unit of force. 6. Fruit fly. 7. Cocci are spherical shaped bacteria and bacilli are rod-shaped. 8. Nitrogen. 9. Millimetre. 10. The liver. 11. Aorta and pulmonary artery. 12. A small, old, relatively cool star. 13. Central processing unit. 14. Nervous tissue linking the left and right hemispheres in the brain. 15. Plaster of Paris.

SESSION 32 · QUIZ 6

Geography

1 Mount Kilimanjaro is the highest mountain in Africa, but which country is it in?

2 Which river runs through Sunderland?

3 Which is the second largest city in France: (a) Lille, (b) Marseille or (c) Lyon?

4 In which country are the limestone mountains *Picos de Europa*?

5 The Flow country of northern Scotland is an important: (a) peatland, (b) natural pine forest or (c) lake system?

6 What happened to the county of Berkshire in April 1998?

7 Which Italian region includes the towns of Assisi, Orvieto and Perugia?

8 A downfold in rock strata resulting from compression of the Earth's crust is: (a) an anticline, (b) a syncline or (c) a rift valley?

9 The River Avon is crossed by Pulteney Bridge in which city?

10 What is the capital of Djibouti?

11 In which country is the Negev desert?

12 Which country receives about a quarter of Australia's exports?

13 In which American state would you find the cities of Seattle and Spokane?

14 The source of the River Amazon is in Peru. True or false?

15 What percentage of the world's ice is contained in Antarctica: (a) 70, (b) 80 or (c) 90 per cent?

ANSWERS

1. Tanzania. 2. River Wear. 3. (b) Marseille. 4. Spain. 5. (a) peatland. 6. It was split into six unitary authorities. 7. Umbria. 8. (b) a syncline. 9. Bath. 10. Djibouti. 11. Israel. 12. Japan. 13. Washington. 14. True. 15. (c) 90 per cent.

SESSION 32 QUIZ 7

The Arts

1 Who wrote *Middlemarch*?

2 Tom Ripley is the amateur villain in the crime novels of which author?

3 'Break, break, break/On thy cold gray stones, O Sea' is the first line of a poem by whom?

4 Who wrote *The Song of Hiawatha*?

5 What type of book is written by Zane Grey?

6 Which cartoon cat is fond of lasagne?

7 How many years did Rip Van Winkle sleep for?

8 Which town did the Pied Piper clear of rats?

9 What is 'life drawing' concerned with?

10 What is the literal meaning of 'terracotta'?

11 Which children's books were famously illustrated by Sir John Tenniel?

12 What is an artist's *oeuvre*?

13 Caravaggio was a leading artist of what style: (a) Baroque, (b) Gothic or (c) Rococo?

14 Which painting medium is made from egg yolk?

15 In the 15th century, who printed the first Bible?

ANSWERS

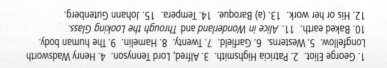

1. George Eliot. 2. Patricia Highsmith. 3. Alfred, Lord Tennyson. 4. Henry Wadsworth Longfellow. 5. Westerns. 6. Garfield. 7. Twenty. 8. Hamelin. 9. The human body. 10. Baked earth. 11. *Alice in Wonderland* and *Through the Looking Glass*. 12. His or her work. 13. (a) Baroque. 14. Tempera. 15. Johann Gutenberg.

SESSION 32 | QUIZ 8

Pot Luck

1 Emmets and Grockles are derogatory terms for what type of people?

2 What is a U-boat?

3 Is a 'paper tiger' someone who: (a) appears to be dangerous but isn't or (b) appears to be safe but isn't?

4 In what situation might you be gazumped?

5 Divorced, beheaded, died. Divorced, beheaded, survived. Who?

6 What is the main ingredient of laver bread?

7 What type of vegetable are described as leguminous?

8 In the Bible who is said to have lived for 969 years?

9 The decibel is named after the inventor of the telephone Alexander Bell. True or false?

10 Where would you find a misericord: (a) police station, (b) a church or (c) a bank?

11 A hagiography is the life story of: (a) a witch, (b) a saint or (c) an artist?

12 Who was Haile Selassie?

13 What is another name for a rowan tree?

14 Who was Ovid?

15 Which numbered Apollo mission made the first manned Moon landing?

ANSWERS

1. Tourists. 2. German submarine. 3. (a) someone who appears to be dangerous but isn't. 4. When buying a house. 5. The six wives of Henry VIII. 6. Seaweed. 7. Peas and beans. 8. Methuselah. 9. True. 10. (b) a church. 11. (b) a saint. 12. Emperor of Ethiopia 1930-74. 13. Mountain ash. 14. A Roman poet. 15. Apollo 11.

SESSION 33 QUIZ 1

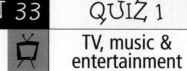

TV, music & entertainment

1 In *Coronation Street*, how did Brian Tilsley die?

2 Which band did Ronnie Wood leave to join the Rolling Stones?

3 Which rock singer played Eddie in *The Rocky Horror Picture Show*?

4 Who are the husband-and-wife team who present the daytime TV show *This Morning*?

5 What was Chuck Berry's only UK No.1 hit single?

6 In which film did the catch phrase 'We're not worthy' feature?

7 Where do the Wombles live and pick up litter?

8 Who is the lead singer with Motorhead?

9 In which film did Martin Sheen and Charlie Sheen play father and son?

10 Who are the two team captains in *They Think It's All Over*?

11 Which jazz musician was nicknamed 'Bird'?

12 What was the first of the *Road* films, starring Bob Hope and Bing Crosby?

13 Who is the longest-serving member of the cast of *Brookside*?

14 Who was the guest vocalist on Take That's hit, 'Relight My Fire'?

15 Which cowboy-film star was the USA's most decorated soldier in World War II?

ANSWERS

1. He was stabbed outside a disco. 2. The Faces. 3. Meat Loaf. 4. Richard Madeley and Judy Finnigan. 5. 'My Ding-a-Ling'. 6. *Wayne's World*. 7. Wimbledon Common. 8. Lemmy. 9. *Wall Street*. 10. Gary Lineker and David Gower. 11. Charlie Parker. 12. *Road to Singapore*. 13. Michael Starke, who plays Sinbad. 14. Lulu. 15. Audie Murphy.

SESSION 33   QUIZ 2

History

1. Which American won the Nobel Peace Prize in 1973?

2. How many British prime ministers were there during World War I?

3. The Minoan civilization flourished on which Mediterranean island?

4. Which king lost the American colonies?

5. The Berlin wall was erected in 1959. True or false?

6. William III defeated James II at which battle?

7. In 1927 conditioned reflexes were observed by which Russian scientist?

8. Who was Charles II's favourite mistress?

9. What did Billy Butlin open in 1936?

10. Where did Britain explode its first H-bomb?

11. What happened to Anwar Sadat of Egypt in 1981?

12. Who was the first head of state to give birth while in office?

13. What is a Salic law?

14. What did the Mason-Dixon line divide?

15. How many Great Ages did ancient Egypt have?

ANSWERS

1. Henry Kissinger. 2. Two. Asquith and Lloyd George. 3. Crete. 4. George III. 5. False. It went up in 1961. 6. The battle of the Boyne. 7. Pavlov. 8. Nell Gwyn. 9. His first holiday camp. 10. Christmas Island. 11. He was assassinated. 12. Benazir Bhutto. 13. It excludes females from inheritance, especially from monarchy. 14. Pennsylvania and Maryland, the north and south states prior to the Civil War. 15. Three. Old, Middle and New.

SESSION 33 — QUIZ 3

Sports

1 Which team has won the European Cup the most times in succession?

2 In what year was the first Rugby League Challenge Cup Final? Was it: (a) 1879, (b) 1897 or (c) 1904?

3 Which English Rugby Union side does New Zealander Zinzan Brooke play for?

4 Where was the 'Rorkes Drift' rugby test match played?

5 Which outspoken manager resigned from football in 1983?

6 Laura Davies won the US Open in which year?

7 What 'came home' in 1996?

8 Gary Lineker began his career at: (a) Leicester, (b) Tottenham or (c) Everton?

9 At what sport did Virginia Holgate win a medal in 1984?

10 Who is Zimbabwe's most famous goalkeeping export?

11 Which team plays at Ninian Park?

12 Pat Eddery won the Oaks on 'Polygamy' in 1975. True or false?

13 Franz Klammer competed at which sport?

14 The playing fields of which school won a victory at Waterloo?

15 In which year did Glen Hoddle step down from being manager of the England football squad?

ANSWERS

1. Real Madrid. 2. (b) 1897. 3. Harlequins. 4. Sydney Cricket Ground in 1914. It was so named because of the incredible defence put up by the British team. 5. Brian Clough. 6. 1987. 7. Football. 8. (a) Leicester. 9. Horse riding. 10. Bruce Grobbelaar. 11. Cardiff City. 12. False. He won on that horse in 1974. 13. Skiing. 14. Eton. 15. 1999.

SESSION 33   QUIZ 4

General knowledge

1   Did the first ever Model A Ford cost: (a) $150, (b) $500 or (c) $850?

2   Whose memoirs were *The Downing Street Years*?

3   Where was the 'Colossus'?

4   What does the word 'Islam' mean?

5   What is the only man-made structure visible from the Moon?

6   In the game Cluedo, how many married female suspects are there?

7   Who found Moses in the bulrushes?

8   What nationality is Edmund Hillary?

9   Alexander Fleming never won the Nobel Prize. True or false?

10   Who was Joseph Jakobs?

11   Which is the largest African country?

12   How many stars are there on New Zealand's flag?

13   Who publishes *En Route*?

14   Alfred Stieglitz, Man Ray and Edward S. Curtis followed which profession?

15   What is Sadler's Wells?

ANSWERS

SESSION 33 QUIZ 5
Technology & science

1 Where in the human body is the pineal gland?

2 Ruby and sapphire are varieties of which mineral?

3 What is the name of the computer software organization founded in 1975 by Bill Gates and Paul Allen?

4 What is the origin of the word 'pixel'?

5 When Armstrong and Aldrin walked on the Moon for the first time in 1969, who remained in the command module?

6 Which chemical element has the symbol Sb?

7 What fish is also called the white whale?

8 What does the symbol 'c' mean to a scientist?

9 What term describes the study of earthquakes?

10 What is the name of the complex carbohydrate that forms the cell wall of most plants?

11 What is the technical name for visual purple, the light-sensitive pigment in the retina of the eye?

12 Which planet was discovered in 1781?

13 What does DDT stand for?

14 Who was the first person to look at space through a telescope?

15 What is the main chemical pollutant that causes acid rain?

ANSWERS

1. In the forehead. 2. Corundum. 3. Microsoft. 4. It is an abbreviation of 'picture element'. 5. Michael Collins. 6. Antimony. 7. Beluga. 8. It represents the velocity of light (in equations etc). 9. Seismology. 10. Cellulose. 11. Rhodopsin. 12. Uranus, discovered by William Herschel. 13. Dichloro-diphenyl-trichloroethane. 14. Galileo Galilei. 15. Sulphur dioxide.

SESSION 33 | QUIZ 6

Geography

1 Which bridge would you cross to travel from Dunfermline to Edinburgh?

2 In which country are the rivers Enns, Mur and Inn?

3 Where is Mount Toubkal?

4 The French region of the Auvergne is in which upland area: (a) Vosges mountains, (b) the Ardennes or (c) the Massif Central?

5 In which island group are Little Abaco and Great Abaco?

6 What is the capital of Hungary?

7 Which English city has districts called Aston, Edgbaston and Perry Barr?

8 Where would 'Rossby waves' occur: (a) in the atmosphere, (b) in the sea or (c) in sedimentary rocks?

9 On which river does Albuquerque in New Mexico stand?

10 Of these three countries, all with a population density of less than five per square kilometre, which has the lowest: (a) Mongolia, (b) Australia or (c) Canada?

11 Which long distance footpath goes from Ivinghoe Beacon to Overton Hill near Avebury, following a prehistoric path for half its length?

12 What wildlife are you likely to encounter on the Svalbard Islands: (a) tigers, (b) polar bears or (c) kangaroos?

13 In which country is the mountain Mulhacen?

14 Darwin is the capital of which region of Australia?

15 Which country on the Red Sea became independent from Ethiopia in 1993?

ANSWERS

1. Forth Bridge. 2. Austria. 3. Morocco. 4. (c) the Massif Central. 5. The Bahamas. 6. Budapest. 7. Birmingham. 8. (a) in the atmosphere. 9. Rio Grande. 10. (a) Mongolia. 11. The Ridgeway Path. 12. (b) polar bears. 13. Spain. 14. Northern Territory. 15. Eritrea.

SESSION 33   QUIZ 7

The Arts

1   Gertrude Jeykll designed: (a) gardens, (b) wallpaper or (c) conservatories?

2   'Chinoiserie' designs, popular in the 18th century, were influenced by the art of which country?

3   Which art and design style at the beginning of the 20th century is associated with Charles Rennie Mackintosh?

4   Clarice Cliff produced brightly coloured: (a) clothes, (b) pottery or (c) curtains?

5   What type of instrument is a flageolet?

6   Who wrote the operas *Turandot* and *Madame Butterfly*?

7   At which farm did 'Flora Poste' visit her relatives the 'Starkadders'?

8   Who created the detective 'Albert Campion'?

9   Who produced the poetry book *The Birthday Letters*?

10   What is Edward Ardizzone known for?

11   Which modern poet writes poems about spectacles?

12   Who is the author of the 'Brother Cadfael' stories?

13   In the 'Calvin and Hobbes' cartoons, what is 'Hobbes'?

14   'Imitations of Immortality' is an ode by which poet?

15   Hyperbole is: (a) rhyming, (b) shouting or (c) exaggerating?

ANSWERS

1. (a) gardens. 2. China. 3. Art Nouveau. 4. (b) pottery. 5. A tin whistle. 6. Puccini. 7. *Cold Comfort Farm*. 8. Margery Allingham. 9. Ted Hughes. 10. Illustrating children's and adults' books. 11. John Hegley. 12. Ellis Peters. 13. A (toy) tiger. 14. William Wordsworth. 15. (c) exaggerating.

SESSION 33 | QUIZ 8

Pot Luck

1   What does the Green Cross Code apply to?

2   What is a Dear John letter?

3   The 'Treasures of Tutankhamun' exhibition at the British Museum attracted how many visitors in 1972: (a) 1.2 million, (b) 1.7 million or (c) 2.4 million?

4   What anti-parking device is known in America as the Denver Boot?

5   In 1997, how many hours per day on average did viewers watch television in the UK?

6   A tintinnabulation is the sound of: (a) horns, (b) bells or (c) sirens?

7   Was the last person to be lawfully beheaded in Britain executed in: (a) 1747, (b) 1856 or (c) 1932?

8   Which letter is represented in Morse Code by dash dash?

9   Which non-existent organization was invited to the opening of the Panama Canal; was it: (a) The Dutch Mountain Guides, (b) The New York Gondoliers or (c) The Swiss Navy?

10 If a person counted at a rate of 100 numbers a minute, 8 hours a day, 5 days a week, how many years would it take to reach one billion?

11 Which Victorian politician was nicknamed 'Dizzy'?

12 What name is given to the period of the rising of the Dog Star Sirius?

13 Whose real name was Cristóbal Colón?

14 What colour is cyan?

15 What is the motto of the British monarch?

ANSWERS

1. Road safety: crossing a road. 2. One that says that a relationship has finished. 3. (b) 1.7 million. 4. Wheel clamp, first used in Denver, Colorado. 5. 3.53 hours. 6. (b) bells. 7. (a) 1747. 8. M. 9. (c) The Swiss Navy. 10. 80 years. 11. Benjamin Disraeli. 12. Dog Days. 13. Christopher Columbus. 14. Blue. 15. *Dieu et Mon Droit*, God and My Right.

SESSION 34 QUIZ 1

TV, music & entertainment

1 Who is the presenter of the TV game show *Supermarket Sweep*?

2 Actors Eric Roberts and Julia Roberts are brother and sister. True or false?

3 How did soul singer Marvin Gaye die?

4 Which member of the Monkees starred in *Circus Boy* as a child actor?

5 Who directed *Reservoir Dogs* and *Pulp Fiction*?

6 Where was conductor Zubin Mehta born?

7 Which member of the *EastEnders* cast also starred in *Are You Being Served*?

8 Which Hollywood musical star's real name is Harold Leek?

9 Who was the keyboard player with the Boomtown Rats?

10 What kind of animal was 'Skippy' in the children's TV programme of the same name?

11 Which of Elizabeth Taylor's husbands did she marry twice?

12 Who duetted with Van Morrison on 'Whenever God Shines His Light'?

13 Who played 'Dr Kildare' in the TV drama series of the same name?

14 Which surrealist painter designed the dream sequence in Alfred Hitchcock's *Spellbound*?

15 Who wrote the opera *Porgy and Bess*?

ANSWERS

1. Dale Winton. 2. True. 3. He was shot by his father. 4. Mickey Dolenz. 5. Quentin Tarantino. 6. Bombay, India. 7. Wendy Richard, who plays Pauline Fowler. 8. Howard Keel. 9. Johnny Fingers. 10. A kangaroo. 11. Cliff Richard. 12. Richard Chamberlain. 14. Salvador Dali. 15. George and Ira Gershwin.

SESSION 34   QUIZ 2

History

1   Did Australia become a nation in: (a) 1801, (b) 1851 or (c) 1901?

2   What relation were Mary and Elizabeth I?

3   Which infamous Italian lady lived from 1480-1519?

4   Who was the first woman to fly across the Atlantic?

5   What was found near the tomb of Shi-Huangdi in 1974?

6   Who died saying 'Et tu Brute'?

7   400,000 went to Moscow but only a tenth of that number returned. Who were they?

8   The siege of Ladysmith took place during which war?

9   Who was Raoul Wallenberg?

10   What was the name of the unbreakable German code machine throughout World War II?

11   What were the names of the American landing beaches on D-Day?

12   Desmond Tutu became the first black bishop of which town?

13   With what city is the name Medici synonymous?

14   In 1672 Isaac Newton was made a member of what?

15   Who became British prime minister in 1927 only to die later the same year?

ANSWERS

1. (c) 1901. 2. Half-sisters. 3. Lucrezia Borgia. 4. Amelia Earhart. 5. Thousands of terracotta soldiers. 6. Julius Caesar. 7. The remnants of Napoleon's army. 8. The Boer War. 9. A Swede who helped many Hungarian Jews during World War II. 10. Enigma. 11. Utah and Omaha. 12. Johannesburg. 13. Florence. 14. The Royal Society. 15. George Canning.

SESSION 34 — QUIZ 3

Sports

1 The Swaythling Cup is awarded in which sport?

2 What horse was kidnapped in 1983?

3 How many goals did Gary Lineker score for England?

4 The golfer Tom Kite was born in which American State?

5 In what sport would you expect to see a pike and a tuck?

6 What racing driver had the nickname 'Shunt'?

7 Did Kornelia Ender swim for: (a) Australia, (b) East Germany or (c) West Germany?

8 Which Scotsman had his teeth restored by a drink?

9 Ken Norton beat Muhammad Ali. True or false?

10 How did Gilles Villeneuve die?

11 In what year did the British Lions win a series over New Zealand for the first time?

12 In what sport is a randolph performed?

13 What is the first event in the decathlon?

14 Tae kwon do and the Triathlon will make their Olympic appearance at Sydney. True or false?

15 Where were the 26th Olympics held?

ANSWERS

1. Table tennis. 2. 'Shergar'. 3. 48. 4. Texas. 5. Diving. 6. James Hunt. 7. (b) East Germany. 8. Joe Jordan, who featured in a Heineken advert. 9. True, but it was a non-title bout. 10. While practising for the Belgian Grand Prix in 1982. 11. 1971. 12. Trampolining. 13. 100 metres. 14. True. 15. Atlanta.

SESSION 34   QUIZ 4

General knowledge

1   How many Oscars did *Ben Hur* win?

2   Who did *The Untouchables* take on?

3   Who said, 'Eureka'?

4   What is the capital of Austria?

5   In which decade were 'Teddy boys' particularly fashionable in Britain?

6   Who did Tony Blair choose to be his first secretary of state for Scotland?

7   Where might you see the Gruenfeld Defence?

8   Which country has the DAX financial index?

9   In which city can you see the Wrigley Building and the Tribune Tower?

10   Enrico Fermi worked to build what?

11   What do the initials DG stand for?

12   By what name is the F-117 better known?

13   By what name was Sri Lanka formerly known?

14   Friedrich Sertürner discovered which drug in 1805?

15   What is ataxia?

ANSWERS

1. 11. 2. Al Capone. 3. Archimedes. 4. Vienna. 5. The 1950s. 6. Donald Dewar. 7. On a chess board. 8. Germany. 9. Chicago. 10. The nuclear reactor. 11. Dei Gratia - by the grace of God. 12. The Stealth Fighter. 13. Ceylon. 14. Morphine. 15. Loss of muscle control.

SESSION 34 QUIZ 5

Technology & science

1 What is the generic name for fuels such as natural gas, coal and oil?

2 What did Alfred Nobel's father, Emmanual, invent?

3 What is the computer scientist Kevin Mitnick famous for?

4 In which year did an astronaut make the first untethered 'walk' in space?

5 Which is the third major planet from the Sun?

6 If you suffer from Bright's disease, which part of the body is affected?

7 What is geotropism?

8 What is a 'black hole'?

9 Which metal is added to steel to make it stainless?

10 What is the literal meaning of the word 'atom'?

11 Name one of the two moons, or satellites, orbiting Mars?

12 Where is Silicon Valley?

13 What does the medical abbreviation LD stand for?

14 What was Linus Yale's invention of 1851?

15 Name the organs that are involved in a triple transplant.

ANSWERS

1. Fossil fuels. 2. Plywood 3. Being the world's most wanted computer hacker (caught in 1994). 4. 1984, by Bruce McCandless. 5. The Earth. 6. The kidneys. 7. The growth of a plant or part of a plant towards the pull of the Earth's gravity. 8. A region of space with a gravitational field that is so strong that nothing can escape. 10. It comes from Greek, meaning 'indivisible'. 11. Phobos, Deimos. 12. California, between Palo Alto and San Jose (site of high technology firms). 13. Lethal dosage. 14. The Yale lock. 15. Heart, lungs and liver.

SESSION 34   QUIZ 6

Geography

1 What is the capital of Oman?

2 What is the currency of Albania? Is it: (a) the lev, (b) the lek or (c) the leu?

3 In which island group would you find Hoy, Stronsay and Westray?

4 What type of rock is granite: (a) igneous, (b) metamorphic or (c) sedimentary?

5 In the highlands of which African country are the lakes Tana, Shala and Abaya?

6 In which type of cloud does hail form: (a) cirrus, (b) alto-stratus or (c) cumulo-nimbus?

7 Which south coast resort would you visit to see the Royal Pavilion?

8 Which country has the largest national park in the world, at seventy million hectares: (a) Australia, (b) Canada or (c) Greenland?

9 Where is the Sierra Nevada mountain range, which includes the peaks Mount Ritter and North Palisade?

10 Which coast of Australia has a Mediterranean type climate: (a) north, (b) east or (c) south?

11 In which ocean are the Cape Verde Islands?

12 Which country is separated from Italy by the Strait of Otranto?

13 Which country surrounds the Sea of Marmara?

14 Which industry has made São Paulo the largest city in the southern hemisphere: (a) coffee, (b) gold mining or (c) oil?

15 What is 'loess'? Is it: (a) a fertile soil transported by wind, (b) a sedimentary rock or (c) a mineral?

ANSWERS

1. Muscat. 2. (b) the lek. 3. Orkney Islands. 4. (a) igneous. 5. Ethiopia. 6. (c) cumulo-nimbus clouds. 7. Brighton. 8. (c) Greenland. 9. USA. 10. (c) south. 11. Atlantic. 12. Albania. 13. Turkey. 14. (a) coffee. 15. (a) a fertile soil transported by wind.

SESSION 34 · QUIZ 7

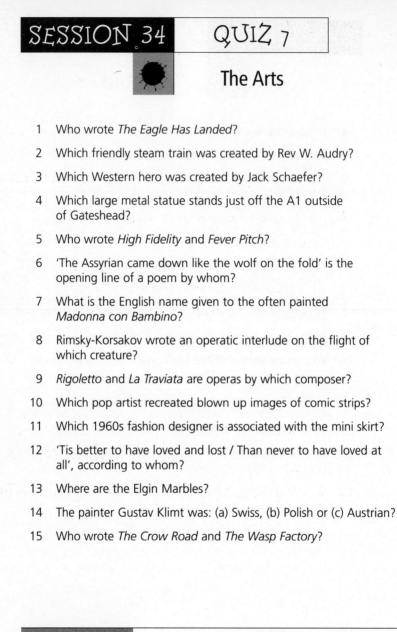

The Arts

1 Who wrote *The Eagle Has Landed*?

2 Which friendly steam train was created by Rev W. Audry?

3 Which Western hero was created by Jack Schaefer?

4 Which large metal statue stands just off the A1 outside of Gateshead?

5 Who wrote *High Fidelity* and *Fever Pitch*?

6 'The Assyrian came down like the wolf on the fold' is the opening line of a poem by whom?

7 What is the English name given to the often painted *Madonna con Bambino*?

8 Rimsky-Korsakov wrote an operatic interlude on the flight of which creature?

9 *Rigoletto* and *La Traviata* are operas by which composer?

10 Which pop artist recreated blown up images of comic strips?

11 Which 1960s fashion designer is associated with the mini skirt?

12 'Tis better to have loved and lost / Than never to have loved at all', according to whom?

13 Where are the Elgin Marbles?

14 The painter Gustav Klimt was: (a) Swiss, (b) Polish or (c) Austrian?

15 Who wrote *The Crow Road* and *The Wasp Factory*?

ANSWERS

1. Jack Higgins. 2. Thomas the Tank Engine. 3. *Shane*. 4. *Angel of the North*. 5. Nick Hornby. 6. Lord Byron. 7. *Lady (Virgin Mary) with Child*. 8. *The Flight of the Bumble Bee*. 9. Verdi. 10. Roy Lichtenstein. 11. Mary Quant. 12. Alfred, Lord Tennyson. 13. In the British Museum. 14. (c) Austrian. 15. Iain Banks.

SESSION 34   QUIZ 8

Pot Luck

1   A dandiprat was a small English coin. True or false?

2   Whom did King Darius cast into the lion's den?

3   What religious group is also known as The Church of the Latter Day Saints?

4   How much does something cost if it is 'gratis'?

5   Which is the higher rank: Field-Marshal or Sergeant-Major?

6   Which was the world's first major library?

7   What happened to Solomon Grundy on Monday?

8   In the American West why was Boot-hill cemetery so-called?

9   Davy Crockett was a real person. True or false?

10   Why is one version of the Bible called 'The Wicked Bible'?

11   Who was 'Old Ironsides'?

12   In army slang what is mufti?

13   What is meant by the phrase 'When Dover and Calais meet'?

14   'The Permissive Society' was used to describe people in which decade?

15   In 1996-97 which author's books were most borrowed from UK libraries?

ANSWERS

1. True, in the 16th century. 2. Daniel. 3. The Mormons. 4. Nothing, it is free. 5. Field-Marshal. 6. Alexandrian Library, Alexandria, Egypt, founded about 300 BC. 7. He was born. 8. Because its occupants 'died with their boots on'. 9. True, he was killed at the Alamo in 1836. 10. The seventh commandment accidentally says 'Thou shall commit adultery'. 11. Oliver Cromwell. 12. Civilian clothes. 13. Never. 14. 1960s. 15. Catherine Cookson.

SESSION 35 QUIZ 1

TV, music & entertainment

1 Who played Tonto in *The Lone Ranger*?

2 Who played '006' in the James Bond film *Goldeneye*?

3 Where is La Scala opera house?

4 Denzel Washington was once a regular in which TV medical drama?

5 What is the name of Elvis Costello's 1981 album of country songs?

6 Who is the famous daughter of Tippi Hedren, star of Hitchcock's *The Birds*?

7 What are the first names of 'The Slobs' from *Harry Enfield and Chums*?

8 Who was Elvis Presley's manager?

9 Which film actor said, 'Anyone who hates small dogs and children can't be all bad'?

10 The actors who play Kim Marchant and Chris Tate in *Emmerdale* are married in real life. True or false?

11 Which pop singer and drummer once played the Artful Dodger in a West End production of *Oliver!*?

12 Which film star played Rowdy Yates in TV's *Rawhide*?

13 Which breakfast-show presenter also presented *Moviewatch*?

14 Who recorded the theme song from the 90s version of *Godzilla*?

15 Who plays the mayor in the sitcom *Spin City*?

ANSWERS

1. Jay Silverheels. 2. Sean Bean. 3. Milan. 4. *St Elsewhere*. 5. *Almost Blue*. 6. Melanie Griffith. 7. Wayne and Waynetta. 8. Colonel Tom Parker. 9. W. C. Fields. 10. True. 11. Phil Collins. 12. Clint Eastwood. 13. Johnny Vaughan. 14. Jamiroquai. 15. Barry Bostwick.

SESSION 35 — QUIZ 2

History

1 What became known as the Queen's trial in 1820?

2 In what month was Napoleon defeated at Waterloo?

3 Who became leader of the Liberal Party in 1867?

4 'America for the Americans' is a pithy way of defining which political idea?

5 In 1925 Churchill made Britain return to what?

6 Who preached his first sermon in 610 AD?

7 How did Harold, Earl of Wessex, die?

8 Good Queen Bess was the nickname of which monarch?

9 Which famous French ecclesiastical building was begun in 1194?

10 By what name was the religious order that whipped itself in the 13th century known?

11 In 1224 Frederich II founded a university at which Italian location?

12 What was constructed from 688-692 in Jerusalem?

13 What was the name of the last resident of Spandau prison?

14 Marie Curie won two Nobel Prizes – the only woman ever to do so. True or false?

15 What did Edward the Confessor found in 1052?

ANSWERS

1. When George IV attempted to divorce his wife, Caroline. 2. June. 3. W. E. Gladstone. 4. The Monroe Doctrine. 5. The gold standard. 6. Mohammed. 7. He was shot by an arrow, at Hastings. 8. Queen Elizabeth I. 9. Chartres Cathedral. 10. The Flagellants. 11. Naples. 12. The Dome of the Rock. 13. Rudolf Hess. 14. True. 15. Westminster Abbey.

SESSION 35   QUIZ 3

Sports

1. Who was first across the line in the 1988 men's 100-metre Olympic final?

2. Which was the first African nation to win the 4 x 400 metres for men at the Olympics?

3. Who was the goalkeeper when England lost to Germany in the 1970 World Cup Finals?

4. In snooker who is known as 'the Whirlwind'?

5. What sport did Nadia Comaneci excel at?

6. What is Japan's national sport?

7. Who was the first Briton to win the Indy 500?

8. Which awesome cricketer was known as Big Bird?

9. How many times did Viv Richards hit the stumps with throws in the cricket World Cup final in 1975?

10. How many times did 'Red Rum' compete in the Grand National?

11. What was the crowning moment of referee Jack Taylor's career?

12. What did Graham Rix do against Valencia in extra time?

13. James Hunt once played at Wimbledon. True or false?

14. Who won the 1974 World Cup Final?

15. What sport do the Pittsburgh Steelers play?

ANSWERS

1. Ben Johnson, but he was disqualified. 2. Kenya. 3. Peter Bonetti. 4. Jimmy White. 5. Gymnastics. 6. Sumo wrestling. 7. Jim Clark. 8. Joel Garner. 9. Three. 10. Five. 11. He refereed the 1974 World Cup Final. 12. He missed a penalty. 13. True. 14. West Germany. 15. American Football.

SESSION 35   QUIZ 4

General knowledge

1   Do what 'in haste and repent at leisure'?

2   What colour is jaundiced skin?

3   To which Christian group did Lord Shaftesbury belong?

4   Who said, 'You can't fool all of the people, all the time'?

5   What is the name of the canine pal of Dennis the Menace?

6   Which was Queen Elizabeth's 'annus horribilis'?

7   The Nabateans built which 'rose-red' city?

8   In which card game can you score 'One for his nob'?

9   Which country has the most turkeys in the world?

10   What is Sirimavo Bandaranaike's claim to fame?

11   Lord Rutherford won the Nobel Prize for which subject?

12   Sherman, T34 and Crusader are all types of what?

13   How many states are there in the US?

14   What are the colours on the Canadian flag?

15   What do *One Million Years BC*, *Jurassic Park* and *Fantasia* have in common?

ANSWERS

1. Marry. 2. Yellow. 3. The Evangelicals. 4. P T Barnum, the showman. 5. Gnasher. 6. 1992. 7. Petra. 8. Cribbage. 9. USA. 10. She was the first woman prime minister in the world. 11. Chemistry. 12. They are all World War II tanks. 13. 50. 14. Red and white. 15. They all feature dinosaurs.

SESSION 35   QUIZ 5

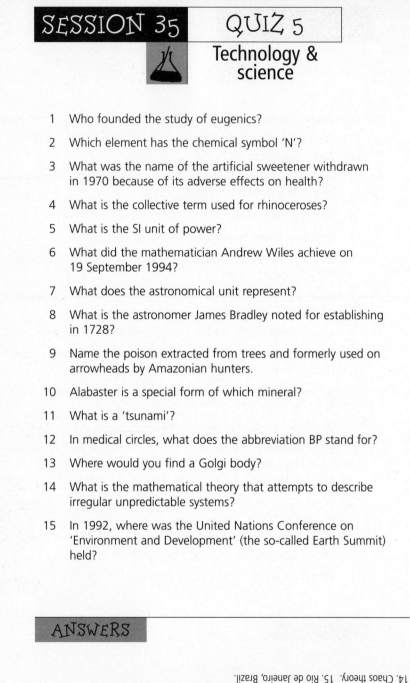

Technology & science

1 Who founded the study of eugenics?

2 Which element has the chemical symbol 'N'?

3 What was the name of the artificial sweetener withdrawn in 1970 because of its adverse effects on health?

4 What is the collective term used for rhinoceroses?

5 What is the SI unit of power?

6 What did the mathematician Andrew Wiles achieve on 19 September 1994?

7 What does the astronomical unit represent?

8 What is the astronomer James Bradley noted for establishing in 1728?

9 Name the poison extracted from trees and formerly used on arrowheads by Amazonian hunters.

10 Alabaster is a special form of which mineral?

11 What is a 'tsunami'?

12 In medical circles, what does the abbreviation BP stand for?

13 Where would you find a Golgi body?

14 What is the mathematical theory that attempts to describe irregular unpredictable systems?

15 In 1992, where was the United Nations Conference on 'Environment and Development' (the so-called Earth Summit) held?

ANSWERS

1. Sir Francis Galton. 2. Nitrogen. 3. Cyclamate. 4. A crash. 5. The watt. 6. Proof of Fermat's Theorem. 7. The mean distance from the centre of the Earth to the centre of the Sun (149,597,870 km). 8. Calculating the speed of light. 9. Curare. 10. Gypsum. 11. A tidal wave. 12. Blood pressure (or British Pharmacopoeia). 13. In a cell (an organelle). 14. Chaos theory. 15. Rio de Janeiro, Brazil.

SESSION 35 QUIZ 6

Geography

1 Which mountain range lies along the border between Poland and the Czech Republic, passes through the Ukraine and into Romania?

2 What is the capital of Libya?

3 Which of these is on the west coast of England: (a) St Abb's Head, (b) St Bee's Head or (c) Beachy Head?

4 Which is the most southerly of the United States?

5 On which Greek island are the ruins of Knossos?

6 Where is the second largest coral reef in the world: (a) Antigua, (b) Belize or (c) Cuba?

7 What are the 'Santa Ana' in California, the 'Brickfielder' in southeast Australia and the 'Haboob' in the Sudan?

8 Which island group includes La Palma, Gomera and Fuerteventura?

9 What is the name for the band of scrub and savanna grassland to the south of the Sahara desert?

10 Temple Meads station is in: (a) Bristol, (b) Cheltenham or (c) Exeter?

11 What is the name of the strait which connects the Sea of Marmara with the Aegean?

12 Canberra was built because Melbourne and Sydney could not decide which should be the capital. True or false?

13 Which is the world's largest producer of tobacco: (a) USA, (b) Brazil or (c) China?

14 Which is the longest of Poland's rivers: (a) the Elbe, (b) the Oder or (c) the Vistula?

15 Which country has the longest coastline in Europe?

ANSWERS

1. Carpathians. 2. Tripoli. 3. St Bee's Head. 4. Hawaii. 5. Crete. 6. (b) Belize. 7. Local winds. 8. Canary Islands. 9. The Sahel. 10. (a) Bristol. 11. Dardanelles. 12. True. 13. (c) China. 14. (c) the Vistula. 15. Norway.

SESSION 35 QUIZ 7

The Arts

1 In which century did Rococo art and architecture develop?

2 How many arms does the *Venus de Milo* have?

3 *The View of Delft* is a painting of his home town by which Dutch artist?

4 Which company is the oldest firm of auctioneers in the world?

5 In sculpture, does 'biomorphic' mean: (a) geometric shapes, (b) organic shapes or (c) changing shapes?

6 Who wrote the *Minute Waltz*, which can be played in a minute?

7 Who is the kidnapped heroine of R. D. Blackmore's only successful novel?

8 Which dramatist wrote *The Birthday Party* and *The Caretaker*?

9 Whom did James Boswell accompany on a tour of the Hebrides in 1784?

10 Boccaccio's tales of *The Decameron* are told in the vicinity of which Italian city?

11 What is a bibliophile?

12 Which zoologist wrote *My Family and Other Animals*?

13 What type of alphabet is Futhorc?

14 Which King's mines are the title of a novel by H. Rider Haggard?

15 Who wrote about the adventures of Flashman?

ANSWERS

15. George Macdonald Fraser.
1. 18th century. 2. None. 3. Vermeer. 4. Sotheby's. 5. (b) organic shapes. 6. Chopin. 7. Lorna Doone. 8. Harold Pinter. 9. Dr Samuel Johnson. 10. Florence. 11. A person who collects or is fond of books. 12. Gerald Durrell. 13. The runic alphabet. 14. King Solomon.

SESSION 35 · QUIZ 8

Pot Luck

1 In what month is Candlemas Day?

2 In which year was Stephen Lawrence stabbed to death?

3 What is a Trojan horse?

4 What did Robert Burns call 'the great chieftain of the pudding race'?

5 Which of these is the definite article: (a) but, (b) the or (c) a?

6 Which salad of celery, apple and walnuts is named after a New York hotel?

7 Kelpies are: (a) tree nymphs, (b) water sprites or (c) mountain pixies?

8 What is bully beef also known as?

9 The invention of Catseyes was inspired by the dark roads of which county?

10 The Christmas Tree in Trafalgar Square is an annual present from which city?

11 Circumlocution means (a) an indirect way of expressing something, (b) a roundabout on a road or (c) an approximate amount?

12 Which game-bird may legally be shot between 1 October and 1 February?

13 What is a coracle?

14 Which real-life heroine lived in Longstone lighthouse?

15 What is the 'OAU'?

ANSWERS

1. February. 2. 1993. 3. A deception or concealed danger. 4. The haggis. 5. (b) the. 6. Waldorf salad. 7. (b) water sprites. 8. Corned beef. 9. Yorkshire. 10. Oslo. 11. (a) an indirect way of expressing something. 12. Pheasant. 13. A one-person fishing boat. 14. Grace Darling. 15. Organization of African Unity.

SESSION 36 | QUIZ 1

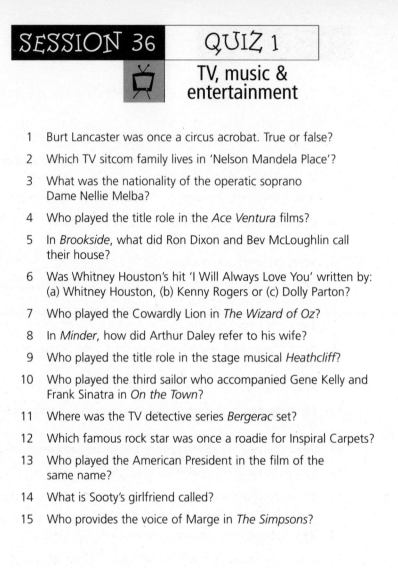

TV, music & entertainment

1 Burt Lancaster was once a circus acrobat. True or false?

2 Which TV sitcom family lives in 'Nelson Mandela Place'?

3 What was the nationality of the operatic soprano Dame Nellie Melba?

4 Who played the title role in the *Ace Ventura* films?

5 In *Brookside*, what did Ron Dixon and Bev McLoughlin call their house?

6 Was Whitney Houston's hit 'I Will Always Love You' written by: (a) Whitney Houston, (b) Kenny Rogers or (c) Dolly Parton?

7 Who played the Cowardly Lion in *The Wizard of Oz*?

8 In *Minder*, how did Arthur Daley refer to his wife?

9 Who played the title role in the stage musical *Heathcliff*?

10 Who played the third sailor who accompanied Gene Kelly and Frank Sinatra in *On the Town*?

11 Where was the TV detective series *Bergerac* set?

12 Which famous rock star was once a roadie for Inspiral Carpets?

13 Who played the American President in the film of the same name?

14 What is Sooty's girlfriend called?

15 Who provides the voice of Marge in *The Simpsons*?

ANSWERS

1. True. 2. 'The Trotters' of *Only Fools and Horses*. 3. Australian. 4. Jim Carrey. 5. 'Casa Bevron'. 6. (c) Dolly Parton. 7. Bert Lahr. 8. 'Er indoors'. 9. Cliff Richard. 10. Jules Munshin. 11. Jersey. 12. Noel Gallagher. 13. Michael Douglas. 14. 'Soo'. 15. Julie Kavner.

SESSION 36   QUIZ 2

History

1 What did St Columba begin in AD 503?

2 What is the name of the family that printed the official reports of debates in the House of Commons from 1774 onwards?

3 Who tried to abolish religious ceremony in the Elizabethan age?

4 Which Christian apologist of the 20th century wrote *The Screwtape Letters*?

5 What occurred in England in 1381?

6 What was the name of the newly promoted Field Marshal who surrendered at Stalingrad?

7 The Royal Navy launched its first what in 1901?

8 By what name is the spy Margarete Gertrude Zelle better known?

9 Who was the first new British monarch of this century?

10 Menno Simmons was one of the leaders of which religious group?

11 Which battle in 1746 marked the end of the Jacobite rebellions?

12 Who was the first president of the fifth French republic?

13 Of whom was it said, 'No man has ever done more to further the use of English as an international language'?

14 Who became president upon the death of Kennedy?

15 What did Winston Churchill talk about at Fulton, Missouri?

ANSWERS

SESSION 36   QUIZ 3

Sports

1   How many hurdles are there in the 110 metre hurdles for men?

2   Whose autobiography is unusually titled *The Working Man's Ballet*?

3   What country did middle-distance runner John Walker compete for?

4   What are the first names of the tennis-playing Williams sisters?

5   Who was the goalkeeper when Sunderland won the FA Cup Final beating Leeds?

6   In addition to Manchester United, what other club did Bobby Charlton play for?

7   How many goals did Gary Lineker score in the 1982 World Cup? Was it: (a) five, (b) six or (c) eight?

8   In what year was the famous White Horse Wembley Final?

9   What was Dean Richards' nickname?

10 What sport do the London Towers play?

11 Wigan won the 1943/44 Rugby League Championships. True or false?

12 Manchester United fans once chanted, 'Oooh Aaah.' Who were they singing about?

13 Which footballing brothers were born in Ashington, Northumberland?

14 Thabiso Moqhali won marathon gold for which country in the 1998 Commonwealth Games?

15 With which club did Terry Butcher finish his playing career?

ANSWERS

1. 10. 2. Alan Hudson. 3. New Zealand. 4. Serena and Venus. 5. Jim Montgomery. 6. Preston. 7. (b) six. 8. 1923. 9. 'Deano'. 10. Basketball. 11. True. 12. Eric Cantona. 13. Bobby and Jack Charlton. 14. Lesotho. 15. Rangers.

SESSION 36 — QUIZ 4

General knowledge

1 Robin Williams played a woman in which film?

2 Who first said that the Earth moves around the Sun?

3 Who first elucidated the double helix model of DNA?

4 Who were originally known as 'Limeys'?

5 Which countries own SAS airlines?

6 What sort of animal is 'Sonic'?

7 What everyday item do sand, limestone and sodium carbonate make?

8 Jack Sprat refused to eat what type of food?

9 The National Trust is a charity. True or false?

10 How did John Madejski make his fortune?

11 What is the commonest pub name in the UK?

12 What lies at the centre of Israel's flag?

13 Which country has the lowest birth rate in the world?

14 Where is the Library of Congress?

15 Is the commonest word in the English language: (a) a, (b) an or (c) the?

ANSWERS

1. *Mrs Doubtfire*. 2. Copernicus. 3. Watson and Crick. 4. British sailors who took lime juice to combat scurvy. 5. Norway, Sweden and Denmark. 6. A hedgehog. 7. Glass. 8. Fat. 9. True. 10. He published *Auto Trader* magazine. 11. 'The Red Lion'. 12. The Star of David. 13. Italy. 14. Washington DC. 15. (c) the.

SESSION 36 — QUIZ 5

Technology & science

1 What is the name of the copper and zinc alloy used in imitation of gold?

2 Which was the earliest known unit of length?

3 When did the physicist Anders Celsius introduce the Celsius scale of temperature?

4 Where in the human body would you find a Graafian follicle?

5 What is gutta-percha?

6 What is the name of Jupiter's brightest Galilean satellite?

7 How is the semi-precious stone amber formed?

8 What is the name of a curve or geometrical figure, each part of which has the same statistical character as the whole?

9 Who was the Austrian physician who pioneered the study of the unconscious mind?

10 In computing, how many 'bits' are in a 'byte'?

11 What are the chemicals that make Bakelite?

12 What is the name of the drug obtained from the nux vomica plant?

13 In 1990 a Surveillance Unit was set up in Edinburgh to monitor which disease?

14 In computing, what does the acronym BASIC represent?

15 What is the process of damascening?

ANSWERS

1. Ormolu. 2. Cubit (length of human forearm). 3. 1742. 4. In the ovary. 5. Juice of various tropical trees which can be hardened and used in electrical appliances. 6. Ganymede. 7. The fossilized resin exuded by extinct coniferous trees. 8. Fractal. 9. Sigmund Freud. 10. Eight. 11. Formaldehyde (methanal) and phenol. 12. Strychnine. 13. CJD. Creutzfeldt-Jakob disease. 14. Beginner's all-purpose symbolic instruction code. 15. Inlaying a metal object with gold or silver.

SESSION 36 — QUIZ 6

Geography

1 In which forest would you find the small town of Lyndhurst?

2 What is the name for a line on a map connecting places with the same barometric pressure?

3 Which city in Israel has the largest population: (a) Tel Aviv, (b) Jerusalem or (c) Haifa?

4 Which river is crossed by the Clifton Suspension Bridge?

5 In which country are the national parks Gran Paradiso and Abruzzo, both former royal hunting preserves?

6 Which Norwegian city is known as the 'Wooden City' and the 'Portal of the Fjords'?

7 In which American state is Death Valley?

8 What percentage of Egypt's population lives in the Nile valley and delta: (a) 86, (b) 92 or (c) 96 per cent?

9 Which is the only Australian city which is not on the coast?

10 Which country is the biggest exporter of rice: (a) China, (b) Thailand or (c) India?

11 The Dnieper River flows through the Ukraine into which sea?

12 Which South American country's name means 'land of silver', although it is not a major producer today?

13 In 1971 six of the seven Trucial States, including Abu Dhabi and Dubai, opted to form which country?

14 Where does the unitary authority of Caerphilly have its administrative headquarters?

15 Which landlocked south African country gains most of its export earnings from diamonds?

ANSWERS

1. The New Forest. 2. Isobar. 3. (a) Tel Aviv. 4. River Avon. 5. Italy. 6. Bergen. 7. California. 8. (c) 96 per cent. 9. Canberra. 10. (b) Thailand. 11. Black Sea. 12. Argentina. 13. United Arab Emirates. 14. Hengoed. 15. Botswana.

SESSION 36   QUIZ 7

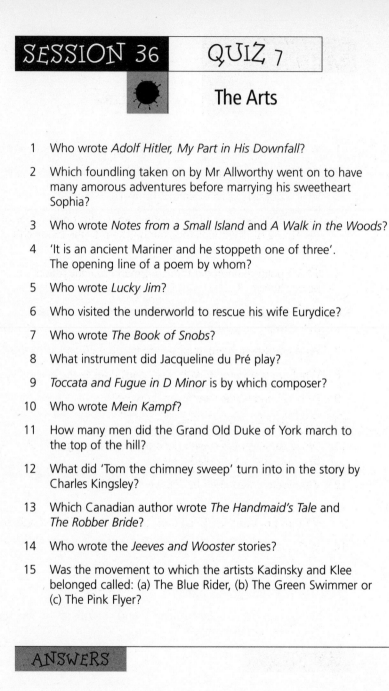

The Arts

1   Who wrote *Adolf Hitler, My Part in His Downfall*?

2   Which foundling taken on by Mr Allworthy went on to have many amorous adventures before marrying his sweetheart Sophia?

3   Who wrote *Notes from a Small Island* and *A Walk in the Woods*?

4   'It is an ancient Mariner and he stoppeth one of three'. The opening line of a poem by whom?

5   Who wrote *Lucky Jim*?

6   Who visited the underworld to rescue his wife Eurydice?

7   Who wrote *The Book of Snobs*?

8   What instrument did Jacqueline du Pré play?

9   *Toccata and Fugue in D Minor* is by which composer?

10   Who wrote *Mein Kampf*?

11   How many men did the Grand Old Duke of York march to the top of the hill?

12   What did 'Tom the chimney sweep' turn into in the story by Charles Kingsley?

13   Which Canadian author wrote *The Handmaid's Tale* and *The Robber Bride*?

14   Who wrote the *Jeeves and Wooster* stories?

15   Was the movement to which the artists Kadinsky and Klee belonged called: (a) The Blue Rider, (b) The Green Swimmer or (c) The Pink Flyer?

ANSWERS

1. Spike Milligan. 2. *Tom Jones* (by Henry Fielding). 3. Bill Bryson. 4. Samuel Taylor Coleridge. 5. Kingsley Amis. 6. Orpheus. 7. W. M. Thackeray. 8. Cello. 9. J. S. Bach. 10. Adolf Hitler. 11. 10,000. 12. A water baby. 13. Margaret Atwood. 14. P. G. Wodehouse. 15. (a) The Blue Rider.

SESSION 36 · QUIZ 8

Pot Luck

1 What is the name of the trade union for actors?

2 Which two languages are combined in 'franglais'?

3 Which Cornish town is famous for its Furry Dance?

4 At the state opening of Parliament who bangs on the door of the House of Commons to summon them to the monarch's presence?

5 Which political party did the statesman Clement Attlee belong to?

6 By what name did the Local Defence Volunteers come to be known?

7 Who was Israeli prime minister from 1984–86 and 1995–96?

8 What word beginning with ph- means a fake?

9 Fructose and lactose are forms of what?

10 What did 'Aiken Drum' play upon?

11 What game is played with decorated pieces, originally of bamboo and ivory, called 'tiles'?

12 Who were entertained by ENSA?

13 The original Monopoly board featured the streets of:
(a) Toronto, Canada, (b) London or (c) Atlantic City, New Jersey?

14. Who was 'Ol' Blue Eyes'?

15 What is provided by Reuters?

ANSWERS

1. Equity. 2. French and English. 3. Helston. 4. 'Black Rod'. 5. Labour. 6. The Home Guard. 7. *Shimon Peres.* 8. Phoney. 9. Sugar, fruit sugar and milk sugar. 10. A ladle. 11. *Mahjong.* 12. The troops in World War II. 13. (c) Atlantic City, New Jersey. 14. Frank Sinatra. 15. News and information.

SESSION 37

QUIZ 1

TV, music & entertainment

1   What is the connection between Cary Grant and the film *A Fish Called Wanda*?

2   Who runs the beauty parlour in *Home and Away*?

3   What does B. B. King call his guitar?

4   Daniel Day Lewis is the son of poet C. Day Lewis. True or false?

5   In *The Prisoner*, what was Patrick McGoohan's number?

6   From where did singer Engelbert Humperdinck take his name?

7   What disability does Academy Award-winning actress Marlee Matlin have?

8   What is the name of the character played by Patricia Routledge in the sitcom *Keeping Up Appearances*?

9   Who was the lead singer with the group Them from 1963 to 1966?

10 Who played Curly in the film *City Slickers*?

11 Which former member of the *Coronation Street* cast was once married to US chat-show host Leeza Gibbons?

12 Which band had a hit with 'Firestarter'?

13 Which Hitchcock film is largely set in 'Bates Motel'?

14 Who is the question master in *Have I Got News For You?*?

15 Which Russian composer wrote the ballets *Swan Lake* and *The Sleeping Beauty*?

ANSWERS

1. The character played by John Cleese in *A Fish Called Wanda* is called Archie Leach, which is Cary Grant's real name. 2. Marilyn Fisher. 3. Lucille. 4. True. 5. Six. 6. From the German composer who wrote the opera *Hansel and Gretel*. 7. She is deaf. 8. Hyacinth Bucket. 9. Van Morrison. 10. Jack Palance. 11. Christopher Quentin, who played Brian Tilsley. 12. The Prodigy. 13. *Psycho*. 14. Angus Deayton. 15. Pyotr Ilych Tchaikovsky.

SESSION 37   QUIZ 2

History

1 By what name was T. E. Lawrence also known as?

2 How did Mary Queen of Scots die?

3 Phil Collins starred in a film about which incident that took place in 1963?

4 Did women in Switzerland gain the vote in: (a) 1943, (b) 1957 or (c) 1971?

5 Who said, 'Let them eat cake'?

6 Which Benedictine Monastery was blown to bits on 15 March 1944?

7 Who formed the first Labour government in 1924?

8 How long did Prohibition last in America?

9 What did René Laënnec invent in 1816?

10 What did Kelvin reach in 1848?

11 Who wrote *The Republic*?

12 Who was murdered by a Hindu gunman in 1948?

13 Why did James VI succeed Elizabeth I?

14 The Ming dynasty reigned in which country?

15 What law did economist Thomas Gresham formulate?

ANSWERS

1. Lawrence of Arabia. 2. She was executed. 3. The Great Train Robbery. 4. (c) 1971. 5. Marie Antoinette. 6. Monte Cassino. 7. Ramsay MacDonald. 8. 13 years, from 1920–33. 9. The stethoscope. 10. Absolute zero. 11. Plato. 12. Gandhi. 13. She died leaving no children. 14. China. 15. 'Bad money drives out good money'.

SESSION 37   QUIZ 3

Sports

1   Richard Meade competed at which sport?

2   An Olympic boxing match has how many rounds?

3   Who was the captain of the 1970 World Cup Winners?

4   Who used to 'bite your legs'?

5   Where do Ireland play their rugby internationals?

6   What was cricketer Derek Randall's nickname?

7   Which year did Mats Wilander win the French Open thus becoming the youngest player to do so?

8   Which horse 'danced' its way to many victories?

9   Fred Perry won titles in 1934, 1935 and 1936 at which sport?

10 What nationality is golfer Bernard Gallacher?

11 Who presents snooker for the BBC?

12 The pole vault is not an event of the decathlon. True or false?

13 Whose hand wobbled when it held the Olympic flame in Atlanta?

14 Where were the 1998 Winter Olympics held?

15 At what football ground was the 1987 Rugby League Premiership Final held for the first time?

ANSWERS

SESSION 37   QUIZ 4

General knowledge

1   Which country has the most universities?

2   Mario Puzo wrote which book that spawned three films?

3   The 'cha cha cha' is a Latin American version of which dance?

4   Where was the 'wondrous' lighthouse?

5   What is the name of the last book in the Old Testament?

6   In mythology the Fates are all female. True or false?

7   Who founded the Quakers?

8   Which actor disappeared from the play *Cell Mates*?

9   Joshua destroyed the walls of which city?

10   Is persiflage: (a) a type of food, (b) frivolous conversation or (c) a component of a body cell?

11   What is a first footer?

12   The word 'latrine' comes from the Latin 'to wash'. True or false?

13   Who shoes horses?

14   Which character said, 'I am a Bear of Very Little Brain, and long words Bother me'?

15   With which country do you associate sputniks?

ANSWERS

1. India with over 7,000. 2. *The Godfather*. 3. The Mambo. 4. Alexandria, Egypt. It was one of the seven wonders of the ancient world. 5. Malachi. 6. True. 7. George Fox. 8. Stephen Fry. 9. Jericho. 10. (b) frivolous conversation. 11. The first person to enter the house in the new year. 12. True. 13. A farrier. 14. Winnie the Pooh. 15. Russia. They were satellites.

SESSION 37   QUIZ 5

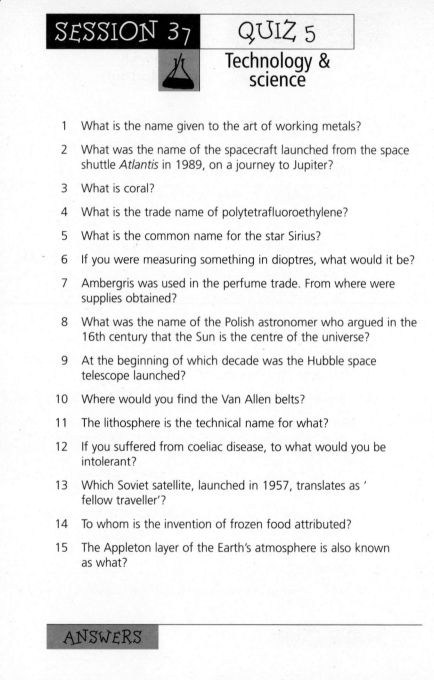

Technology & science

1   What is the name given to the art of working metals?

2   What was the name of the spacecraft launched from the space shuttle *Atlantis* in 1989, on a journey to Jupiter?

3   What is coral?

4   What is the trade name of polytetrafluoroethylene?

5   What is the common name for the star Sirius?

6   If you were measuring something in dioptres, what would it be?

7   Ambergris was used in the perfume trade. From where were supplies obtained?

8   What was the name of the Polish astronomer who argued in the 16th century that the Sun is the centre of the universe?

9   At the beginning of which decade was the Hubble space telescope launched?

10   Where would you find the Van Allen belts?

11   The lithosphere is the technical name for what?

12   If you suffered from coeliac disease, to what would you be intolerant?

13   Which Soviet satellite, launched in 1957, translates as 'fellow traveller'?

14   To whom is the invention of frozen food attributed?

15   The Appleton layer of the Earth's atmosphere is also known as what?

ANSWERS

1. Metallurgy. 2. Galileo. 3. The hard calcium carbonate skeleton of sea living polyps. 4. Teflon. 5. The Dog Star. 6. Focal length of a lens. 7. The intestines of the sperm whale. 8. Nicolas Copernicus (1473-1543). 9. In the 1990s (in 1990). 10. Zones of electrically charged particles circling the Earth. 11. Earth's crust and upper mantle. 12. Gluten. 13. 'Sputnik'. 14. Clarence Birdseye. 15. The F-layer.

SESSION 37   QUIZ 6

Geography

1   On which sea is the Italian port of Brindisi?

2   Which mountains lie to the south of the plateau of Tibet?

3   What is the capital of Sierra Leone?

4   In which natural harbour would you find Brownsea island?

5   Which is the deepest lake in the world: (a) Lake Baikal,
    (b) Wast Water or (c) Lake Superior?

6   The main gases coming from erupting volcanoes are hydrogen
    sulphide and ammonia. True or false?

7   'The Backs' is open ground next to which English river?

8   In which city are the headquarters of the International
    Atomic Agency?

9   The 'puszta' is a grassland and saline steppe landscape unique
    in Europe. In which country?

10 The Serengeti National Park is the largest in Africa. Which
    country is it in?

11 Lake Tahoe in America is partly in California and partly in which
    other state?

12 The Australian outback town of Coober Pedy developed because
    of gold mining. True or false?

13 Which is the longest river in Europe: (a) the Danube, (b) the
    Rhine or (c) the Volga?

14 Where in South America is there a territory which is a
    department of France?

15 Which of these cities is furthest south: (a) Toronto, (b) Montreal
    or (c) Seattle?

ANSWERS

1. Adriatic Sea. 2. Himalayas. 3. Freetown. 4. Poole harbour. 5. (a) Lake Baikal. 6. False. The main gases are water vapour and carbon dioxide. 7. River Cam. 8. Vienna. 9. Hungary. 10. Tanzania. 11. Nevada. 12. False. It is in the opal fields. 13. (c) the Volga. 14. French Guiana. 15. (a) Toronto.

SESSION 37 QUIZ 7

The Arts

1 Was Henry Moore: (a) an architect, (b) a potter or (c) a sculptor?

2 What name is given to artists' paint-brushes made from the fur of the Siberian mink?

3 What four letter word describes an image of a saint in art?

4 Which Dutch town was the birthplace of Rembrandt? Was it: (a) Delft, (b) Leiden or (c) Amsterdam?

5 When are dirges played?

6 What fraction of a whole note is a quaver?

7 Who wrote the operas *Don Giovanni* and *Cosi Fan Tutte*?

8 In which century did the English composer Henry Purcell live?

9 Who wrote the novels of *The Alexandria Quartet*?

10 In drama is a droll: (a) a farce, (b) a thriller or (c) a tragedy?

11 Who is the supposed author of *The Iliad* and *The Odyssey*?

12 Who wrote *Steppenwolf* and *The Glass Bead Game*?

13 Who wrote *The Time Machine* and *The Invisible Man*?

14 What colour was Andrew Lang's first Fairy Book?

15 Which was the first of Beatrix Potter's stories to be published?

ANSWERS

1. (c) sculptor. 2. Sable. 3. Icon. 4. (b) Leiden. 5. At funerals. 6. One eighth. 7. Wolfgang Amadeus Mozart. 8. 17th. 9. Lawrence Durrell. 10. (a) a farce. 11. Homer. 12. Hermann Hesse. 13. H. G. Wells. 14. Blue. 15. *The Tale of Peter Rabbit*

SESSION 37 — QUIZ 8

Pot Luck

1 What type of cake is named after a young woman of Bath?

2 Scotland Yard was originally based in Edinburgh. True or false?

3 Who or what is the 'Old Lady of Threadneedle Street'?

4 What was the speciality of Tiller Girls?

5 What are whistle-blowers?

6 With what is the Wiltshire town of Wilton associated?

7 Where would you find the 'Five Sisters' window?

8 What are alms?

9 What modern game developed from 'battledore and shuttlecock'?

10 Who was Princess Diana's companion who was killed with her in the car crash on 31 August 1997?

11 What is the main ingredient of *pâté de foie gras*?

12 Who chooses the winning numbers of premium bonds?

13 The Roman road Ermine Street ran from London to which northern city?

14 Which royal title is abbreviated to 'FD' or 'FID DEF' on British coins?

15 What berries are used to flavour gin?

ANSWERS

1. Sally Lunn. 2. False, it has always been in London. 3. The Bank of England. 4. High-kicking in a line, they were dancers. 5. People who risk their jobs by complaining about malpractices at work. 6. Carpets. 7. York Minster. 8. Charity for the poor. 9. Badminton. 10. Dodi Fayed. 11. Goose liver. 12. ERNIE, a computer. 13. York. 14. Defender of the Faith. 15. Juniper.

SESSION 38   QUIZ 1

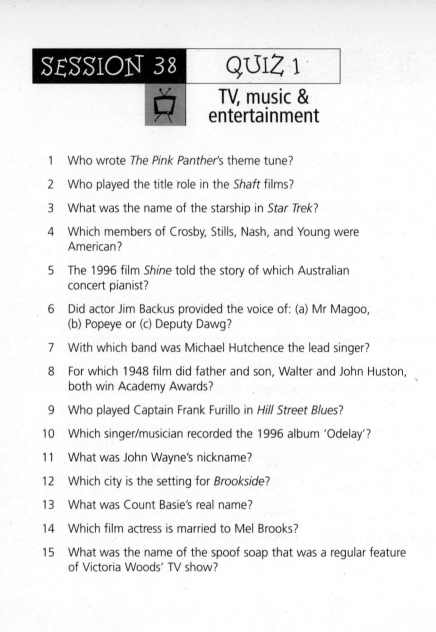

TV, music & entertainment

1. Who wrote *The Pink Panther*'s theme tune?

2. Who played the title role in the *Shaft* films?

3. What was the name of the starship in *Star Trek*?

4. Which members of Crosby, Stills, Nash, and Young were American?

5. The 1996 film *Shine* told the story of which Australian concert pianist?

6. Did actor Jim Backus provided the voice of: (a) Mr Magoo, (b) Popeye or (c) Deputy Dawg?

7. With which band was Michael Hutchence the lead singer?

8. For which 1948 film did father and son, Walter and John Huston, both win Academy Awards?

9. Who played Captain Frank Furillo in *Hill Street Blues*?

10. Which singer/musician recorded the 1996 album 'Odelay'?

11. What was John Wayne's nickname?

12. Which city is the setting for *Brookside*?

13. What was Count Basie's real name?

14. Which film actress is married to Mel Brooks?

15. What was the name of the spoof soap that was a regular feature of Victoria Woods' TV show?

ANSWERS

1. Henry Mancini. 2. Richard Roundtree. 3. *USS Enterprise*. 4. David Crosby and Stephen Stills. 5. David Helfgott. 6. 'Mr Magoo'. 7. INXS. 8. *The Treasure of the Sierra Madre*. 9. Daniel J. Travanti. 10. Beck. 11. Duke. 12. Liverpool. 13. William Basie. 14. Anne Bancroft. 15. *Acorn Antiques*.

SESSION 38   QUIZ 2

History

1   Which musical prodigy began his grand tour in 1703?

2   Who was elected MP for Old Sarum in 1735?

3   What item of clothing was it forbidden to wear in England in 1746?

4   What was the Cato Street conspiracy of 1820?

5   Which ship was built for the first time in 1906?

6   How many children did Henry VIII have by Anne of Cleves?

7   Where did the Great Fire of London begin?

8   What did American Paul Revere do?

9   Who married who on 10 February 1840?

10   What was the British Commonwealth called prior to 1931?

11   Where was the 'Bridge Too Far'?

12   Tintern and Rievaulx were founded in 1131. What are they?

13   From 605-610 AD the Grand Canal was built in China connecting which two rivers?

14   Did Edward the Confessor die in: (a) 1043, (b) 1066 or (c) 1095?

15   Sören Kierkegaard was a famous Dutch philosopher of the 19th century. True or false?

ANSWERS

1. Mozart. 2. William Pitt. 3. Tartans, after the Jacobite rebellions. 4. It was an attempt to murder the Cabinet. 5. *Dreadnought* (the first modern battleship). 6. None. 7. Pudding Lane. 8. He rode all night to Lexington to warn of the arrival of the British. 9. Victoria and Albert. 10. The British Empire. 11. Arnhem, Holland in World War Two. 12. Abbeys. 13. The Yangtze and the Yellow. 14. (b) 1066. 15. False. He was Danish.

SESSION 38

QUIZ 3

Sports

1   What was the name of Liverpool's 'Supersub'?

2   Where is England's largest racecourse?

3   Which club did Andy Gregory join for £130,000 in 1987?

4   Which was the only Soviet bloc country to attend the 1984 Olympic Games?

5   What gave Olympic champion Ray Ewry such phenomenal strength?

6   Who scored for Wimbledon in their 1988 FA Cup win over Liverpool?

7   Martin Peters played for West Ham, Tottenham and which other club?

8   Only one country has attended every Olympic Games since their beginning. Which is it?

9   Which Greek philosopher played for Brazil?

10   Rachel Heyhoe-Flint played which sports competitively?

11   If you are about to begin at the south stake, which sport are you playing?

12   Who scored two goals at Wembley against Fulham in 1975?

13   How many times has Great Britain topped the medal rankings in the Olympic Games?

14   What was the prize money paid to the winner of the men's singles in Wimbledon's first year as an open tournament?

15   What sport do the Edmonton Oilers play?

ANSWERS

1. David Fairclough. 2. Newmarket. 3. Wigan. 4. Romania. 5. He did leg exercises when he had polio as a child. 6. Lawrie Sanchez. 7. Norwich. 8. Great Britain. 9. Socrates. 10. Hockey and cricket. 11. Croquet. 12. Alan Taylor of West Ham. 13. Once in 1908. 14. £2,000. 15. Ice hockey.

SESSION 38   QUIZ 4

General knowledge

1 What seabird was seen for the last time in 1844?

2 On which bird is a parson's nose?

3 Traditionally, on which day are pancakes eaten?

4 What date is Battle of the Boyne day in Northern Ireland?

5 What has a gravitational pull so strong that it attracts light?

6 What could cars switch to for the first time in 1979?

7 Which are the primary colours?

8 What artificial object is 6,400 km long?

9 How many presidents are carved at Mount Rushmore?

10 Which philosophy places pleasure as the highest good?

11 Who was the Roman equivalent of Aphrodite, the Greek goddess of love and marriage?

12 Where is the car manufacturer FIAT based?

13 Where is the Epcot Centre?

14 What is the English word for American 'fall'?

15 What created Lake Mead in America?

ANSWERS

1. The Great Auk. 2. Chicken. 3. Shrove Tuesday. 4. 12 July. 5. A black hole. 6. Catalytic convertors. 7. Red, yellow and blue. 8. The Great Wall of China. 9. Four. 10. Hedonism. 11. Venus. 12. Turin, Italy. 13. Disney World, Florida. 14. Autumn. 15. The Boulder Dam.

SESSION 38

QUIZ 5

Technology & science

1 What metal is the main constituent of brass?

2 In which field of science did Michael Faraday carry out experiments?

3 The term SSSI was introduced in 1991 by English Nature. What do the initials represent?

4 What does the chemical formula D_2O represent?

5 In which year was Bill Gates born?

6 Calcium fluoride is the chemical constituent of which semi-precious stone?

7 What is the smallest bone in the human body?

8 What is the 17th-century astronomer Johann Kepler noted for?

9 What is the technical name for the control centre of a cell?

10 What is the average pulse rate for an adult male?

11 In which month is it possible to have no full Moon?

12 What are measured in megatons?

13 What do the initials SPF on suntan lotion represent?

14 What is the name of Saturn's largest satellite?

15 In which year was teletext introduced into Britain?

ANSWERS

1. Copper. 2. Electricity and electromagnetism. 3. Site of Special Scientific Interest. 4. Heavy water. 5. 1955. 6. Fluorspar. 7. Stirrup bone in the ear. 8. Kepler's laws of motion: he described how planets orbit the Sun. 9. The nucleus. 10. 70–72 beats per minute. 11. February (too short). 12. The explosive power of a nuclear weapon. 13. Sun Protection Factor. 14. Titan. 15. 1973.

SESSION 38   QUIZ 6

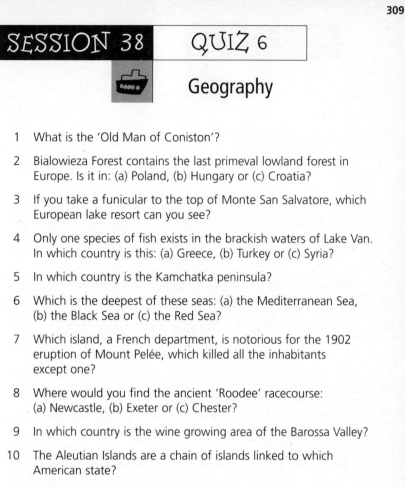

Geography

1 What is the 'Old Man of Coniston'?

2 Bialowieza Forest contains the last primeval lowland forest in Europe. Is it in: (a) Poland, (b) Hungary or (c) Croatia?

3 If you take a funicular to the top of Monte San Salvatore, which European lake resort can you see?

4 Only one species of fish exists in the brackish waters of Lake Van. In which country is this: (a) Greece, (b) Turkey or (c) Syria?

5 In which country is the Kamchatka peninsula?

6 Which is the deepest of these seas: (a) the Mediterranean Sea, (b) the Black Sea or (c) the Red Sea?

7 Which island, a French department, is notorious for the 1902 eruption of Mount Pelée, which killed all the inhabitants except one?

8 Where would you find the ancient 'Roodee' racecourse: (a) Newcastle, (b) Exeter or (c) Chester?

9 In which country is the wine growing area of the Barossa Valley?

10 The Aleutian Islands are a chain of islands linked to which American state?

11 Montreux lies at the western end of which lake?

12 In which country is Benin City?

13 The island of Gozo is south of Malta. True or false?

14 Which estuary separates the coastlines of Argentina and Uruguay?

15 Which is the most northerly of these three islands: (a) Corsica, (b) Sardinia or (c) Sicily?

ANSWERS

1. A peak in the Lake District. 2. (a) Poland. 3. Lugano. 4. (b) Turkey. 5. Russia. 6. (a) The Mediterranean. 7. Martinique (the survivor was saved by the thick walls of his jail cell). 8. (c) Chester. 9. Australia. 10. Alaska. 11. Lake Geneva. 12. Nigeria. 13. False. It is north of Malta. 14. Rio de la Plata (River Plate). 15. (a) Corsica.

SESSION 38 | QUIZ 7

The Arts

1 What type of novels were written by Ngaio Marsh?

2 Which children's book about a family during the English Civil War was written by Captain Frederick Marryat?

3 In a novel what is a purple passage?

4 "Just the place for a Snark!' the bellman cried'. The first line of a poem by whom?

5 Who wrote the ballet *Bolero*?

6 During which English king's reign is *Ivanhoe* set?

7 Where would you find *The Song of Solomon*?

8 In what century was Dr Johnson's Dictionary published?

9 Who wrote *The Metamorphosis* and *The Trial*?

10 Kimball O'Hara is the central character of which novel by Kipling?

11 What is the name of Kingsley Amis's son who is also a writer?

12 A pastoral novel is set: (a) abroad, (b) in a monastery or (c) in the countryside?

13 Virginia Woolf and Lytton Strachey were members of which literary clique?

14 What is a 'Kitchen Sink Drama'?

15 Of which religion is the Koran (Qur'an) the sacred book?

ANSWERS

1. Detective fiction. 2. *Children of the New Forest*. 3. An over-elaborate piece of writing. 4. Lewis Carroll. 5. Maurice Ravel. 6. Richard I. 7. In the Bible, the Old Testament. 8. 18th, in 1755. 9. Franz Kafka. 10. *Kimball*. 11. Martin Amis. 12. (c) in the countryside. 13. The Bloomsbury Group. 14. A story based on domestic realities, usually of working class life. 15. Muslim or Islam.

SESSION 38   QUIZ 8

Pot Luck

1 In which country did chop suey originate?

2 When is St Patrick's Day?

3 Which stamp, first issued in 1911, was advertised with the slogan 'This stamp will take some licking'?

4 What four letter word means both fair-skinned and a fence or fenced area?

5 In 1989 who announced, 'We are a grandmother'?

6 By what name was Erich Weiss, 'The Handcuff King', better known?

7 What sweet was first described as 'treacle thickened by boiling and made into hard cakes'?

8 What is added to alcohol and sugar to make a syllabub?

9 The phrase 'the thin red line' was first used during which war?

10 What name is given to found gold and silver objects which have been hidden by someone who intended to return for them and who cannot now be traced?

11 Which family of languages does English belong to?

12 What shape are the cells of a honeycomb?

13 Which title ranks higher: a viscount or an earl?

14 If 'power tends to corrupt', what, according to 1st Baron Acton, does 'absolute power' do?

15 The 'rotten borough' of Old Sarum had two MPs and how many voters: (a) 7 (b) 70 or (c) 700?

ANSWERS

1. The USA. 2. 17 March. 3. National Health Insurance stamp. 4. Pale. 5. Margaret Thatcher. 6. Harry Houdini. 7. Toffee. 8. Cream. 9. Crimean. 10. Treasure trove. 11. Indo-European. 12. Hexagonal. 13. An earl. 14. It 'corrupts absolutely'. 15. (a) 7.

SESSION 39 | QUIZ 1

TV, music & entertainment

1 What was the name of Roy Rogers' horse?

2 What was the name of the policeman in *Noddy*?

3 In Marvin Gaye's song, 'Abraham, Martin, and John', who are Abraham, Martin, and John?

4 Who provided the voice of 'Jessica Rabbit' in the film *Who Framed Roger Rabbit?*?

5 In *Brookside*, how did Damon Grant die?

6 The 1979 film *The Rose* was loosely based on the life of which rock singer?

7 In which film did Arnold Schwarzenegger famously say, 'I'll be back'?

8 Who played Hudson in *Upstairs Downstairs*?

9 What was the name of Renée and Renato's number one hit?

10 In their 1996 feature film, which country did Beavis and Butthead 'do'?

11 In *The Simpsons*, what is Homer's boss's name?

12 Who played Bodie and Doyle in *The Professionals*?

13 Who was the first actor to refuse an Oscar?

14 What is the name of the talking car in the TV show *Knight Rider*?

15 Who duetted with Meat Loaf on 'Dead Ringer for Love'?

ANSWERS

1. Trigger. 2. Mr Plod. 3. Abraham Lincoln, Martin Luther King and John F. Kennedy. 4. Kathleen Turner. 5. He was stabbed on a trip to York. 6. Janis Joplin. 7. *Terminator*. 8. Gordon Jackson. 9. 'Save your Love'. 10. America. 11. Mr Burns. 12. Lewis Collins and Martin Shaw. 13. George C. Scott. 14. Kit. 15. Cher.

SESSION 39 · QUIZ 2

History

1 Which ancient beauty triggered the Trojan Wars?

2 Which philosopher killed himself by drinking hemlock?

3 About whom was the World War II book *Reach for the Sky* written?

4 Where did the Valentine's Day massacre take place in 1929?

5 What explosive invention appeared in China about AD 870?

6 Who was condemned to death in AD 30?

7 Who succeeded John Masefield as Poet Laureate?

8 Who were transported to Australia instead of being executed in 1834?

9 Which piece of architecture was built in Bath from 1767–74?

10 Who left Britain for the last time in AD 409?

11 Towards the end of the 7th century some famous Gospels were produced by monks in which northern island?

12 Who was known as the Scourge of God?

13 Which union leader led his members into a ten-month long national strike in 1984?

14 For several years protest marches were made from the atomic weapons establishment in a Berkshire village to London. What was the name of the Berkshire village?

15 What was the former name of Ethiopia?

ANSWERS

1. Helen of Troy. 2. Socrates. 3. Douglas Bader. 4. Chicago. 5. Gunpowder. 6. Jesus of Nazareth. 7. C. Day Lewis. 8. The Tolpuddle Martyrs. 9. The Royal Crescent. 10. Roman Legions. 11. Lindisfarne. 12. Attila, king of the Huns. 13. Arthur Scargill. 14. Aldermaston. 15. Abyssinia.

SESSION 39　QUIZ 3

Sports

1　What position did Welsh legend Barry John play?

2　Who won all Olympic discus gold medals from 1956 to 1968?

3　Which county team did Clive Lloyd play for?

4　When did Peter Shilton play his last game for England?

5　Did Jimmy Greaves play for: (a) AC Milan, (b) Juventus (b) or (c) Roma?

6　At which sport were Broughton Rangers a top-class team at the turn of the century?

7　Who plays at the Dell?

8　How many players are there in a handball team?

9　What are Flying Dutchman, Soling and Star?

10　What nationality is tennis player Slobodan Zivojinovic?

11　At what sport did Precious McKenzie compete?

12　Which sporting brothers retired on 28 April 1973?

13　What poisoned the taste of South Africa's rugby World Cup victory?

14　Which country won Rugby League's first World Cup Final Series?

15　What did the heptathlon replace in 1984?

ANSWERS

1. Outside half. 2. Al Oerter of USA. 3. Lancashire. 4. Against Italy in 1990. 5. (a) AC Milan. 6. Rugby league. 7. Southampton. 8. Seven. 9. Classes of Olympic yachting. 10. Yugoslav. 11. Weightlifting. 12. Bobby and Jack Charlton. 13. Allegations that their opponents, New Zealand had been deliberately poisoned. 14. Great Britain beat France 16–12. 15. The pentathlon.

SESSION 39 QUIZ 4

General knowledge

1 Where can you find the Sierra Nevada?

2 Matt draws cartoons for which paper?

3 What is guano?

4 What are the Christian names of P. G. Wodehouse?

5 Who was the drummer in 'The Beatles'?

6 In the US, what exactly is impeachment?

7 What is 'hajj'?

8 What does RADAR stand for?

9 What was The Great Eastern?

10 What is the stretch of water that separates Malaysia from Singapore called?

11 What is the Sanskrit word for union?

12 According to the ancient Greeks what were the four elements?

13 How many faces does a dodecahedron have?

14 What do the initials FGS stand for?

15 Clarice Cliff is known for which art period?

ANSWERS

1. Spain. 2. *The Daily Telegraph*. 3. The dried excrement of fish-eating birds. 4. Pelham Grenville. 5. Ringo Starr. 6. The charging of a public official with an offence committed while in office. 7. The once in a lifetime pilgrimage to Mecca. 8. Radio detecting and ranging. 9. The first combined steam and sail liner. 10. Johore Strait. 11. Yoga. 12. Earth, air, fire and water. 13. 12. 14. Fellow of the Geological Society. 15. Art Deco.

SESSION 39 QUIZ 5

Technology & science

1 Who proposed the scientific principle that states for a body immersed in water the apparent loss in weight is equal to the weight of the water displaced?

2 CERN was established in 1954. What is it?

3 What did Cassini discover in 1672?

4 What is the substance obtained from acacia trees that is used in medicine and confectionery?

5 In which year was *Skylab* launched?

6 Who received the Nobel Prize for Physiology or Medicine in 1904 for work on conditioned reflexes?

7 What is a scruple?

8 Which is the longest bone in the human body?

9 What is the name of the element with the symbol Al?

10 What is the name of the 20th century astronomer who promoted the public understanding of astronomy through his books and television series?

11 What is the chemical constituent of iron pyrites?

12 Ichthyology is the study of what?

13 What is the name of the bone at the base of the human spine?

14 Which invention is credited to Isaac Merritt Singer?

15 In a game of poker, what are the odds of getting four of a kind?

ANSWERS

SESSION 39   QUIZ 6

Geography

1   Which is the largest desert in the world?

2   Which of these Scandinavian countries has the largest population: (a) Denmark, (b) Norway or (c) Sweden?

3   The River Wear flows around a hill topped with a castle and a cathedral. In which city?

4   Which city has previously been called Byzantium and Constantinople?

5   In which city are the Spanish Steps: (a) Madrid, (b) Paris or (c) Rome?

6   The Bighorn Mountains are in Wyoming, but the Little Bighorn River flows north through which state?

7   The ice sheet around the North Pole is floating on the sea. True or false?

8   Which country produces half of the world's platinum: (a) South Africa, (b) Brazil or (c) Russia?

9   The town of Fremantle, at the mouth of the Swan River, has almost been absorbed into which Australian city?

10   Which is the largest of the Channel islands?

11   On which lake is the Swiss city of Lausanne?

12   Which is the northernmost county of Eire: (a) Donegal, (b) Mayo or (c) Sligo?

13   In which country is the city of Marrakech?

14   Which Asian country has a green flag, for the fertility of the land, with a central red disc as the Sun of Independence?

15   In which country do 70% of the people live near the Blue and White Niles?

ANSWERS

1. The Sahara. 2. (c) Sweden. 3. Durham. 4. Istanbul. 5. (c) Rome. 6. Montana. 7. True. 8. (b) Brazil. 9. Perth. 10. Jersey. 11. Lake Geneva. 12. (a) Donegal. 13. Morocco. 14. Bangladesh. 15. Sudan.

SESSION 39 QUIZ 7

The Arts

1. What is Thomas doing in Caravaggio's painting *Doubting Thomas*?

2. Who painted *Self-Portrait with Bandaged Ear*?

3. What is the name of the gamekeeper and lover of Lady Chatterley?

4. Which School was the subject of a play by Richard Sheridan?

5. The court 'masques' written by Ben Jonson were: (a) dances, (b) plays or (c) political speeches?

6. Who wrote the 'Aubrey and Maturin' seafaring novels?

7. What nationality was the poet and novelist Herman Melville?

8. Which book by Michael Ondaatje won the Booker Prize?

9. What was the name of Dr Johnson's cat?

10. Sergei Prokofiev wrote an opera called *The Love for*: (a) *Four Apples*, (b) *Three Oranges* or (c) *Two Lemons*?

11. What were collected by Peter and Iona Opie?

12. Who wrote *Stalky and Co.*?

13. Which weekly literary paper is known as the 'TLS'?

14. What nationality is the composer Sir Michael Tippett?

15. Which artist's name is sometimes given to the colour of hair, a reddish-auburn, that he favoured in his paintings?

ANSWERS

1. Putting his finger in one of Christ's wounds. 2. Van Gogh. 3. Mellors. 4. *The School for Scandal*. 5. Plays. 6. Patrick O'Brian. 7. American. 8. *The English Patient*. 9. Hodge. 10. (b) *The Love for Three Oranges*. 11. Nursery rhymes. 12. Rudyard Kipling. 13. *Times Literary Supplement*. 14. British. 15. Titian.

319

SESSION 39 — QUIZ 8

Pot Luck

1 What two words which sound the same mean 'the burrow of badgers' and 'a group of similar objects'?

2 A curlew may also be called: (a) a paw-paw, (b) a pee-wit or (c) a pooler?

3 Which island was awarded the George Cross in the 1940s?

4 What colour is the Australian swan?

5 Which star is known as the Lodestar?

6 What are the Pawnee and the Nez Percé?

7 What is special about the curtana, the sword carried by British monarchs at their coronation?

8 How is meat cooked if it is described as carbonado?

9 What does the prefix 'cardio-' mean?

10 In the 1920s why were young girls called flappers?

11 Was Jack Ketch: (a) a sauce manufacturer, (b) a painter or (c) a hangman?

12 From which Yorkshire town do Pomfret cakes originate?

13 What is the common name of the bird *Didus ineptus* which became extinct in the 1680s?

14 At what point during an opera is the overture played?

15 In Greek mythology, a siren was half-woman; was her other half: (a) fish, (b) goat or (c) bird?

ANSWERS

1. Sett / set. 2. (b) pee-wit, which is the noise it makes. 3. Malta. 4. Black. 5. The North Star or Pole Star. 6. Native American Indian tribes. 7. It does not have a point. 8. Grilled. 9. Concerning the heart. 10. Because of their flapping pigtails. 11. (c) a hangman. 12. Pontefract. 13. Dodo. 14. At the beginning. 15. (c) bird.

SESSION 40 QUIZ 1

TV, music & entertainment

1 What is the name of Scooby Doo's nephew?

2 Actress Barbara Bach is married to which former Beatle?

3 The film *Scandal* was about which political scandal?

4 Who played Mr Darcy in the 1995 TV production of *Pride and Prejudice*?

5 Which singer/songwriter had a hit with the theme song from *Robin Hood: Prince of Thieves*?

6 What was Mickey Mouse's original name?

7 In the TV sitcom *Rab C. Nesbitt*, what is the name of Rab's wife?

8 Who was the subject of Don McLean's hit *Vincent*?

9 In which film did Anthony Perkins say, 'A boy's best friend is his mother'?

10 In which US city was *Cheers* set?

11 Who were Buddy Holly's backing group?

12 Who played F. Scott Fitzgerald in the film *Beloved Infidel*?

13 Comedian Mark Little played which character in *Neighbours*?

14 The boy band Three T are all nephews of which pop superstar?

15 Whose life story was depicted in the film *What's Love Got To Do With It?*?

ANSWERS

1. Scrappy. 2. Ringo Starr. 3. The Profumo affair. 4. Colin Firth. 5. Bryan Adams. 6. Mortimer Mouse. 7. Mary Doll. 8. Vincent Van Gogh. 9. *Psycho*. 10. Boston. 11. The Crickets. 12. Gregory Peck. 13. Joe Mangel. 14. Michael Jackson. 15. Tina Turner.

SESSION 40 QUIZ 2

History

1 Which American evangelist was born in North Carolina in 1918?

2 What name is given to the Germanic people that settled in Italy from about AD 568?

3 What sought to maintain Catholic orthodoxy in Spain from the 15th to the 17th century?

4 In 1791 Toussaint-L'Ouverture led a revolt of Black slaves in which country?

5 What is generally considered to be the most well-known date in English history?

6 Who was responsible for the deaths of Cranmer, Latimer and Ridley?

7 Which violent people made their presence felt on the shores of Britain for the first time in AD 787?

8 Who was Lee Harvey Oswald alleged to have killed?

9 By what heavenly name was Louis XIV also known?

10 Who was Malcolm Little?

11 Who did Ramon del Rio (alias Jacques Mornard) assassinate?

12 When Italy was united in 1861 which two cities were not included?

13 Who ushered in Glasnost?

14 Which cunning Italian published *The Prince* in 1532?

15 What did James Watt invent in 1769?

ANSWERS

1. Billy Graham. 2. The Lombards. 3. The Spanish Inquisition. 4. Haiti. 5. 1066. 6. Queen Mary I. 7. The Vikings. 8. John F. Kennedy. 9. 'The Sun King'. 10. Malcolm X, the Black rights activist. 11. Leon Trotsky. 12. Rome and Venice. 13. Mikhail Gorbachev. 14. Niccolò Machiavelli. 15. The steam engine.

SESSION 40 — QUIZ 3

Sports

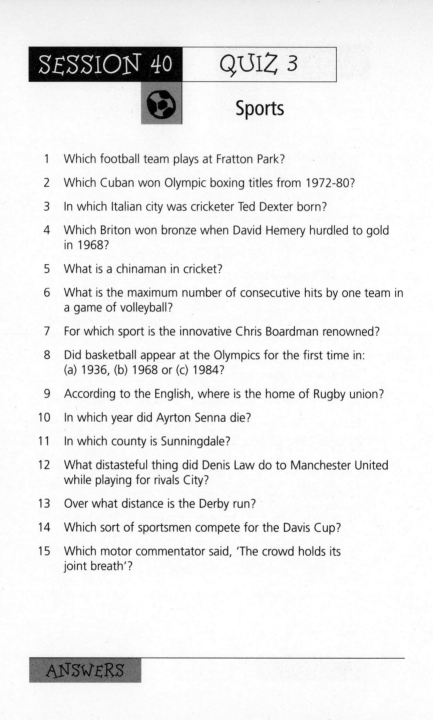

1 Which football team plays at Fratton Park?

2 Which Cuban won Olympic boxing titles from 1972-80?

3 In which Italian city was cricketer Ted Dexter born?

4 Which Briton won bronze when David Hemery hurdled to gold in 1968?

5 What is a chinaman in cricket?

6 What is the maximum number of consecutive hits by one team in a game of volleyball?

7 For which sport is the innovative Chris Boardman renowned?

8 Did basketball appear at the Olympics for the first time in:
(a) 1936, (b) 1968 or (c) 1984?

9 According to the English, where is the home of Rugby union?

10 In which year did Ayrton Senna die?

11 In which county is Sunningdale?

12 What distasteful thing did Denis Law do to Manchester United while playing for rivals City?

13 Over what distance is the Derby run?

14 Which sort of sportsmen compete for the Davis Cup?

15 Which motor commentator said, 'The crowd holds its joint breath'?

ANSWERS

1. Portsmouth. 2. Teofilo Stevenson. 3. Milan. 4. John Sherwood. 5. A left-hander bowling to a right-handed batsman. 6. Three. 7. Cycling. He has broken many records. 8. (a) 1936. 9. Twickenham. 10. 1994. 11. Berkshire. 12. He scored the goal that relegated them from Division One. 13. Twelve furlongs (1.5 miles, 2.4 km). 14. Tennis players. 15. Murray Walker.

SESSION 40 · QUIZ 4

General knowledge

1 What does an orthotist make?

2 How many teeth does a child have?

3 What did Sir James Simpson introduce for the first time in 1847?

4 What is the common name for hydrophobia?

5 What is the American name for 'nappy'?

6 Who said, 'Religion is the opium of the people'?

7 Which animal looked after 'Romulus' and 'Remus'?

8 Was Bill Clinton America's: (a) 42nd, (b) 50th or (c) 57th president?

9 Which member of the Royal family became a Catholic in January 1994?

10 What number lies between 18 and 13 on a dartboard?

11 Camel hair brushes are made from camel's hair. True or false?

12 What is a howitzer?

13 What nickname was given to the V1 rocket?

14 Who was James Bond in the film *Octopussy*?

15 Elizabeth Fry is linked with the reform of what?

ANSWERS

1. Orthopaedic appliances. 2. 20. 3. Chloroform. 4. Rabies. 5. Diaper. 6. Karl Marx. 7. A she-wolf. 8. (a) 42nd. 9. The Duchess of Kent. 10. 4. 11. False. They are made from squirrels' tails. 12. A military cannon. 13. The 'Doodlebug'. 14. Roger Moore. 15. Prisons.

SESSION 40

QUIZ 5

Technology & science

1 What is the name of the science that describes the study of the flow of fluids?

2 In genetics, what is the significance of X and Y?

3 Name the biologist who had a fierce debate with Samuel Wilberforce over evolution in 1860.

4 In what field of physics would you come across 'superstring theory'?

5 In Internet jargon, what does 'spamming' mean?

6 In telecommunications what do the letters ISDN stand for?

7 Which is the fifth major planet from the Sun?

8 In computing, what does WORM represent?

9 The Soviet *Soyuz* series of spacecraft were used for ferrying astronauts to space stations. What does *Soyuz* mean?

10 What is the name of the element with the symbol Zn?

11 In which year was Stephen Hawking born?

12 What vitamin is ascorbic acid?

13 What is henbane?

14 In astronomy, what is syzygy?

15 What is the informal name for the 'lunar roving vehicle'?

ANSWERS

1. Hydraulics (or fluid mechanics). 2. X = female chromosome, Y = male chromosome. 3. Thomas Huxley (1825-95). 4. Atomic physics, elementary particles. 5. Advertising on the Internet to many or all newsgroups, indiscriminately. 6. Integrated Services Digital Network. 7. Jupiter. 8. Write Once Read Many (times). 9. 'Union'. 10. Zinc. 11. 1942. 12. Vitamin C. 13. A plant related to the nightshade family, used for drugs. 14. The alignment of three celestial bodies (usually the Sun, the Earth and the Moon). 15. Moon buggy.

SESSION 40 QUIZ 6

Geography

1   Which is colder, the Arctic or the Antarctic?

2   If your train journey ended at Waverley station, which city would you be in?

3   In which English county would you find the natural features Lulworth Cove and Durdle Door?

4   Which is the largest island in the Mediterranean?

5   Which city, in the centre of the Amazon Basin, has a world-famous opera house, built on the profits of the rubber trade?

6   Which sea does the Volga river flow into: (a) the Barents Sea, (b) the Black Sea or (c) the Caspian Sea?

7   Which Italian city, build on three red clay hills, gave its name to a colour?

8   In which African country has Kano been an important trading centre since pre-Colonial days?

9   In which country is Chittagong, the country's second largest city, and a place prone to flooding?

10   Which one of these South American countries is on the equator: (a) Venezuela, (b) Bolivia or (c) Colombia?

11   In which American state could you visit Plymouth Rock and Cape Cod?

12   Is the 'Skeleton Coast' off the coast of: (a) Namibia, (b) Somalia or (c) Tanzania?

13   What is the capital of New Zealand?

14   Which is the shallowest of these three seas: (a) the East China Sea, (b) the South China Sea or (c) the Sea of Japan?

15   In which country is the volcano Popocatépetl?

ANSWERS

SESSION 40   QUIZ 7

The Arts

1 Who wrote *The Phoenix and the Carpet* and *The Railway Children*?

2 In which part of England did the poets Coleridge, Southey and Wordsworth all live?

3 Which Alpine village performs a Passion Play every ten years?

4 What is the name of Rossini's *Barber of Seville*?

5 Which English poet painted a picture of God entitled *The Ancient of Days*?

6 Which poet wrote *The Journey of the Magi*?

7 Who wrote *Howard's End* and *A Room with a View*?

8 Which journalist and novelist wrote the farce *Noises Off*?

9 What instrument is played by James Galway?

10 A boy called Leo carries messages between two lovers in which novel by L. P. Hartley?

11 Who declared that Christmas was 'humbug!'?

12 Who wrote the play *Look Back in Anger*?

13 A Sarabande is: (a) a dance, (b) a hat or (c) a musical instrument?

14 How does the 23rd Psalm begin?

15 What is the *Mappa Mundi*?

ANSWERS

1. E. Nesbit. 2. The Lake District. 3. Oberammergau. 4. 'Figaro'. 5. William Blake. 6. T. S. Eliot. 7. E. M. Forster. 8. Michael Frayn. 9. Flute. 10. *The Go-Between*. 11. 'Ebenezer Scrooge'. 12. John Osborne. 13. (a) a dance. 14. *The Lord is my shepherd*. 15. A circular map of the world from the 13th century.

SESSION 40   QUIZ 8

Pot Luck

1 Which is bigger in area: Lake Superior or Ireland?

2 For how many days were ships carrying infection traditionally kept in quarantine (hence the origin of the word)?

3 What is added to stout to make the drink Black Velvet?

4 What is seized in a coup d'état?

5 Which anniversary does a golden wedding celebrate?

6 Where is Timbuktu?

7 Which came first, the Palaeolithic or the Neolithic Age?

8 What is special about the phrase 'Madam, I'm Adam'?

9 Which nocturnal bird was once called a Goatsucker because it was believed that it fed off goats' milk?

10 Which coin was called a 'bob'?

11 Which US city is the home of jazz?

12 In which month is the spring equinox?

13 In the tax system what do the letters PAYE stand for?

14 Which animals' young are called elvers?

15 Which jazz club owner said of his club, 'Even the mice eat next door'?

ANSWERS

1. Lake Superior. 2. Forty, *quaranta* is Italian for 40. 3. Champagne. 4. Power. 5. The fiftieth. 6. In Mali, West Africa, on the edge of the Sahara. 7. Palaeolithic. 8. It reads the same backwards as forwards. 9. Nightjar. 10. A shilling (5p). 11. New Orleans. 12. March. 13. Pay As You Earn. 14. Eels. 15. Ronnie Scott.

SESSION 41 QUIZ 1

TV, music & entertainment

1 Who played President Nixon in the film *Nixon*?

2 Was impressionist Rory Bremner born in: (a) London, (b) Oxford or (c) Edinburgh?

3 Who is the lead singer with the band Texas?

4 Who played Emma Thompson's younger sister in the film of Jane Austen's *Sense and Sensibility*?

5 Who is the only original cast member still appearing in *Coronation Street*?

6 The 1984 concert film *Stop Making Sense* featured which band?

7 Who played Glenn Miller in *The Glenn Miller Story*?

8 Who played the Roman Emperor Claudius I in the TV production of *I, Claudius*?

9 Who is Lara Croft?

10 Which famous entertainer started out as Bette Midler's pianist?

11 What is Bollywood?

12 What is the name of the arch-enemy in *Star Trek: the Next Generation*?

13 Who was the Belgian-born jazz guitarist who played with Stéphane Grappelli in the Quintet of the Hot Club of France?

14 In which film is the opening line 'Last night I dreamed I went to Manderley again'?

15 Whose catch phrase is 'I'm free'?

ANSWERS

1. Anthony Hopkins. 2. Edinburgh. 3. Sharleen Spiteri. 4. Kate Winslet. 5. William Roache, who plays Ken Barlow. 6. Talking Heads. 7. James Stewart. 8. Derek Jacobi. 9. The heroine in the *Tomb Raider* computer games. 10. Barry Manilow. 11. The Indian film industry, based in Bombay. 12. The Borg. 13. Django Reinhardt. 14. *Rebecca*. 15. John Inman.

SESSION 41 QUIZ 2

History

1   Who was Aneurin Bevan describing when he said, 'His ear is so sensitively tuned to the bugle note of history that he is often deaf to the more raucous clamour of everyday life'?

2   How many years did Nelson Mandela spend in prison?

3   By what name is the Chinese philosopher K'ung Fu-tzu better known?

4   Which English composer was born in 1872, wrote nine symphonies, including the 'London Symphony', and died in 1958?

5   What high-flying innovation was used in a battle for the first time at the battle of Fleurus in 1794?

6   In 1895 who became colonial secretary in the Conservative government?

7   Who is the founder of the colony of Singapore?

8   Which North American Indian is buried by the River Thames?

9   Did the storming of the Bastille take place in: (a) 1789, (b) 1799 or (c) 1809?

10   Who sailed in the Antarctic ship *Discovery*?

11   What party did the Whigs become?

12   Where is the home of the African Mau Maus?

13   Who was the most famous member of the Hellfire Club?

14   Who was the longest reigning British king?

15   What took place from 20 November 1945 – 31 August 1946?

ANSWERS

1. Winston Churchill. 2. 26. 3. Confucius (a renowned philosopher). 4. Ralph Vaughan Williams. 5. A balloon that was used for observation. 6. Joseph Chamberlain. 7. Sir Thomas Raffles. 8. Pocahontas. 9. (a) 1789. 10. Captain Scott. 11. The Liberals. 12. Kenya. 13. John Wilkes. 14. George III. 15. The Nuremberg War Trials.

SESSION 41   QUIZ 3

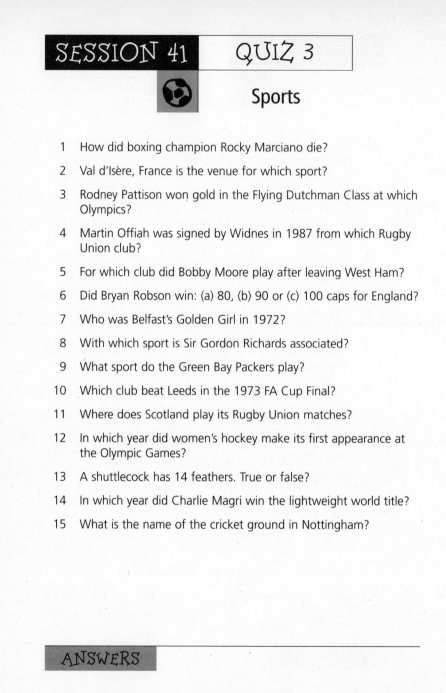

Sports

1. How did boxing champion Rocky Marciano die?

2. Val d'Isère, France is the venue for which sport?

3. Rodney Pattison won gold in the Flying Dutchman Class at which Olympics?

4. Martin Offiah was signed by Widnes in 1987 from which Rugby Union club?

5. For which club did Bobby Moore play after leaving West Ham?

6. Did Bryan Robson win: (a) 80, (b) 90 or (c) 100 caps for England?

7. Who was Belfast's Golden Girl in 1972?

8. With which sport is Sir Gordon Richards associated?

9. What sport do the Green Bay Packers play?

10. Which club beat Leeds in the 1973 FA Cup Final?

11. Where does Scotland play its Rugby Union matches?

12. In which year did women's hockey make its first appearance at the Olympic Games?

13. A shuttlecock has 14 feathers. True or false?

14. In which year did Charlie Magri win the lightweight world title?

15. What is the name of the cricket ground in Nottingham?

ANSWERS

1. He died in a plane crash. 2. Skiing. 3. 1972, Munich. 4. Rosslyn Park. 5. Fulham. 6. (b) 90. 7. Mary Peters, who won gold in the Olympic pentathlon. 8. Horse racing. He was British champion 26 times. 9. American Football. 10. Sunderland. 11. Murrayfield. 12. 1980. 13. False. It has 16. 14. 1983. 15. Trent Bridge.

SESSION 41   QUIZ 4

General knowledge

1 At what branch of science did the monk Gregor Mendel make his mark on the world?

2 Who was Louise Brown?

3 Which rank is below captain in the British army?

4 Where is O'Hare airport?

5 What did the American Christopher Latham Sholes invent in the 1860s?

6 What is the PDSA?

7 Who is William Henry Gates III?

8 'All because the lady loves...' refers to which confectionery?

9 Where is the University of Harvard?

10 Which language is spoken by the greatest number of people?

11 What sort of tricky situation did Joseph Heller find himself in?

12 Who in the Bible said, 'What is truth?'?

13 Why is the play *Venus and Adonis* so important?

14 Of which country is Nairobi the capital?

15 What is a centaur?

ANSWERS

1. Genetics. 2. The first test-tube baby. 3. Lieutenant. 4. Chicago. 5. The typewriter. 6. People's Dispensary for Sick Animals. 7. Bill Gates of Microsoft. 8. 'Milk Tray'. 9. Cambridge, Massachusetts. 10. Mandarin Chinese, spoken by over nine hundred million people. 11. *Catch-22*. He wrote the novel. 12. Pontius Pilate. 13. It is thought to be Shakespeare's first play. 14. Kenya. 15. Half-man, half-horse.

SESSION 41

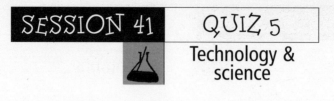

QUIZ 5
Technology & science

1 Who is the French chemist known as the founder of modern chemistry?

2 For what was William Libby awarded the 1960 Nobel prize for chemistry?

3 What is the principle of Boolean algebra?

4 What is a zwitterion?

5 Who produced the first coloured photograph of the visible spectrum?

6 It is commonly called the funny bone, but what is it?

7 Ernest Rutherford carried out experiments in which field of science?

8 What is the phon used to measure?

9 The semi-precious stone malachite is composed of carbonate of copper. What colour is it?

10 What is the name of the element with the symbol Mg?

11 Who first carried out studies of heredity in the 19th century?

12 What is a Mercator Projection?

13 Where would you find the thinnest skin on your body?

14 Who was the crystallographer who determined the structure of haemoglobin and myoglobin?

15 Which is the largest tendon in the body?

ANSWERS

1. Antoine Lavoisier. 2. His development of radioactive carbon-14 dating. 3. Two-valued system (with a property, without a property). 4. An ion with a positive and negative charge. 5. Gabriel Lippmann. 6. It's a nerve in the elbow. 7. Atomic science. 8. Loudness. 9. Green. 10. Magnesium. 11. Gregor Mendel. 12. A map using the map-making methods of Gerardus Mercator (1512-94). 13. On your eyelids. 14. Max Perutz. 15. Achilles tendon, between the calf and the heel.

SESSION 41 QUIZ 6

Geography

1 Which area of water does the Strait of Hormuz link to the Gulf of Oman?

2 The area of Austria called the Salzkammergut now gains most of its income from tourism, but what was its previous important industry?

3 What are 'Nanga Parbat', 'Makalu' and 'Dhaulagiri'?

4 Princetown is a village at the junction of roads across a National Park in Devon, but it is better known for which building rather than for the surrounding scenery?

5 Which is the driest desert in the world: (a) the Atacama, (b) the Kalahari or (c) the Sahara?

6 In 1960 the Brazilian capital moved to Brasilia from which city?

7 The Whitsunday Islands are growing in popularity as tourist resorts. In which country are they?

8 In which country are the Reichenbach Falls, which were used by Conan Doyle in his novels?

9 Which is the longest strait in the world: (a) the Taiwan Strait, (b) the Malacca Strait or (c) the Strait of Otranto?

10 In which National Park are the three peaks of Whernside, Ingleborough and Pen-y-ghent?

11 Which river flows through the Grand Canyon in Arizona?

12 Which is the remotest of the British Isles: (a) St Kilda, (b) Muckle Flugga or (c) Rockall?

13 The circumference of the Earth at the equator is approximately: (a) 40,000, (b) 60,000 or (c) 80,000 kilometres?

14 What is the capital of Malta?

15 Which of these American states borders Canada: (a) Oregon, (b) Montana or (c) Wisconsin?

ANSWERS

1. Persian Gulf. 2. Salt. 3. Mountain peaks in the Himalayas. 4. Dartmoor Prison. 5. (a) Atacama. 6. Rio de Janeiro. 7. Australia. 8. Switzerland. 9. (b) The Malacca Strait. 10. The Yorkshire Dales. 11. Colorado River. 12. (c) Rockall. 13. (a) 40,000 kilometres. 14. Valletta. 15. (b) Montana.

SESSION 41   QUIZ 7

The Arts

1   'Beware the Ides of March' is a line from which play?

2   Ma and Pop Larkin are the central characters in which novel by H. E. Bates?

3   How many lines does a sonnet have?

4   In which county is D. H. Lawrence's *Sons and Lovers* set?

5   Whom does Elizabeth Bennett marry in *Pride and Prejudice*?

6   What did the poet Herrick urge young girls to gather 'while ye may'?

7   'How the Camel got his hump' and 'How the Leopard got his Spots' are in which collection of stories by Rudyard Kipling?

8   Who wrote the poem *The Pied Piper of Hamlyn*?

9   In which county is *Anna of the Five Towns* set?

10   What royal position is held by the composer Malcolm Williamson?

11   Which book by Kit Williams involved a real-life treasure hunt for a golden hare?

12   Who visited a chocolate factory and had an adventure in a great glass elevator?

13   What happened to Albert Ramsbottom when he went to Blackpool Zoo?

14   What object is the subject of a quest by Sir Galahad and the other knights of the Round Table?

15   What did Nostradamus write?

ANSWERS

1. *Julius Caesar* by Shakespeare. 2. *The Darling Buds of May*. 3. 14. 4. Nottinghamshire. 5. Mr Darcy. 6. Rosebuds. 7. *Just-so Stories*. 8. Robert Browning. 9. Staffordshire. 10. Master of the Queen's Music. 11. *Masquerade*. 12. Charlie Bucket. 13. He was eaten by a lion (*Albert and the Lion* by Stanley Holloway). 14. The Holy Grail. 15. Prophecies.

SESSION 41   QUIZ 8

Pot Luck

1   What Victorian drink was flavoured with wormwood?

2   What ceremony is performed with Bell, Book and Candle?

3   At sea during which hours is the second dog-watch?

4   What is a futon?

5   Were the 'gnomes of Zurich': (a) magicians, (b) clock-makers or (c) bankers?

6   What is the 'gogglebox'?

7   In which sport did the catchphrase, 'We wuz robbed' originate?

8   What is saccharin a substitute for?

9   What two words which sound similar mean 'an animal's pelt' and 'an evergreen coniferous tree'?

10   If you were born on Christmas Day what would be your sign of the zodiac?

11   Who plays Inspector Morse in the TV series of that name?

12   Palmists study palms; what do phrenologists study?

13   A morganatic marriage is one between people of different: (a) social status, (b) ages or (c) race?

14   In heraldry is the colour 'gules': (a) red, (b) white or (c) blue?

15   Where is Herne's Oak, reputedly haunted by Herne the Hunter?

ANSWERS

1. Absinthe. 2. Excommunication. 3. 6.00 pm to 8.00 pm. 4. A bed. 5. (c) bankers. 6. Television. 7. Boxing. 8. Sugar. 9. Fur/fir. 10. Capricorn. 11. John Thaw. 12. Heads, the surface of the skull. 13. (a) social status. 14. (a) red. 15. Windsor Great Park.

336

QUIZ 1

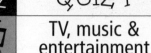

TV, music & entertainment

1 In which film did Henry Fonda and Jane Fonda play father and daughter?

2 Murray Walker is a commentator on which sport?

3 Roxy Music had a number one hit in 1981 with 'Jealous Guy'. Who wrote the song?

4 Who played Elliott's little sister, Gertie, in *E.T.*?

5 Beverley Callard, who played Liz McDonald in *Coronation Street*, is a practising aerobics instructor. True or false?

6 Who was the lead singer with the Undertones?

7 Who provided the voice of the evil spirit, 'Captain Howard', in *The Exorcist*?

8 Robson Green and Jerome Flynn first worked together in which TV drama serial?

9 Which rapper starred as a cop in the film *New Jack City*?

10 Which actor's original name was William Henry Pratt?

11 Which TV presenter used to be the girl in Boddington's beer advert?

12 Which Norwegian composer wrote the incidental music for *Peer Gynt*?

13 Jada Pinkett, who starred in *The Nutty Professor* with Eddie Murphy, is married to him in real life. True or false?

14 Michael Aspel was once a BBC newsreader. True or false?

15 Who wrote and recorded 'Streets of Philadelphia', the theme song from the film *Philadelphia*?

ANSWERS

1. *On Golden Pond*. 2. Motor racing. 3. John Lennon. 4. Drew Barrymore. 5. True. 6. Feargal Sharkey. 7. Debra Winger. 8. *Soldier, Soldier*. 9. Ice-T. 10. Boris Karloff. 11. Melanie Sykes. 12. Edvard Grieg. 13. False. She is married to Will Smith. 14. True. 15. Bruce Springsteen.

SESSION 42 QUIZ 2

History

1 Where was the *Marie Céleste* bound for on its fateful journey?

2 What were the opposing factions in the War of the Roses?

3 Which was the last country to declare independence from the United Kingdom?

4 What was the occupation of Joseph Guillotin?

5 Who was the third American president?

6 Who said, 'My God, what have we done?'?

7 Which Scottish author went for a *Tour of the Hebrides*?

8 Which of these three World War II leaders died first? Was it: (a) Churchill, (b) Stalin or (c) Roosevelt?

9 The 1748 Treaty of Aix-la-Chapelle ended which war?

10 Who were the 'Patriots'?

11 Which battle did the horse Comanche survive?

12 Which Bay did Cook discover in 1770?

13 Did the Catholic Emancipation Act occur in: (a) 1829, (b) 1856 or (c) 1878?

14 Who fought Russia in the Crimean War?

15 What was a 'Rotten Borough'?

ANSWERS

1. Genoa, Italy. 2. York and Lancaster. 3. Rhodesia. 4. A doctor. He wished to devise a humane method of execution. 5. Thomas Jefferson. 6. Captain Robert Lewis who had just dropped the first atomic bomb on Hiroshima in 1945. 8. (c) Roosevelt in 1945. 7. Boswell. 9. The Austrian War of Succession. 10. The Americans during the War of Independence. 11. The Battle of Little Big Horn. 12. Botany Bay. 13. (a) 1829. 14. Britain, France, Turkey and Sardinia. 15. A political district with very few voters. They existed before the Reform Act of 1832.

SESSION 42 · QUIZ 3

Sports

1   What sport is Jack Dempsey famous for?

2   Goodison is in the same city as another famous ground. What is that location called?

3   How many times has Britain won an Olympic marathon?

4   What sport do the Philadelphia 76ers play?

5   What took place in Perth during January 1998?

6   What do the initials FIFA stand for?

7   Which African country does Halle Gebrselassie come from?

8   Which Argentinian player went to Tottenham for £325,000 in 1978?

9   Jarmila Kratochilova holds the longest-standing athletics world record at which distance?

10   Which politician raced the 'Morning Cloud' yachts?

11   Which Manchester City player wore number 7 for England in the 1970 World Cup?

12   The Vauxhall End is to be found at Lords. True or false?

13   What is the name of Boston's basketball team?

14   In 1962, how long did it take Sonny Liston to knock out Floyd Patterson for the title of heavyweight champion of the world?

15   The Irishman Pat O'Callaghan won Olympic Gold in an event for which the Irish were renowned at the beginning of the century. What was it?

ANSWERS

1. Boxing. 2. Anfield, home of Liverpool. 3. Never. 4. Basketball. 5. The World Swimming Championships. 6. Fédération Internationale de Football Association. 7. Ethiopia. 8. Ossie Ardiles. 9. 800 metres. 10. Sir Edward Heath. 11. Francis Lee. 12. False. It is at the Oval. 13. Celtics. 14. Two minutes, six seconds. 15. The hammer.

SESSION 42   QUIZ 4

General knowledge

1 What type of vehicle competed for the Schneider Trophy?

2 How often should a sabbatical be taken?

3 What did entertainer Kenny Everett die from?

4 What rocked America on 19 April 1995?

5 Who changed his name to Paul after his conversion to Christianity?

6 What is the study of armorial bearings?

7 What is the name of the state-sponsored medical aid system in America?

8 Napier's bones are useful for doing what?

9 If something is cultrate, what shape is it?

10 Which German philosopher placed man at the centre of the universe?

11 Which emperor said, 'Would that the Roman people had but one neck'?

12 What happened on 12 April 1961?

13 What is celebrated on 29 September according to the Christian calendar?

14 What fruit, found by Columbus, originates in Guadeloupe?

15 Who said, 'Give me a firm place to stand, and I will move the earth'?

ANSWERS

1. Seaplanes. 2. Every seven years. 3. AIDS. 4. The Oklahoma City bomb. 5. Saul. 6. Heraldry. 7. Medicare. 8. Mathematics. They were rods used for division and multiplication. 9. Knife-shaped. 10. Immanuel Kant. 11. Caligula. 12. Yuri Gagarin became the first man in space. 13. Michaelmas. 14. Pineapple. 15. Archimedes.

SESSION 42

QUIZ 5

Technology & science

1 What is the chemical symbol for mercury?

2 What is the name of the cloud of gases around the Sun?

3 Who was the 16th-century physician who revolutionized anatomy by performing post-mortem dissections?

4 What is the chemical symbol for bismuth?

5 How many days does it take Mercury to orbit the Sun?

6 In computing, what does the acronym BIOS represent?

7 What are the two main metals found in the semi-precious stone turquoise?

8 In which year was 'Velcro' invented?

9 What class of essential food is biotin?

10 How many tides are there each day?

11 In retailing, what does EPOS stand for?

12 Where would you find the thickest layer of skin on the human body?

13 What is the function of a biopsy?

14 What is phlogiston?

15 What is the name of our galaxy?

ANSWERS

1. Hg. 2. Corona. 3. Andreas Vesalius (1514–64). 4. Bi. 5. 88 days. 6. *Basic Input-Output System*. 7. Copper and aluminium. 8. 1948. 9. A vitamin of the B complex (also-called vitamin H). 10. Two high tides and two low tides. 11. *Electronic point of sale*. 12. The soles of the feet. 13. To remove living tissue from a body to discover the presence, cause or extent of a disease. 14. A substance that was believed to have been formed during combustion. 15. The Milky Way.

SESSION 42   QUIZ 6

Geography

1　Of which country is Amman the capital?

2　On which firth is Dundee situated: (a) the Firth of Tay, (b) the Firth of Forth or (c) the Moray Firth?

3　Where is Mount Ararat: (a) Syria, (b) Iraq or (c) Turkey?

4　What is the 'white gold' that is produced on the Cape York peninsula in Queensland, Australia?

5　On which island could you visit the towns of Jaffna, Kandy and Trincomalee?

6　Which of these countries produces most of the world's diamonds: (a) South Africa, (b) Russia or (c) Australia?

7　What is the name for the landscape of coniferous forests in Siberia between the tundra and the steppe?

8　In which country is Lake Taupo: (a) Mexico, (b) New Zealand or (c) Nigeria?

9　Which river flows through Lancaster?

10　On which coastline of Spain is the Costa Verde: (a) east, (b) south or (c) north?

11　Which African country is surrounded by Namibia, Zimbabwe and South Africa?

12　In which province of Canada could you watch the Calgary Stampede?

13　The remotest inhabited island in the world is Tristan da Cunha. Is its nearest neighbour: (a) the Falkland Islands, (b) St Helena or (c) Ascension Island?

14　In North Africa is a 'wadi': (a) a village with a well, (b) a river-bed that is dry except for the rainy season or (c) an oasis?

15　The equator passes through the Galapagos Islands. True or false?

ANSWERS

1. Jordan. 2. (a) the Firth of Tay. 3. (c) Turkey. 4. Sugar. 5. Sri Lanka. 6. (c) Australia. 7. Taiga. 8. (b) New Zealand. 9. River Lune. 10. (c) north. 11. Botswana. 12. Alberta. 13. (b) St Helena. 14. (b) a river-bed that is dry except in the rainy season. 15. True.

SESSION 42   QUIZ 7

The Arts

1   Who wrote the sonnet which contains the line 'the darling buds of May'?

2   Which artist painted the picture of bubbles used in adverts for Pears soap?

3   A hurdy-gurdy is: (a) musical instrument, (b) a form of yodelling or (c) a folk dance?

4   In which Austrian city was Mozart born?

5   What colour was Johann Strauss' Danube?

6   Who wrote the series of novels collectively called *A Dance to the Music of Time*?

7   What was Frankenstein's first name: (a) Ernest, (b) Victor or (c) Hermann?

8   How is Air Detective Inspector Bigglesworth better known?

9   What was the name of the 'hard-boiled' detective in *The Maltese Falcon*?

10   What type of animal was Rikki Tikki Tavi?

11   Who wrote *The Pirates of Penzance*?

12   Which Peruvian bear was the creation of Michael Bond?

13   Who painted *The Scapegoat*?

14   In *The Winter's Tale* who was a 'snapper up of unconsidered trifles'?

15   What was the Empress of Blandings in P. G. Wodehouse's stories?

ANSWERS

1. William Shakespeare. 2. John Everett Millais. 3. (a) a musical instrument. 4. Salzburg. 5. Blue. 6. Anthony Powell. 7. (b) Victor. 8. Biggles. 9. Sam Spade. 10. A mongoose. 11. Gilbert and Sullivan. 12. 'Paddington'. 13. William Holman Hunt. 14. Autolycus. 15. A prize sow.

SESSION 42 — QUIZ 8

Pot Luck

1 What type of summer is predicted if 'the oak's before the ash'?

2 What nationality was Erik the Red?

3 What is another name for groundnuts or monkey nuts?

4 Which bird was depicted on the farthing coin?

5 What is *esprit de corps*?

6 To whom is a person espoused?

7 What is Betelgeuse?

8 What type of animal is a cob, is it: (a) a fish, (b) a dog or (c) a horse?

9 In World War II what was a 'Moaning Minnie'?

10 What is the smallest letter of the Greek alphabet?

11 Which Italian city is famous for its leaning tower?

12 Is the *Aurora Borealis* seen in the northern or southern hemisphere?

13 Does 'a bed of roses' describe a pleasant or unpleasant situation?

14 Who was Beau Brummel?

15 When is 'the witching hour'?

ANSWERS

1. A wet one. 2. Norwegian. 3. Peanuts. 4. Wren. 5. Respect for the organization you belong to. 6. Their wife or husband. 7. A star. 8. (c) a horse. 9. A German bomb or an English air-raid siren. 10. Iota. 11. Pisa. 12. Northern. 13. Pleasant. 14. A very fashion-conscious friend of George, the Prince Regent. 15. Midnight.

SESSION 43 QUIZ 1

TV, music & entertainment

1 Melissa Mathison, the screenwriter who wrote *E.T.*, is married to which Hollywood star?

2 In *Friends*, what is Ross's profession?

3 Which jazz musician was nicknamed 'Satchmo'?

4 Who played Big Daddy in the film *Cat on a Hot Tin Roof*?

5 Which TV series featured Clarence, the cross-eyed lion?

6 Which rock singer starred opposite Mel Gibson in *Mad Max Beyond Thunderdome*?

7 Who was the boxer portrayed by Robert De Niro in *Raging Bull*?

8 Who did we hear, but never see, in *Charlie's Angels*?

9 The Space hit, 'We've Gotta Get Out of this Place', was originally a hit for which group in 1965?

10 What were the robots called in the film *Blade Runner*?

11 Which children's TV programme features 'Big Bird'?

12 Who was the subject of Stevie Wonder's song, 'Sir Duke'?

13 Who played 'Freddy Kruger' in the *Nightmare on Elm Street* films?

14 Who played 'Wonder Woman' in the 70s TV series of the same name?

15 Where was singer Gloria Estefan born?

ANSWERS

15. Havana, Cuba.

11. *Sesame Street*. 12. Duke Ellington. 13. Robert England. 14. Lynda Carter.

6. Tina Turner. 7. Jake La Motta. 8. Charlie. 9. The Animals. 10. Replicants.

1. Harrison Ford. 2. Palaeontologist. 3. Louis Armstrong. 4. Burl Ives. 5. *Daktari*.

SESSION 43   QUIZ 2

History

1   Who did Flora MacDonald help in 1746?

2   What did Carthage lose in 241 BC?

3   What established basic Christian doctrine in AD 325?

4   Why did Edward VIII abdicate?

5   How long did the General Strike of 1926 last?

6   Who was the Red Baron?

7   In 1517 Luther nailed his 95 theses to the church door of which castle?

8   Which part of India did Francis Xavier arrive at in 1542?

9   Who lay siege to Vienna in 1683?

10   What religion were the French refugees, the Huguenots?

11   What book did Izaak Walton write in the 1650s?

12   What was the name of the floating harbours employed for the invasion of Europe?

13   How old was Britain's youngest ever prime minister?

14   Which country suffered most military losses during World War II?

15   Who was Hitler's Armaments minister?

ANSWERS

1. Charles Edward Stuart, after his defeat at Culloden. 2. The First Punic War. 3. The Council of Nicaea. 4. To marry divorcee, Mrs Simpson. 5. 3 May - 12 May. 6. Manfred von Richthofen. 7. Wittenberg. 8. Goa. 9. The Turks. 10. Protestant. 11. *The Compleat Angler.* 12. Mulberry Harbours. 13. 24. It was William Pitt. 14. Russia. 15. Albert Speer.

SESSION 43   QUIZ 3

Sports

1   What team was Gary Sobers playing for when he hit six sixes?

2   In which year did the infamous 'Battle of Highbury' take place?

3   Only two men have retained the 100 metre Olympic title.
One was Archie Hahn, who was the other one?

4   Who scored the most goals in the English football league in the
season 1927–28?

5   What sporting arena is twelve foot square?

6   What were invented in 1927 in order to help athletes?

7   Which club team did Bill Beaumont play rugby for?

8   What film was set around the 1924 Olympics?

9   Is Mario Andretti: (a) Italian, (b) Swiss or (c) American?

10   Which footballer did the Portuguese dub 'El Beatle' in 1966?

11   Which football team plays at Gay Meadow?

12   In which county is the Royal Liverpool golf course?

13   When did the career of 'Arkle' come to an end?

14   What do the rings on the Olympic symbol represent?

15   Kenny Dalglish scored more than 100 goals in both England and
Scotland leagues. True or false?

ANSWERS

1. Nottingham. 2. 1934 against Italy. 3. Carl Lewis. 4. Dixie Dean. 5. Gymnastics' floor exercise area. 6. Starting blocks. 7. Fylde. 8. *Chariots of Fire*. 9. (c) American. 10. George Best. 11. Shrewsbury. 12. Cheshire. 13. In the King George VI Chase in December 1966. 14. The five continents. 15. True.

SESSION 43   QUIZ 4

General knowledge

1. Before being embalmed, mummies were placed in what for 40 days?

2. Who patented the diesel engine?

3. Which country gave the Statue of Liberty to America?

4. Which philosopher is remembered for his work on language and its relation to the world?

5. Nemesis is the god of what?

6. Which is the ruby wedding anniversary?

7. Karol Wojtyla is better known as who?

8. How does one express the letter 'S' in Morse Code?

9. Where is the company Daewoo based?

10. Which city is called the 'Venice of Belgium'?

11. According to the proverb, whose house is his castle?

12. What was constructed to contain the Minotaur?

13. What was the occupation of Josiah Wedgwood?

14. In which month do Muslims fast from dawn to dusk?

15. What is the Chinese meditation in motion called?

ANSWERS

1. Salt. 2. Rudolf Diesel in 1892. 3. France. 4. Ludwig Wittgenstein. 5. Retribution. 6. Fortieth. 7. Pope John Paul II. 8. Three dots. 9. South Korea. 10. Bruges. 11. An Englishman's. 12. The Labyrinth. 13. A potter. 14. Ramadan. 15. T'ai chi (or t'ai ch'uan).

SESSION 43 QUIZ 5

Technology & science

1 Which soft, unreactive metal has the chemical symbol Pt?

2 Which is the brightest planet in the night sky?

3 What is catabolism?

4 What are the two main metals in pewter?

5 René Thom developed a mathematical theory in 1972. What did he call it?

6 What was the first substance ever used to anaesthetise a patient for a medical operation?

7 Dian Fossey is a zoologist noted for her studies on which animal?

8 How many kilobytes in a megabyte?

9 What is the chemical name for caustic soda?

10 Which is the longest muscle in the human body?

11 What makes a patient anaemic?

12 What is the name of the pouch on marsupials?

13 Diamond is the hardest mineral known to humans. What is the second hardest?

14 In the human body, what does the CNS comprise?

15 In computing, what does the abbreviation PCB represent?

ANSWERS

1. Platinum. 2. Venus. 3. The breakdown of living tissue into energy and waste products. 4. Lead and tin. 5. Catastrophe Theory. 6. Ether. 7. Mountain gorilla. 8. 1,024. 9. Sodium hydroxide. 10. The sartorius, from the hip to the knee. 11. Lack of iron carrying protein, haemoglobin, in the blood (hence less oxygen in the body). 12. The marsupium. 13. Corundum. 14. The central nervous system comprises the brain and spinal cord. 15. Printed circuit board.

SESSION 43 QUIZ 6

Geography

1 Is the 'Hindu Kush': (a) a river delta, (b) an Indian state or (c) a mountain range?

2 Khartoum lies at the junction of two rivers. One is the White Nile, what is the other?

3 The Cullin Hills are on the Isle of Skye. True or false?

4 Which of these types of clouds forms at the greatest height: (a) nimbostratus, (b) cirrus or (c) altocumulus?

5 In which country is the Kakadu National park?

6 On which island can you visit the Blue Grotto, Mount Solaro and Jupiter's Villa?

7 Motherwell is the administrative headquarters of which Scottish unitary authority?

8 On which island of New Zealand is the city of Christchurch?

9 Toronto is on the shore of which of the Great Lakes?

10 Which city is at the confluence of the Missouri and Mississippi rivers: (a) Memphis, (b) St Louis or (c) New Orleans?

11 What natural disaster occurred in Colombia in January 1999?

12 Which one of these German cities is on the Rhine: (a) Frankfurt, (b) Cologne or (c) Stuttgart?

13 Tokyo is on the island of Hokkaido. True or false?

14 The Suez Canal links the Mediterranean with which sea?

15 What is the name of the strait which separates Anglesey from Wales?

ANSWERS

1. (c) a mountain range. 2. The Blue Nile. 3. True. 4. (b) cirrus. 5. Australia. 6. Capri. 7. North Lanarkshire. 8. South Island. 9. Lake Ontario. 10. (b) St Louis. 11. An earthquake. 12. (b) Cologne. 13. False. It is on Honshu. 14. The Red Sea. 15. The Menai Strait.

SESSION 43 QUIZ 7

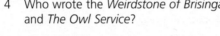

The Arts

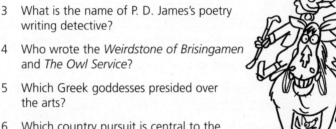

1 Which red-haired heroine was created by L. M. Montgomery?

2 Who were Hazel, Fiver and Bigwig?

3 What is the name of P. D. James's poetry writing detective?

4 Who wrote the *Weirdstone of Brisingamen* and *The Owl Service*?

5 Which Greek goddesses presided over the arts?

6 Which country pursuit is central to the novels of R. S. Surtees?

7 Who wrote *The Fall of the House of Usher* and other gothic stories?

8 What does it mean if a novel's hero is 'eponymous'?

9 Who wrote *Gulliver's Travels*?

10 Who wrote *The Magic Toyshop* and *Nights at the Circus*?

11 What technique for dyeing fabric involves blocking parts of the cloth with wax?

12 Which Dutch artist drew pictures of visual illusion including one in which a pair of hands are drawing themselves?

13 In which artistic field was Edwin Lutyens a leading figure?

14 What is japanning a form of?

15 What is a kilim?

ANSWERS

1. *Anne of Green Gables*. 2. Rabbits in *Watership Down*. 3. Adam Dalgleish. 4. Alan Garner. 5. The Muses. 6. Fox hunting. 7. Edgar Allan Poe. 8. His name is the title of the book. 9. Jonathan Swift. 10. Angela Carter. 11. Batik. 12. M. C. Escher. 13. Architecture. 14. Varnishing. 15. A (Turkish) rug.

SESSION 43   QUIZ 8

Pot Luck

1 What is unusual about a Manx cat?

2 How many inches high is a horse measuring 16 hands?

3 What direction is withershins?

4 What number is represented by the roman numerals CXV?

5 What is onomatophobia a fear of?

6 What in law used to be the difference between robbery and burglary?

7 Which tree is associated with graveyards?

8 What happened to the peeping Tom who looked at Lady Godiva as she rode naked through Coventry?

9 What is the difference between libel and slander?

10 What stretches from Bowness to Wallsend?

11 What happens to deciduous trees in autumn?

12 What is meant by the prefix 'poly-', as in 'polygamy' and 'polygon'?

13 Where is the Sun when it is at its zenith?

14 Do stalactites form up or down?

15 What speed are you travelling at if you are doing 'a ton'?

ANSWERS

1. It has no tail. 2. 64. 3. Anti-clockwise. 4. 115. 5. Names. 6. Burglary was at night only.
7. Yew. 8. He was struck blind. 9. Libel is written, slander is spoken. 10. Hadrian's Wall.
11. Their leaves fall off. 12. Many. 13. Its highest point. 14. Down. 15. 100 mph.

SESSION 44 QUIZ 1

TV, music & entertainment

1   What was the name of the nose-twitching witch in the sitcom *Bewitched*?

2   Who played comedian Lenny Bruce in the feature film *Lenny*?

3   The Band Aid song 'Do They Know It's Christmas?' was written by whom?

4   What was the name of the diminutive actor who starred in the TV series *Fantasy Island*?

5   Who played a twelve-year-old prostitute in the film *Taxi Driver*?

6   Who originally recorded the All Saints hit, 'Under the Bridge'?

7   Who played Beth Jordache in *Brookside*?

8   Stan Laurel was Clint Eastwood's father. True or false?

9   Who recorded the 1970 album *Abraxas*?

10 What was the name of the character played by Olympia Dukakis in the TV serial *Tales from the City*?

11 Which Irish writer and painter was portrayed by Daniel Day Lewis in the film *My Left Foot*?

12 Frank and Nancy Sinatra duetted on which hit record?

13 Where was the TV detective series *Magnum* set?

14 In which country was actor Bela Lugosi born?

15 Who wrote the musical score for the film *Local Hero*?

ANSWERS

1. Samantha Stevens. 2. Dustin Hoffman. 3. Bob Geldof and Midge Ure. 4. Herve Villechaize. 5. Jodie Foster. 6. The Red Hot Chili Peppers. 7. Anna Friel. 8. False. 9. Santana. 10. Anna Madrigal'. 11. Christy Brown. 12. 'Somethin' Stupid'. 13. Hawaii. 14. Hungary. 15. Mark Knopfler.

SESSION 44 QUIZ 2

History

1 Which Spanish mystic and priest was a leading advocate of quietism?

2 What important manuscripts were discovered in 1947?

3 Whose regime did Castro overthrow in 1959?

4 When was the First International founded?

5 Which battle was the turning point of the American Civil War?

6 What forward base used in the Crimean War gave its name to a type of head covering?

7 Which popular Paris amusement location opened in 1889?

8 Where did Robert the Bruce defeat Edward II?

9 The battle of Bosworth Field ended which wars?

10 Who succeeded John Betjeman as Poet Laureate?

11 Which country did Italy invade in 1935?

12 Which famous scholar and engineer was killed in the Roman sack of Syracuse?

13 Where was the German ship the *Graf Spee* scuttled?

14 What did Henry Grattan ask for in 1780?

15 Who said, 'I am just going outside and may be some time'?

ANSWERS

1. Miguel de Molinos. 2. The Dead Sea Scrolls. 3. Batista. 4. 1864. 5. Gettysburg. 6. Balaclava. 7. 'The Moulin Rouge'. 8. Bannockburn. 9. The Wars of the Roses. 10. Ted Hughes. 11. Abyssinia. 12. Archimedes. 13. The River Plate, South America. 14. Irish Home Rule. 15. Captain Lawrence Oates.

SESSION 44   QUIZ 3

Sports

1   Which team did American sports star George Halas play for?

2   Lee Trevino is Mexican. True or False?

3   How many oars does a sculler hold?

4   Which footballer had the nickname 'Crazy Horse'?

5   Ian Botham once had a trial with Crystal Palace football club. True or false?

6   Which tennis player suggested to an umpire that 'he could not be serious'?

7   How many players take part in a rugby union scrum?

8   What was once labelled 'Hardaker's Folly'?

9   Who was the Flying Finn?

10 In what year did Coventry win the FA Cup for the first time?

11 Where is the Hockenheim racing circuit?

12 What are the colours of Aston Villa?

13 What nationality was Wimbledon champion Maria Bueno?

14 How many players are there in a rugby league team?

15 What is a pugilist?

ANSWERS

1. The Chicago Bears. 2. False. He is American. 3. Two. 4. Emlyn Hughes. 5. True. 6. John McEnroe. 7. 16. Eight from each side. 8. The League Cup. 9. Paavo Nurmi. 10. 1987. 11. Germany. 12. Claret and blue. 13. Brazilian. 14. 13. 15. A boxer.

SESSION 44 QUIZ 4

General knowledge

1 According to the proverb, what should not be washed in public?

2 What is the number 500 in Roman numerals?

3 What does BSE stand for?

4 The 'didgeridoo' is an Australian Aboriginal instrument. True or false?

5 What disease does an oncologist work against?

6 By what other name is 'lockjaw' known?

7 Who wrote *Pensées*?

8 Who wrote the pamphlet *The First Blast of the Trumpet against the Monstrous Regiment of Women*?

9 What is the Heptateuch?

10 Who was Charles Lutwidge Dodgson?

11 Who was Castor's brother in Greek mythology?

12 Who place an advertisement in *The Times* in May 1994 saying how happily married they were?

13 What according to the Bible was created on the fourth day?

14 What is Pelmanism?

15 Which country produces the most oranges?

ANSWERS

1. Dirty linen. 2. D. 3. *Bovine spongiform encephalopathy*. 4. True. 5. Cancer. 6. Tetanus. 7. Blaise Pascal. 8. John Knox. 9. The first seven books of the Bible. 10. Lewis Carroll. 11. Pollux. 12. Richard Gere and Cindy Crawford. 13. The Sun and the Moon. 14. A system of memory improvement and a game with this as its main purpose. 15. Brazil.

SESSION 44

QUIZ 5

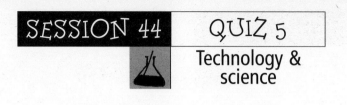

Technology & science

1 What is the chemical symbol for tin?

2 Which is the largest planet in the Solar System?

3 What is a deliquescent substance?

4 What was Thomas Edison's invention of 1877?

5 Who was director of the Jodrell Bank radio astronomy station from 1951–81?

6 What is the structure of DNA?

7 In medicine, what is the abbreviation ECT short for?

8 What is Babbit metal?

9 What drug relieves the rigidity in muscles and assists movement, and is used to treat Parkinson's Disease?

10 What is Bakelite?

11 What is the alternative name for meerschaum?

12 Jane Goodall is a conservationist and a world authority on which animal?

13 The word 'linoleum' comes from Latin *lini oleum* because of its naturally occurring constituent. What is the constituent?

14 Why is legionnaires' disease so named?

15 What is the name of a one-sided continuous surface made by twisting a strip of paper through 180 degrees and joining the ends?

ANSWERS

1. Sn. 2. Jupiter. 3. One that absorbs water from the atmosphere. 4. The gramophone.
5. Sir Alfred Charles Bernard Lovell. 6. A double helix. 7. Electroconvulsive therapy.
8. An alloy of tin, lead, copper and antimony (used in bearings). 9. Dopamine. 10. The first
synthetic plastic. 11. Sepiolite. 12. Chimpanzees in the wild. 13. Linseed oil. 14. It was first
identified when it broke out at a convention of the American Legion in Philadelphia in 1976.
15. The Möbius strip.

SESSION 44 QUIZ 6

Geography

1   Karachi is the chief port of which country?

2   Which desert covers much of Botswana and Namibia?

3   Which country has its capital on the island of Zealand or Sjaelland?

4   What is the capital of Zimbabwe?

5   Which canal joins Loch Ness to the Moray Firth?

6   Which type of cloud can form an 'anvil head': (a) cumulonimbus, (b) cirrus or (c) stratocumulus?

7   In which English city would you be able to get a main line train from Piccadilly Station?

8   In which European capital could you see the Atomium, built for the 1958 World Fair?

9   Sarajevo is the capital of: (a) Bosnia-Herzegovinia, (b) Croatia or (c) Yugoslavia?

10 The Namib desert gains an important part of its water from fog. True or false?

11 Which bay do you cross when sailing north from Capri?

12 In which country is the Sinai Peninsula?

13 Where in Australia is Uluru (Ayers Rock): (a) Western Australia, (b) South Australia or (c) Northern Territory?

14 Which is the deepest of the Great Lakes on the border of Canada and America?

15 Which of these islands does not lie on the equator: (a) Borneo, (b) Java or (c) Sumatra?

ANSWERS

1. Pakistan. 2. Kalahari desert. 3. Denmark. 4. Harare. 5. Caledonian Canal. 6. (a) cumulonimbus. 7. Manchester. 8. Brussels. 9. (a) Bosnia-Herzegovinia. 10. True. 11. The Bay of Naples. 12. Egypt. 13. (c) Northern Territory. 14. Lake Superior. 15. (b) Java.

SESSION 44

QUIZ 7

The Arts

1. What type of fabric can be described as Bobbin, Pillow or Needlepoint?

2. In paintings are 'putti': (a) imps, (b) cherubs or (c) dogs?

3. Giorgio Vasari's 16th-century book of *Lives* contained biographies of : (a) artists, (b) saints or (c) musicians?

4. What colours are usually used on 'willow pattern' china?

5. Which Flemish artist's name has become synonymous with the large full-figured women which he portrayed?

6. What is a pastiche?

7. What issue is central to Harriet Beecher Stowe's novel *Uncle Tom's Cabin*?

8. Which Greek lyric poet was born on Lesbos?

9. 'Dr Kay Scarpetta' is a forensic scientist in the novels of which writer?

10. Who wrote *Catch-22*?

11. What type of instrument is played with a plectrum?

12. Which of Dickens' novels features 'Sir Leicester Dedlock'?

13. What is taught at the RADA?

14. Which Florentine sculptor was born Donato di Niccolo?

15. Arthur Rackham illustrated: (a) fairy stories, (b) political cartoons or (c) railway timetables?

ANSWERS

1. Lace. 2. (b) cherubs. 3. (a) artists. 4. Blue and white. 5. Rubens, hence 'rubenesque'. 6. A work of art that mixes styles or is an imitation of another artist's work. 7. Slavery. 8. Sappho. 9. Patricia Cornwell. 10. Joseph Heller. 11. A stringed one. 12. *Bleak House*. 13. Dramatic arts, especially acting. 14. Donatello. 15. (a) fairy stories.

SESSION 44   QUIZ 8

Pot Luck

1   Which festival is also called Yule?

2   What kind of creature was the Ibis, which was sacred to Egyptians?

3   What is the motto of the Prince of Wales?

4   What people sometimes adopted a surname beginning 'Fitz-'?

5   What is being signalled when a ship's ensign is flown upside down?

6   In the Bible who was known for his patience?

7   Which side of a boat is starboard?

8   Which English boy's name is in other languages Sean, Hans and Giovanni?

9   What was the first month of the Roman calendar?

10   Who was Lord Haw Haw?

11   Which herb represents remembrance?

12   What is a Portuguese man-of-war?

13   According to an old warning, you 'should not cast a clout' until which month is out?

14   Which part of a graveyard was considered the devil's side?

15   What is supposed to happen if it rains on St Swithin's Day?

ANSWERS

1. Christmas. 2. Bird. 3. *Ich dien*, I serve. 4. Illegitimate children of royalty. 5. The ship is in distress. 6. Job. 7. Right-hand side looking forward. 8. John. 9. March. 10. A British man who broadcast Nazi propaganda to the British. 11. Rosemary. 12. A jelly fish. 13. May. 14. North, probably because it received the least sun. 15. It will rain for 40 days.

SESSION 45 QUIZ 1

TV, music & entertainment

1   Who played James Bond in the film *Casino Royale*?

2   Which musical instrument does Vanessa-Mae play?

3   Who was the only *Coronation Street* character to have a spin-off series?

4   What is the name of the character played by Sigourney Weaver in the *Alien* films?

5   What kind of music did singer Mahalia Jackson specialize in?

6   Where was Inspector Morse set?

7   Who was the Danish author played by Meryl Streep in *Out of Africa*?

8   Nirvana had a hit with 'Smells Like Teen Spirit'. What is Teen Spirit?

9   Who is the question master in *Fifteen to One*?

10   What was the name of the 1978 Black version of *The Wizard of Oz*?

11   The Beatles' 'Penny Lane' was on one side of a double A-side. What was on the other side?

12   What is the name of the character played by Helen Mirren in *Prime Suspect*?

13   Which historical event was depicted in the 1953 film *From Here To Eternity*?

14   Which band made an album in 1975 called 'A Night at the Opera'?

15   What was the name of the character played by Antonio Fargas in *Starsky and Hutch*?

ANSWERS

1. David Niven. 2. Violin. 3. Leonard Swindley, played by Arthur Lowe. 4. Ripley.
5. Gospel. 6. Oxford. 7. Isak Dinesen, a.k.a. Karen Blixen. 8. A US brand of deodorant.
9. William G. Stewart. 10. *The Wiz*. 11. 'Strawberry Fields Forever'. 12. Jane Tennison.
13. The Japanese attack on Pearl Harbor. 14. Queen. 15. Huggy Bear.

SESSION 45   QUIZ 2

History

1   Before he crossed the Alps, Hannibal had already traversed another mountain range. What was it?

2   What was the name of the group of Nottinghamshire frameworkers who destroyed labour-saving machinery in 1811?

3   What broke out causing untold misery in Ireland in 1845?

4   The name 'Assassin' comes from a secret sect established in 1090 that specialized in suicide missions. True or false?

5   Who was the first Earl of Beaconsfield?

6   Zola wrote *J'accuse* in protest at which legal trial?

7   'It's wonderful, but it isn't war' was said of which heroic action?

8   Who was the Soviet leader at the time of the Cuban missile crisis?

9   Who did John Wilkes Booth kill?

10   Leopold I was king of which European country?

11   Who was the first president of Cyprus in 1960?

12   Who was the Irish president once and the prime minister three times?

13   What was the name of the plan to provide war-torn Europe with US aid?

14   What did the Romans call York?

15   What language did the 1549 Act of Uniformity abolish from English churches?

ANSWERS

1. The Pyrenees. 2. The Luddites. 3. The potato blight causing the Irish potato famine. 4. True. 5. Benjamin Disraeli. 6. The Dreyfuss trial. 7. The Charge of the Light Brigade. 8. Nikita Khrushchev. 9. Abraham Lincoln. 10. Belgium. 11. Archbishop Makarios. 12. Eamon De Valera. 13. The Marshall Plan. 14. Eboracum. 15. Latin.

SESSION 45 QUIZ 3

Sports

1 In what sport is there a 'prostitute'?

2 Which country did England play in the semi-finals of their World Cup winning year?

3 At which sport does Kelly Holmes compete?

4 Which club side plays at the Oval?

5 In which sport do you have the parallel bars and the beam?

6 Who was the first player sent off in an FA Cup Final?

7 Which footballer played their last game, appropriately, against Germany in 1972?

8 What number of points is a game of squash normally played up to?

9 With which sport do you associate Monza and Imola?

10 Abraham Saperstein began which basketball team in 1927?

11 What is a jockey's uniform known as?

12 Lionel Richie performed at the end of which Olympic Games?

13 Mike Hailwood competed at which sport?

14 Which top ranking tennis player did John Lloyd marry?

15 In cricket is a slip fielder in front or behind the receiving batsman?

ANSWERS

1. Rugby. The number 2 is known as the hooker. 2. Portugal. 3. Middle distance running. 4. Surrey. 5. Gymnastics. 6. Kevin Moran of Manchester United. 7. Geoff Hurst. 8. Nine. 9. Motor racing. 10. The Harlem Globetrotters. 11. Silks. 12. 1984 Los Angeles. 13. Motor cycling. 14. Chris Evert. 15. Behind.

SESSION 45 — QUIZ 4

General knowledge

1 Was the Transport and General Workers Union founded in: (a) 1910, (b) 1917 or (c) 1922?

2 Which country lost the greatest number of merchant ships during World War I?

3 The 'Sun of May' lies at the centre of which country's flag?

4 Actor Harrison Ford appeared in the film *Apocalypse Now*. True or false?

5 What is the literal meaning of 'malaria'?

6 Against what did the Temperance Movement battle?

7 Where can one find a Parliament called the Tynwald?

8 According to the Jews, who are the Goys?

9 What did Sir Frederick Banting isolate?

10 What is the medical name for the windpipe?

11 Who died saying, 'Thank God I have done my duty'?

12 How many plagues did Moses inflict upon the Egyptians?

13 In a standard domino set are there: (a) 24, (b) 26 or (c) 28 tiles?

14 Who directed *Psycho* and *The Birds*?

15 In what industry did Paul Raymond make his fortune?

ANSWERS

1. (c) 1922. 2. The United Kingdom. 3. Argentina. 4. True. He appeared in a cameo role. 5. Bad air. 6. Abuse of alcohol. 7. The Isle of Man. 8. The Gentiles. 9. Insulin. 10. Trachea. 11. Lord Nelson. 12. Ten. 13. (c) 28. 14. Alfred Hitchcock. 15. Adult entertainment.

SESSION 45   QUIZ 5

Technology & science

1   Which planet in the Solar System has the greatest number of moons?

2   What is the clotting protein in blood called?

3   Who is the electrical engineer credited as one of the pioneers of television?

4   Who proposed three laws of motion in 1687?

5   For which other part of the body does bone marrow produce cells?

6   Ambroise Paré is known as the founder of what?

7   What is bovine somatotrophin?

8   Hansen's disease has another name. What is it?

9   Ground that is permanently frozen is known as what?

10   What is the chemical symbol for lead?

11   What is unusual about the name Nicolas Bourbaki?

12   In which part of the brain does the cerebellum lie?

13   Who founded the Institute for Sex Research in 1942?

14   Where in the human body would you find a Bowman's capsule?

15   In medicine, what would you use boric acid for?

ANSWERS

1. Saturn (at least 18). 2. Fibrinogen. 3. John Logie Baird (1888-1946). 4. Isaac Newton. 5. Blood. 6. Modern surgery. 7. A hormone that when injected increases a cow's milk yield. 8. Leprosy. 9. Permafrost. 10. Pb. 11. It's a pseudonym, for a group of French scientists who published a definitive survey of mathematics from 1939 onwards. 12. At the back of the skull. 13. Alfred Charles Kinsey (1894-1956). 14. In the kidney. 15. As an antiseptic.

SESSION 45 QUIZ 6

Geography

1 Which of these towns is on the north coast of Scotland:
(a) Wick, (b) Kirkwall or (c) Thurso?

2 What is the capital of Uganda?

3 What is the name for the lowest level of the atmosphere:
(a) the thermosphere, (b) the stratosphere or (c) the troposphere?

4 In which south coast port would you be able to look out to sea
from The Hoe?

5 What is the peninsula called in the north of Queensland:
(a) Arnhem Land, (b) Cape York or (c) Eyre Peninsula?

6 Is the coast of Ghana called: (a) the Gold Coast,
(b) the Grain Coast or (c) the Ivory Coast?

7 In which American city are the districts of Burbank and
Beverly Hills?

8 Which is greater: the diameter of the Earth at the equator or
the diameter between the poles?

9 In which African country is the Tsavo National Park?

10 What is significant about Mount Erebus in Antarctica; is it:
(a) the only peak yet to be climbed, (b) the highest mountain in
Antarctica or (c) the most southerly volcano?

11 In which country is the ski resort of Cortina d'Ampezzo?

12 Which country pioneered meat processing at the town of
Fray Bentos?

13 On the shore of which Cumbrian lake are the villages of
Glenridding, Pooley Bridge and Watermillock?

14 Which mountainous country is completely surrounded by
South Africa?

15 In which country is the town of Maastricht?

ANSWERS

1. (c) Thurso. 2. Kampala. 3. (c) the troposphere. 4. Plymouth. 5. (b) Cape York. 6. (a) the
Gold Coast. 7. Los Angeles. 8. The diameter at the equator. 9. Kenya. 10. (c) the most
southerly volcano. 11. Italy. 12. Uruguay. 13. Ullswater. 14. Lesotho. 15. The Netherlands.

SESSION 45   QUIZ 7

The Arts

1   What type of art is based on inner-city spray can vandalism?

2   Which London school of fine art opened in 1871?

3   Who wrote *The Tin Drum*?

4   What were the Emperor's new clothes made of?

5   Who wrote *Titus Groan* and *Gormenghast*?

6   In which novel by Graham Greene does Harry Lime appear?

7   In which poem by Milton is the word 'pandemonium' first used, meaning the city of Satan?

8   In *Pickwick Papers* which county is described as being the home of 'apples, cherries, hops and women'?

9   Which king commissioned the new translation of the Bible, known as the Authorized Version and published in 1611?

10   Who wrote the epic poem *Childe Harold's Pilgrimage*?

11   Tussore, Mulberry and Mussel are what types of fabric?

12   What art technique uses small squares of glass or marble called tesserae?

13   René Lalique was: (a) a stone mason, (b) a copper etcher or (c) a glassmaker?

14   Which South Kensington museum was originally called the Museum of Ornamental Art?

15   What is the English translation of the title of Johann Strauss's opera *Die Fledermaus*?

ANSWERS

1. Graffiti. 2. The Slade. 3. Günter Grass. 4. Nothing; they were non-existent. 5. Mervyn Peake. 6. *The Third Man*. 7. *Paradise Lost*. 8. Kent. 9. King James I. 10. Lord Byron. 11. Silk. 12. Mosaic. 13. (c) a glassmaker. 14. The Victoria and Albert. 15. *The Bat*.

SESSION 45   QUIZ 8

Pot Luck

1   What word beginning with g means a judge's hammer?

2   How deep is a fathom?

3   Is a *fata morgana*: (a) a fairy, (b) a mirage or (c) a poisonous mushroom?

4   Which sign of the zodiac is represented by the Twins?

5   How many sheets of paper are there now in a ream?

6   In which German city does the Oktoberfest take place?

7   What name is given to a female deer?

8   A kindergarten is a nursery school. What is the literal meaning of this German word?

9   On what day does the Queen distribute alms to the needy?

10   On which day is it lucky to kiss a chimney sweep?

11   What shops were legalized on 1 May 1961?

12   Which Greek youth fell in love with his own reflection?

13   What is chowder?

14   On which of the Channel Islands are motorized vehicles banned?

15   What is All Saint's Eve usually called?

ANSWERS

1. Gavel. 2. Six feet. 3. (b) a mirage. 4. Gemini. 5. 500. 6. Munich. 7. Doe. 8. Children's garden. 9. Maundy Thursday. 10. Your wedding day. 11. Betting shops. 12. Narcissus. 13. A thick soup. 14. Sark. 15. Hallowe'en.

SESSION 46 QUIZ 1

TV, music & entertainment

1 Who wrote the musical scores for *Lawrence of Arabia*, *Dr Zhivago* and *Ryan's Daughter*?

2 In which city is the TV detective show *Taggart* set?

3 Singer Glen Campbell was once a member of the Beach Boys. True or false?

4 What was the name of the character played by Anthony Hopkins in *Silence of the Lambs*?

5 On which TV programme was singer Sheena Easton discovered?

6 Which jazz pianist had his own group called the Red Hot Peppers?

7 Of which Hollywood star was it said 'Wet she was a star'?

8 Who played Herman Munster in the sitcom *The Munsters*?

9 Who co-wrote the song *Fame* with David Bowie?

10 Who was actress Isabella Rosselini's famous mother?

11 Which TV detective's catchphrase was 'Who loves ya, baby?'

12 What was the Spice Girls' first hit record?

13 Who played 'Oskar Schindler' in the film *Schindler's List*?

14 Which film actor played Tom Jordache in the TV drama serial *Rich Man, Poor Man*?

15 Which US band had a hit in 1992 with 'Everybody Hurts'?

ANSWERS

1. Maurice Jarre. 2. Glasgow. 3. True. 4. Hannibal Lecter. 5. Esther Rantzen's *Big Time*. 6. Jelly Roll Morton. 7. Esther Williams. 8. Fred Gwynne. 9. John Lennon. 10. Ingrid Bergman. 11. Kojak. 12. 'Wannabe'. 13. Liam Neeson. 14. Nick Nolte. 15. R.E.M.

SESSION 46 QUIZ 2

History

1 Where did the Pilgrim Fathers settle in 1620?

2 What dastardly deed were John Wright, Thomas Percy and Robert Catesby involved in?

3 What did the German family Krupp manufacture?

4 What happened to Iceland and Yugoslavia on 1 December 1918?

5 What was the year of the Easter Rising?

6 Which Frenchman was the 'Hero of Verdun'?

7 Who was prime minister during the General Strike?

8 Catherine de Medici was queen of which country in the 16th century?

9 The illuminated manuscript of the Gospels the *Book of Kells* was produced in: (a) the 3rd century, (b) the 8th century or (c) the 10th century?

10 In which country were the Mysore Wars fought?

11 Where were Cavendish and his undersecretary murdered in 1882?

12 What did Robert Peel establish in 1829?

13 What did Winston Churchill call his depressive moods?

14 What did Lord Baden-Powell found in 1907?

15 Which revolutionary was killed with an ice pick in Mexico?

ANSWERS

1. Plymouth, Massachusetts. 2. The Gunpowder Plot. 3. Armaments. 4. They achieved sovereignty. 5. 1916. 6. Henri Philippe Pétain. 7. Stanley Baldwin. 8. France. 9. (b) the 8th century. 10. India. 11. Phoenix Park, Dublin. 12. The Metropolitan Police Force, nicknamed the Peelers. 13. Black Dog. 14. The Boy Scouts. 15. Leon Trotsky.

SESSION 46   QUIZ 3

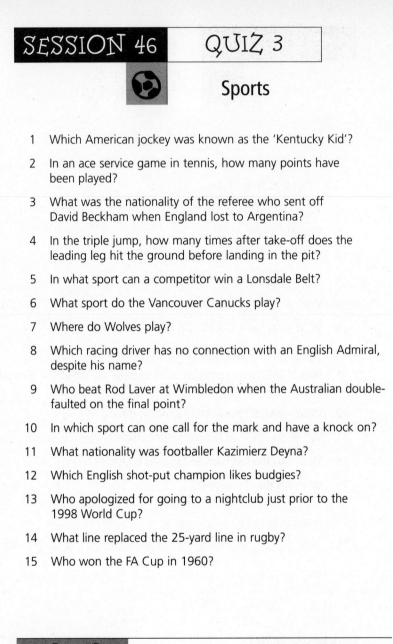

Sports

1 Which American jockey was known as the 'Kentucky Kid'?

2 In an ace service game in tennis, how many points have been played?

3 What was the nationality of the referee who sent off David Beckham when England lost to Argentina?

4 In the triple jump, how many times after take-off does the leading leg hit the ground before landing in the pit?

5 In what sport can a competitor win a Lonsdale Belt?

6 What sport do the Vancouver Canucks play?

7 Where do Wolves play?

8 Which racing driver has no connection with an English Admiral, despite his name?

9 Who beat Rod Laver at Wimbledon when the Australian double-faulted on the final point?

10 In which sport can one call for the mark and have a knock on?

11 What nationality was footballer Kazimierz Deyna?

12 Which English shot-put champion likes budgies?

13 Who apologized for going to a nightclub just prior to the 1998 World Cup?

14 What line replaced the 25-yard line in rugby?

15 Who won the FA Cup in 1960?

ANSWERS

1. Steve Cauthen. 2. Four. 3. Danish. 4. Once. 5. Boxing. 6. Ice hockey. 7. Molineux. 8. Nelson Piquet. 9. Roger Taylor. 10. Rugby. 11. Polish. 12. Geoff Capes. He is an avid collector. 13. Teddy Sheringham. 14. The 22-metre line. 15. Wolves.

SESSION 46

QUIZ 4

General knowledge

1 What do the initials RSI stand for?

2 What would you do with a Château Lafite?

3 What was Piper Alpha?

4 Which country has the most English-language speakers?

5 What is vexillology?

6 Who wrote the *Little Red Book*?

7 What does the name Andrew mean?

8 Who is Dr Jack Kevorkian?

9 With what weapons did David defeat Goliath?

10 Who said, 'Cogito ergo sum'?

11 Which BBC news correspondent became an MP at the general election in 1997?

12 Which rank is above Air Marshal in the RAF?

13 Which country has the longest coastline?

14 Who was the last woman hanged in the UK?

15 Where is the JFK airport?

ANSWERS

1. Repetitive strain injury. 2. Drink it, it's a very expensive wine. 3. An oil rig in the North Sea that caught fire on 6 July 1988. 4. USA. 5. The study of flags and related emblems. 6. Mao Tse-tung. 7. Manly. 8. An exponent of assisted suicide. 9. A stone and sling. 10. René Descartes. 11. Martin Bell. 12. Air Chief Marshal. 13. Canada. 14. Ruth Ellis, on 13 July 1955. 15. New York.

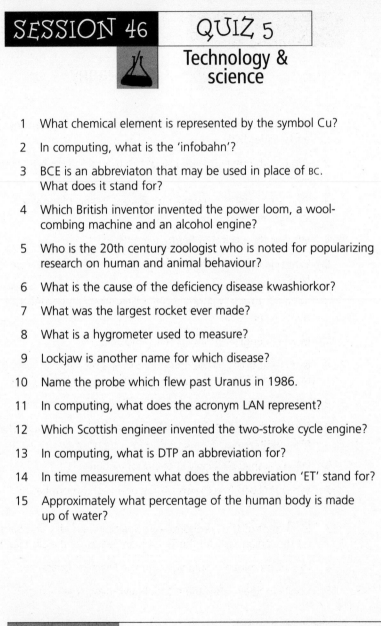

SESSION 46

QUIZ 5

Technology & science

1 What chemical element is represented by the symbol Cu?

2 In computing, what is the 'infobahn'?

3 BCE is an abbreviaton that may be used in place of BC.
   What does it stand for?

4 Which British inventor invented the power loom, a wool-combing machine and an alcohol engine?

5 Who is the 20th century zoologist who is noted for popularizing research on human and animal behaviour?

6 What is the cause of the deficiency disease kwashiorkor?

7 What was the largest rocket ever made?

8 What is a hygrometer used to measure?

9 Lockjaw is another name for which disease?

10 Name the probe which flew past Uranus in 1986.

11 In computing, what does the acronym LAN represent?

12 Which Scottish engineer invented the two-stroke cycle engine?

13 In computing, what is DTP an abbreviation for?

14 In time measurement what does the abbreviation 'ET' stand for?

15 Approximately what percentage of the human body is made up of water?

ANSWERS

1. Copper. 2. A high speed computer network, especially the Internet. 3. Before the Common Era. 4. Edmund Cartwright. 5. Desmond Morris (1928–). 6. Lack of protein in the diet (usually in young children in developing countries). 7. *Saturn V* (it carried the first astronauts that landed on the Moon). 8. Humidity of the atmosphere (or any other gas). 9. Tetanus. 10. *Voyager 2*. 11. Local area network. 12. Sir Dugald Clerk. 13. Desk-top publishing. 14. Ephemeris time. 15. 60 – 80 per cent.

SESSION 46 QUIZ 6

Geography

1 On which island could you visit the towns of Peel, Ramsey and Castletown?

2 What is the name of the lake created on the River Nile by the Aswan Dam?

3 Tien Shan, the 'Mountains of Heaven', are in Mongolia. True or false?

4 What is the capital of South Australia?

5 Which is the last American city on the Pacific coast before Mexico?

6 In which African country are the Masai Mara and Amboseli game reserves?

7 In which English county is the Fylde coast?

8 Is the end point of the Ebro delta in Spain called: (a) Cap de Tortosa, (b) Cap de la Nau or (c) Cabo de Palos?

9 Which is the highest capital city in the world?

10 What is the strait between Malaysia and the Indonesian island of Sumatra?

11 Where is the USA's only subtropical wetland?

12 What do Loch Fyne, Loch Linnhe and Loch Broom have in common?

13 Is the part of the Mediterranean Sea between Italy and Sardinia: (a) the Ionian Sea, (b) the Tyrrhenian Sea or (c) the Ligurian Sea?

14 In which country would you find the Malabar Coast?

15 Seville in Spain is on the Guadalquivir river. True or false?

ANSWERS

1. The Isle of Man. 2. Lake Nasser. 3. False. They are in Kyrgyzstan and China. 4. Adelaide. 5. San Diego. 6. Kenya. 7. Lancashire. 8. Cap de Tortosa. 9. La Paz in Bolivia. 10. Strait of Malacca. 11. The Everglades in Florida. 12. They are all sea lochs. 13. (b) the Tyrrhenian Sea. 14. India. 15. True.

SESSION 46 — QUIZ 7

The Arts

1 At what speed should music marked 'andante' be played?

2 'Land of Hope and Glory' is from which set of marches by Edward Elgar?

3 Who wrote the long running play *The Mousetrap*?

4 Which girl did Tennyson invite to 'Come into the garden...'?

5 Who wrote *Heart of Darkness* and *Lord Jim*?

6 On which island were Ralph, Jack and Peterkin shipwrecked in a novel by R. M. Ballantyne?

7 Who wrote *James and the Giant Peach* and *Matilda*?

8 Which composer wrote the popular piece of music 'Morning' from his *Peer Gynt*?

9 Which cartoonist created drawings of ludicrously elaborate machinery designed to achieve simple tasks?

10 Which artist's autobiography is called *My Secret Life*?

11 What nationality were the majority of the Impressionist painters?

12 By what title is Velazquez's painting *Toilet of Venus* better known?

13 Which hymn is believed to have been written when its author took shelter in Cheddar Gorge?

14 The discovery of which stone slab in 1799 enabled hieroglyphics to be deciphered?

15 'If music be the food of love' is a line from which play?

ANSWERS

1. Slowly. 2. *Pomp and Circumstance*. 3. Agatha Christie. 4. Maud. 5. Joseph Conrad. 6. *The Coral Island*. 7. Roald Dahl. 8. Edvard Grieg. 9. William Heath Robinson. 10. Salvador Dali. 11. French. 12. *The Rokeby Venus*, because it used to be at Rokeby Hall. 13. *Rock of Ages*. 14. The Rosetta stone. 15. *Twelfth Night*.

SESSION 46 · QUIZ 8

Pot Luck

1 Which British female singer of the sixties, famous for her dusky voice and beehive hairstyle, died in 1999?

2 Is faro: (a) a card game, (b) a horse or (c) a type of flour?

3 Who was El Cid?

4 The drachma is the currency of which country?

5 What are niacin, thiamine and riboflavin?

6 In hot countries what name is given to an afternoon rest or nap?

7 What size of paper is 148 x 210 mm?

8 What word beginning with 'f' means wreckage found floating on the sea?

9 Kirsch is a spirit made from which fruit?

10 What disease may be prevented or cured by quinine?

11 How old is a nonagenarian?

12 What colour is a garnet?

13 What do flags flying at half mast indicate?

14 What is Mammon?

15 Would you wear a shako on: (a) your hand, (b) your foot or (c) your head?

ANSWERS

SESSION 47

QUIZ 1

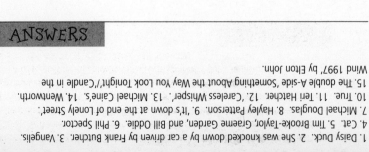

TV, music & entertainment

1 What is Donald Duck's girlfriend called?

2 In *EastEnders*, how did Tiffany Mitchell die?

3 Who wrote the musical score for the film *Chariots of Fire*?

4 What was the name of Holly Golightly's cat in *Breakfast at Tiffany's*?

5 Who were *The Goodies*?

6 Which record producer created the 'Wall of Sound' production technique?

7 What is actor Michael Keaton's real name?

8 What is the name of the transsexual character in *Coronation Street*?

9 In the Elvis Presley hit, where is 'Heartbreak Hotel' located?

10 Action-film hero Chuck Norris is a former world champion in karate. True or false?

11 Who plays Lois Lane in TV's *The New Adventures of Superman*?

12 What was George Michael's first solo single?

13 Which film star's original name was Maurice Micklewhite?

14 What is the name of the women's prison in *Prisoner: Cell Block H*?

15 What is the best-selling single of all time?

ANSWERS

1. Daisy Duck. 2. She was knocked down by a car driven by Frank Butcher. 3. Vangelis. 4. Cat. 5. Tim Brooke-Taylor, Graeme Garden, and Bill Oddie. 6. Phil Spector. 7. Michael Douglas. 8. Hayley Patterson. 9. 'It's down at the end of Lonely Street'. 10. True. 11. Teri Hatcher. 12. 'Careless Whisper'. 13. Michael Caine's. 14. Wentworth. 15. The double A-side 'Something About the Way You Look Tonight'/'Candle in the Wind 1997' by Elton John.

SESSION 47   QUIZ 2

History

1   Which German battleship was sunk on 27 May 1941?

2   By what other name is the third Ypres battle known?

3   What did King Canute order to go back?

4   Which monarch succeeded William of Orange?

5   What gold coins were struck for the first time in Florence in 1252?

6   What did Henry VIII dissolve?

7   Who 'came, saw and conquered'?

8   Who were the Fenians?

9   Who was president of Kenya from 1964–78?

10   Who was the unwitting hero of Operation Mincemeat?

11   In which Egyptian city is the Karnak temple?

12   What were the ziggurats?

13   Which brothers invented the hot air balloon?

14   In which year did the *Titanic* sink?

15   Where did Burgess and Maclean escape to?

ANSWERS

1. *The Bismarck*. 2. Passchendaele. 3. The sea. 4. Anne. 5. Florins. 6. The monasteries. 7. Julius Caeser. 8. A revolutionary Irish organization formed to fight for an independent Ireland. 9. Jomo Kenyatta. 10. A dead man. His body was 'dumped' so that the Germans would find it and read 'classified' information that falsely predicted the Allies would choose Greece rather than Sicily for the invasion of southern Europe. 11. Luxor. 12. Ancient Mesopotamian brick-built temple towers, constructed of rectangular terraces of diminishing size. 13. Montgolfier. 14. 1912. 15. Moscow.

SESSION 47   QUIZ 3

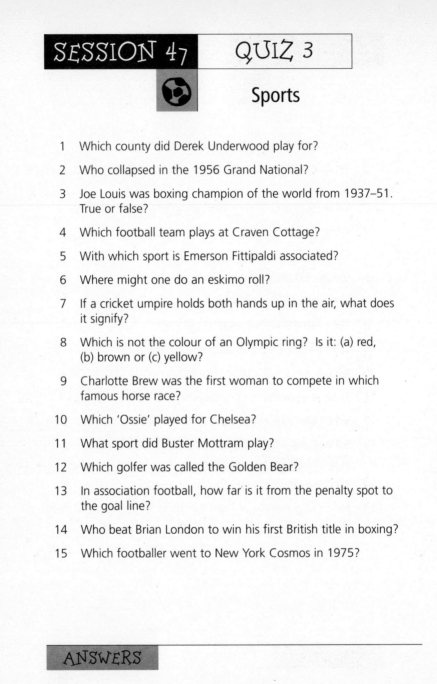

Sports

1   Which county did Derek Underwood play for?

2   Who collapsed in the 1956 Grand National?

3   Joe Louis was boxing champion of the world from 1937–51. True or false?

4   Which football team plays at Craven Cottage?

5   With which sport is Emerson Fittipaldi associated?

6   Where might one do an eskimo roll?

7   If a cricket umpire holds both hands up in the air, what does it signify?

8   Which is not the colour of an Olympic ring? Is it: (a) red, (b) brown or (c) yellow?

9   Charlotte Brew was the first woman to compete in which famous horse race?

10   Which 'Ossie' played for Chelsea?

11   What sport did Buster Mottram play?

12   Which golfer was called the Golden Bear?

13   In association football, how far is it from the penalty spot to the goal line?

14   Who beat Brian London to win his first British title in boxing?

15   Which footballer went to New York Cosmos in 1975?

ANSWERS

1. Kent. 2. 'Devon Loch'. 3. False. It was from 1937–49. 4. Fulham. 5. Motor racing. 6. In a canoe. 7. A six. 8. (b) brown. 9. The Grand National. 10. Peter Osgood. 11. Tennis. 12. Jack Nicklaus. 13. 12 yards. 14. Henry Cooper. 15. Pelé.

SESSION 47

QUIZ 4

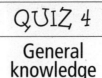

General knowledge

1 What did Melville Bissell invent?

2 What did Lt. Thomas Selfridge have the misfortune to become in 1908?

3 Where is the capital of the Mormons?

4 What is a gillion?

5 How many Pius Popes have there been?

6 Where do Sikhs originate?

7 What nationality is the electronics giant, Siemens?

8 What do the initials NIMBY stand for?

9 A yurt is the home of which nomadic peoples?

10 Do people go to find gold quickly or slowly?

11 Edith Holden had a surprise bestseller with which book?

12 Who was the first king of Israel?

13 'How is the empire?' were the last words of which English monarch?

14 Who was the first man to walk in space?

15 How many men were hung after the Nuremberg War Trials?

ANSWERS

1. The carpet sweeper. 2. He was the first plane crash fatality. 3. Salt Lake City, Utah. 4. One thousand million. 5. 12. 6. The Punjab. 7. German. 8. Not in my back yard. 9. Nomads in Mongolia, Siberia and Turkey. 10. Quickly, they 'rush'. 11. *The Country Diary of an Edwardian Lady*. 12. Saul. 13. George V. 14. Alexei Leonov in 1965. 15. Ten.

SESSION 47 QUIZ 5

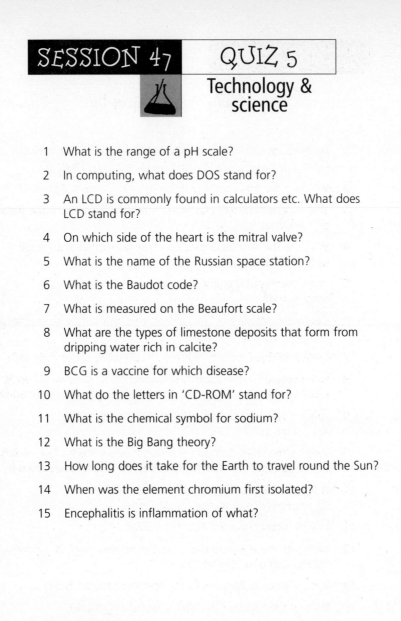

Technology & science

1   What is the range of a pH scale?

2   In computing, what does DOS stand for?

3   An LCD is commonly found in calculators etc. What does LCD stand for?

4   On which side of the heart is the mitral valve?

5   What is the name of the Russian space station?

6   What is the Baudot code?

7   What is measured on the Beaufort scale?

8   What are the types of limestone deposits that form from dripping water rich in calcite?

9   BCG is a vaccine for which disease?

10   What do the letters in 'CD-ROM' stand for?

11   What is the chemical symbol for sodium?

12   What is the Big Bang theory?

13   How long does it take for the Earth to travel round the Sun?

14   When was the element chromium first isolated?

15   Encephalitis is inflammation of what?

ANSWERS

1. 0 – 14, from acid to alkaline. 2. Disk operating system. 3. Liquid-crystal display. 4. Left side. 5. Mir. 6. A code used in telecommunications. 7. Wind velocity. 8. Stalactites and stalagmites. 9. Tuberculosis. 10. Compact disk read-only memory. 11. Na. 12. A postulated explosive event that marked the beginning of time. 13. 365 days. 14. 1797. 15. The brain.

SESSION 47   QUIZ 6

Geography

1   At the Banc d'Arguin National park, the wardens patrol on camels. Is this in: (a) Mali, (b) Mauritania or (c) Niger?

2   Which is the most easterly of the United States of America?

3   Which Australian city was virtually destroyed by Hurricane Tracy on Christmas Day 1974?

4   Where is the world's largest tin mine: (a) Australia, (b) Brazil or (c) Canada?

5   Which lake is at the junction of Germany, Austria and Switzerland?

6   Ceuta and Melilla are Spanish enclaves on the African mainland, within which country?

7   In which English county is the area called the Isle of Purbeck?

8   Is the greatest tidal range in the world at: (a) the Bay of Fundy, Nova Scotia, (b) the Severn estuary or (c) the Gulf of Honduras?

9   Around which land mass are the Weddell, Ross and Amundsen seas?

10   What is the strait, through the islands of southern Chile, which bears the name of the Portuguese sailor who first navigated it?

11   Is the source of the Dordogne river in: (a) the Alps, (b) the Pyrenees or (c) the Massif Central?

12   In which country is the Kola peninsula?

13   Which of these principalities has the smallest area: (a) Andorra, (b) Monaco or (c) Liechenstein?

14   Which National Park lies to the north of Merthyr Tydfil?

15   What is the name of the largest island in Canada?

ANSWERS

1. (b) Mauritania. 2. Maine. 3. Darwin. 4. (b) Brazil. 5. Lake Constance, or the Bodensee. 6. Morocco. 7. Dorset. 8. (a) Bay of Fundy, Nova Scotia. 9. Antarctica. 10. The Strait of Magellan. 11. (c) The Massif Central. 12. Russia. 13. (b) Monaco. 14. The Brecon Beacons. 15. Baffin Island.

SESSION 47   QUIZ 7

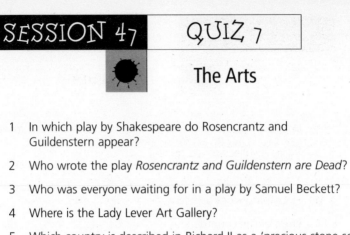

The Arts

1 In which play by Shakespeare do Rosencrantz and Guildenstern appear?

2 Who wrote the play *Rosencrantz and Guildenstern are Dead*?

3 Who was everyone waiting for in a play by Samuel Beckett?

4 Where is the Lady Lever Art Gallery?

5 Which country is described in Richard II as a 'precious stone set in the silver sea'?

6 Who came to call in the 1947 mystery play by J. B. Priestley?

7 Which fictional teacher did Muriel Spark describe as being in her prime?

8 Which architect designed the cathedrals of Newcastle, Birmingham, Nottingham and Southwark?

9 In book sizes, which is larger: a quarto or a folio?

10 Who is on trial at the end of *Alice in Wonderland*?

11 'My Luve's like a red, red rose'. The first line of a poem by whom?

12 Which poet was a librarian at Hull University in the 1950s?

13 Whose wife, called Jane, was the model for many of Dante Gabriel Rossetti's paintings?

14 Which country is the setting of the novel *Cry, the Beloved Country*?

15 In which century were Beaumont and Fletcher writing plays together?

ANSWERS

1. *Hamlet*. 2. Tom Stoppard. 3. Godot (*Waiting for Godot*). 4. Port Sunlight. 5. Britain. 6. An inspector (*An Inspector Calls*). 7. 'Miss Jean Brodie'. 8. August Pugin. 9. Folio. 10. 'The Knave of Hearts'. 11. Robert Burns. 12. Philip Larkin. 13. William Morris. 14. South Africa. 15. 17th.

SESSION 47 QUIZ 8

Pot Luck

1 The spice called mace is the outer covering of which other spice?

2 What is collected into quires?

3 What do you do if you 'pick up the gauntlet'?

4 How many sides does a dodecahedron have?

5 From which country does goulash originate?

6 What is a polymath?

7 In what year was the Festival of Britain; was it: (a) 1941, (b) 1951 or (c) 1961?

8 What word means both a holder for arrows and to tremble?

9 What name is given to curried chicken and vegetable soup?

10 What is the profession of a 'silk'?

11 What is the opposite of 'yin'?

12 Which country's car registration letters are PNG?

13 Where would you find the Dutch House, the Palm House and the Orangery?

14 How many gallons of wine are in a hogshead?

15 Is an isthmus: (a) a narrow piece of land, (b) an island or (c) a river crossing?

ANSWERS

1. Nutmeg. 2. Paper. 3. Take up a challenge. 4. 12. 5. Hungary. 6. Someone with knowledge of many subjects. 7. (b) 1951. 8. Quiver. 9. Mulligatawny. 10. A barrister, specifically a QC. 11. Yang. 12. Papua New Guinea. 13. Kew Gardens. 14. 52.5 imperial gallons or 63 US gallons. 15. (a) a narrow piece of land.

384

QUIZ 1

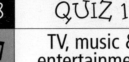

TV, music & entertainment

1   Who wrote the songs in Walt Disney's *The Lion King*?

2   Which major Hollywood star made a cameo appearance at the end of the film *Fairy Tale*?

3   In the TV drama series *Quincy*, what was 'Quincy''s profession?

4   Which US composer wrote 'St Louis Blues' and 'Loveless Love'?

5   Which British animator has won three Oscars for his short films featuring 'Wallace and Gromit'?

6   Who was Dudley Moore's comedy partner in TV's *Not Only... But Also*?

7   Which US singer's real name is Richard Penniman?

8   In which film did James Cagney say, 'Made it, Ma – of the world'?

9   Who wrote the songs for *The Wombles*?

10   Which actor guested on Blur's hit single 'Parklife'?

11   Which actor delivered the eulogy at the funeral in *Four Weddings and A Funeral*?

12   What is Joey's surname in *Home and Away*?

13   Who was the lead singer with the band Madness?

14   In which film did Peter Finch urge people to yell, 'I'm mad as hell and I'm not going to take this any more!'?

15   Who is the presenter of TV's *Masterchef*?

SESSION 48 · QUIZ 2

History

1 What did Molotov and Ribbentrop sign on 23 August 1939 that helped Hitler invade Poland?

2 Who was the only prominent supporter of Edward VIII at the time of his abdication?

3 In what year did Vesuvius erupt covering the town of Pompeii?

4 What devastated Europe in the 14th century?

5 Which city did Joan of Arc set out to relieve?

6 Which country did Cortes invade in the period from 1519–20?

7 Which country divided along the 17th parallel in 1954?

8 In which year did King Hussein of Jordan die?

9 Which country declared 'UDI'?

10 The word 'Boycott' was first used in Ireland in the 1890s. True or false?

11 Who revolted against the Romans in AD 66?

12 What useful item was invented by the Chinese in AD 105?

13 What did Edward I take from Scotland in 1296?

14 Which explorer reached the Cape of Good Hope in 1487–88?

15 By what name is Charles Edward Stuart better known?

ANSWERS

1. A non-aggression pact. 2. Churchill. 3. AD 79. 4. The Black Death. 5. Orleans. 6. Mexico. 7. Vietnam. 8. 1999. 9. Rhodesia. 10. True, after Captain Boycott, a land agent in the country. 11. Boudicca. 12. Paper. 13. The Stone of Scone. 14. Bartholomew Diaz. 15. The 'Young Pretender' or 'Bonnie Prince Charlie'.

SESSION 48   QUIZ 3

Sports

1   Which Suffolk club side did Alf Ramsey manage?

2   When did 'Red Rum' win the Grand National for the third time?

3   How long is an Olympic swimming pool?

4   What did 'Pickles' find in 1966?

5   What item cannot be drunk on a golf course?

6   Who rode 'Shergar' for his first Derby win?

7   What colour signifies danger in motor racing?

8   In football, who are known as 'The Gunners'?

9   How many points are scored for a try in rugby union?

10   What is a golden duck?

11   Where was Ivan Lendl born?

12   Charlie George never played for England. True or false?

13   Which London club was managed by John Lyall?

14   In which year was the Tour de France inaugurated?

15   What is a 'spoon' in golf?

ANSWERS

1. Ipswich. 2. 1977. 3. 50 metres. 4. The Jules Rimet trophy. 5. The tee. 6. Walter Swinburn. 7. Yellow. 8. Arsenal. 9. Five. 10. Out first ball in cricket. 11. Czechoslovakia. 12. False, he played once. 13. West Ham. 14. 1903. 15. A 3-wood.

SESSION 48 QUIZ 4

General knowledge

1 Which is the smallest country in the world?

2 What did Whitcombe Judson invent in 1891?

3 What type of instrument is a Moog?

4 Which countries make up the Baltic States?

5 The roadrunner bird is the state animal of New Mexico. True or false?

6 What is Nike the goddess of?

7 The Incas lived in which mountain range?

8 What did Sir Alexander Fleming isolate in 1928?

9 The Jolly Roger is the traditional flag of what?

10 Who directed *Raiders of the Lost Ark*?

11 What is a Job's comforter?

12 Who wrote *The Lord of the Rings*?

13 What is strabismus?

14 Who is Abbadon?

15 What does 'pis aller' mean?

ANSWERS

1. Vatican City. 2. The safety zip. 3. A keyboard synthesiser. 4. Estonia, Latvia and Lithuania. 5. True. 6. The goddess of victory. 7. The Andes. 8. Penicillin. 9. Pirates. 10. Steven Spielberg. 11. Someone who, trying to sympathize, only makes matters worse. 12. J. R. R. Tolkien. 13. Eye mis-alignment, such as cross eye. 14. The devil. 15. A last resort, literally, the worst going.

SESSION 48   QUIZ 5

Technology & science

1 Leo Baekeland created the first synthetic plastic in 1909. What did he call it?

2 From which mineral is emerald obtained?

3 Which Greek mathematician first measured the Earth's circumference by using geometry?

4 In biology, what is the abbreviation BMR short for?

5 What is produced in the Bessemer process?

6 Where would you find a base pair?

7 What creature acts as carrier of the disease bilharzia?

8 What was the 'Flying Bedstead'?

9 Mica is: (a) a measurement in printing, (b) mucous substance or (c) a rock-forming mineral?

10 What practice is involved in geophagy?

11 In which year did Alexander Graham Bell invent the telephone?

12 What is a hydrometer used for?

13 What is the popular name for vitamin B_1?

14 What is the full name of E. Coli?

15 What is a quark?

ANSWERS

1. Bakelite. 2. Beryl. 3. Eratosthenes. 4. Basal metabolic rate. 5. Steel. 6. In a molecule of DNA. 7. Freshwater snails. 8. The first vertical take-off aircraft (1954). 9. (c) a rock-forming mineral. 10. Eating soil. 11. 1876. 12. Measuring density of liquids. 13. Thiamine. 14. *Escherichia coli*. 15. A subatomic particle.

SESSION 48 — QUIZ 6

Geography

1   In which English county are Babbacombe Bay and Start Bay?

2   What is the name of the Spanish coast between Barcelona and the French border?

3   From which city could you visit the islands of Burano, Murano and Torcello?

4   In which African country is the port of Dar es Salaam?

5   Which of the Leeward Islands derives its name from its long, thin shape, which reminded its Spanish discoverers of an eel?

6   Which is the most westerly of Canada's territories: (a) British Columbia, (b) North West Territories or (c) Yukon Territory?

7   Which country is sandwiched between Guyana and French Guiana?

8   From which country could you look out into the Gulf of Lions: (a) France, (b) Italy or (c) Greece?

9   In which state is the American side of the Niagara Falls?

10   Which two counties border the Wash?

11   Which of these small countries has the largest population: (a) Andorra, (b) Liechtenstein or (c) San Marino?

12   Which canal opened in 1869 and is 173 kilometres long?

13   In which Indian city are the Red Fort and the Taj Mahal?

14   What is the capital of Latvia?

15   After the Tokyo-Yokohama conurbation, which is the next largest city in Japan, with over ten million people?

ANSWERS

1. Devon. 2. Costa Brava. 3. Venice. 4. Tanzania. 5. Anguilla. 6. (c) Yukon Territory. 7. Suriname. 8. (a) France. 9. New York. 10. Lincolnshire and Norfolk. 11. (a) Andorra. 12. The Suez Canal. 13. Agra. 14. Riga. 15. Osaka.

SESSION 48 · QUIZ 7

The Arts

1 Who wrote the lines 'Come, friendly bombs, and fall on Slough/ It isn't fit for humans now'?

2 What is known as 'The Scottish Play'?

3 Who wrote *Decline and Fall* and *A Handful of Dust*?

4 What is an allegory?

5 In a nonsense poem by Edward Lear what did the Pobble lose?

6 Which Scottish artist painted the *Reverend Robert Walker Skating on Duddington Loch*?

7 *Aladdin* and *Ali Baba and the Forty Thieves* come from which collection of stories?

8 Which vet was the central character in the book *If Only They Could Talk*?

9 Which Dutch artist's favourite subject was beautiful Greek and Roman girls in marbled halls?

10 Which composer is the subject of Peter Shaffer's play *Amadeus*?

11 Which newspaper has published the comic strip *Andy Capp* since 1956?

12 Who wrote *Frankenstein*?

13 In which year did Otis Redding die?

14 On what date is Burns Night?

15 In which city is Keats buried?

ANSWERS

1. John Betjeman. 2. *Macbeth*. 3. Evelyn Waugh. 4. A story or picture in which things have symbolic meaning. 5. His toes (*The Pobble who has no toes*). 6. Henry Raeburn. 7. *The Arabian Nights*. 8. James Herriot. 9. Lawrence Alma-Tadema. 10. Wolfgang Amadeus Mozart. 11. *Daily Mirror*. 12. Mary Shelley. 13. 1967. 14. 25 January (Robert Burns' birthday). 15. Rome.

SESSION 48   QUIZ 8

Pot Luck

1 How many miles are there in seven leagues?

2 What is a virago?

3 What is contained in a bottle marked with a skull and crossbones?

4 How many gallons of beer in two firkins?

5 The word 'dekko', meaning to take a look, comes originally from: (a) Spanish, (b) Hindi or (c) Egyptian?

6 What cake was traditionally eaten on Mothering Sunday?

7 What is one dice called?

8 An ocarina is: (a) a fish, (b) a wind instrument or (c) a fruit?

9 Which day of the week is named after the god Odin?

10 What word, used to describe army uniforms, means 'dust-coloured' in Hindi?

11 What was 'wampum' for North American Indians?

12 A greave is a piece of armour which protects: (a) the head, (b) the shoulder or (c) the shin?

13 When was the single European currency, the euro, introduced?

14 Does simian mean: (a) ape-like, (b) pig-like or (c) cat-like?

15 What five-letter word means someone who falsely claims to have medical skill and knowledge?

ANSWERS

1. 21. 2. A strong or fierce woman. 3. Poison. 4. 18 gallons. 5. (b) Hindi. 6. Simnel. 7. A die. 8. (b) a wind instrument. 9. Wednesday, Odin's or Woden's day. 10. khaki. 11. Money. 12. (c) the shin. 13. 1 January 1999. 14. (a) ape-like. 15. Quack.

SCORE SHEET

SCORE SHEET